HBJ TREASURY OF LITERATURE

BEYOND EXPECTATIONS

SENIOR AUTHORS
ROGER C. FARR
DOROTHY S. STRICKLAND

AUTHORS
RICHARD F. ABRAHAMSON
ELLEN BOOTH CHURCH
BARBARA BOWEN COULTER
MARGARET A. GALLEGO
JUDITH L. IRVIN
KAREN KUTIPER
JUNKO YOKOTA LEWIS
DONNA M. OGLE
TIMOTHY SHANAHAN
PATRICIA SMITH

SENIOR CONSULTANTS
BERNICE E. CULLINAN
W. DORSEY HAMMOND
ASA G. HILLIARD III

CONSULTANTS
ALONZO A. CRIM
ROLANDO R. HINOJOSA-SMITH
LEE BENNETT HOPKINS
ROBERT J. STERNBERG

HARCOURT BRACE & COMPANY
Orlando   Atlanta   Austin   Boston   San Francisco   Chicago   Dallas   New York
Toronto   London

Printed in the United States of America

ISBN 0-15-300426-6

3 4 5 6 7 8 9 10   048   96   95   94   93

Acknowledgments continue on page 623, which constitutes an extension of this copyright page.

Acknowledgments

For permission to reprint copyrighted material, grateful acknowledgment is made to the following sources:

Atheneum Publishers, an imprint of Macmillan Publishing Company: "Mother Doesn't Want a Dog" from *If I Were In Charge of the World and Other Worries* by Judith Viorst. Text copyright © 1981 by Judith Viorst.

Avon Books: Cover illustration by Alan Daniel from *Bunnicula* by Deborah and James Howe. Illustration copyright © 1979 by Alan Daniel.

Bantam Books, a division of Bantam Doubleday Dell Publishing Group, Inc.: From pp. 113-126 in *B-Ball: The Team That Never Lost a Game* by Ron Jones. Text copyright © 1990 by Ron Jones.

Susan Bergholz Literary Services, New York: "Name/Nombres" by Julia Alvarez. Text copyright © 1985 by Julia Alvarez.

Camden House Publishing: Cover photograph by François Gohier from *Meeting the Whales: The Equinox Guide to Giants of the Deep* by Erich Hoyt. Copyright © 1991 by Erich Hoyt.

Curtis Brown, Ltd.: From pp. 7-24 in *Courage, Dana* (Retitled: "Mystery Girl Saves Tot's Life") by Susan Beth Pfeffer. Text copyright © 1983 by Susan Beth Pfeffer.

Deborah Chandra: "Sleeping Simon" by Deborah Chandra from *Dog Poems*, selected by Myra Cohn Livingston. Text copyright © 1990 by Deborah Chandra. Published by Holiday House.

Myra J. Ciardi: "The Dollar Dog" from *Doodle Soup* by John Ciardi. Text copyright © 1985 by Myra J. Ciardi. Published by Houghton Mifflin Company.

Clarion Books, a Houghton Mifflin Company imprint: From pp. 7–25 in *Lincoln: A Photobiography* (Retitled: "A Backwoods Boy") by Russell Freedman. Text copyright © 1987 by Russell Freedman.

Coward-McCann, Inc.: From "The Stories Behind the Words" in *What's Behind the Word?* by Harold Longman, cover illustration by Susan Perl. Text and cover illustration copyright © 1968 by Harold Longman. From *Phoebe and the General* by Judith Berry Griffin, illustrated by Margot Tomes. Text copyright © 1977 by Judith Berry Griffin; illustrations copyright © 1977 by Margot Tomes.

Dell Books, a division of Bantam Doubleday Dell Publishing Group, Inc.: From pp. 1-25 in *Make Like a Tree and Leave* (Retitled: "The Mummy Project") by Paula Danziger, cover illustration by Joe Csatari. Text copyright © 1990 by Paula Danziger; cover illustration copyright © 1990 by Joe Csatari.

Dial Books for Young Readers, a division of Penguin Books USA Inc.: Cover illustration by Barry Moser from *George Washington: Leader of a New Nation* by Mary Pope Osborne. Copyright © 1991 by Mary Pope Osborne.

Doubleday, a division of Bantam Doubleday Dell Publishing Group, Inc.: "The Wonderful Words" from *Words Words Words* by Mary O'Neill. Text copyright © 1966 by Mary O'Neill.

Dilys Evans Fine Illustration: Cover illustration by Leslie H. Morrill from *Mrs. Frisby and the Rats of NIMH* by Robert C. O'Brien. Copyright © 1971 by Robert C. O'Brien.

Angel Flores: "The Stub-Book" by Pedro Antonio de Alarcón from *Spanish Stories*, edited by Angel Flores.

Four Winds Press, an imprint of Macmillan Publishing Company: Cover illustration by Eileen McKeating from *Summer of the Dodo* by Patricia Baehr. Illustration copyright © 1990 by Eileen McKeating. From pp. 1-7, with map redrawn from p. 5 in *Earth's Changing Climate* (Retitled: "A Rendezvous with Ice") by Roy A. Gallant. Text copyright © 1979 by Roy A. Gallant.

Greenwillow Books, a division of William Morrow & Company, Inc.: Cover illustration by Peter Sis from *The Whipping Boy* by Sid Fleischman. Illustration copyright © 1986 by Peter Sis.

Harcourt Brace Jovanovich, Inc.: From pp. 39-41 in *How Smart Are Animals?* (Retitled: "How Smart Are Dolphins?") by Dorothy Hinshaw Patent. Text copyright © 1990 by Dorothy Hinshaw Patent. "Sea Slant" from *Slabs of the Sunburnt West* by Carl Sandburg. Text copyright © 1922 by Harcourt Brace Jovanovich, renewed 1950 by Carl Sandburg. "Seventh Grade" from *Baseball in April and Other Stories* by Gary Soto. Text copyright © 1990 by Gary Soto. Pronunciation Key from *HBJ School Dictionary*, Third Edition. Text copyright © 1990 by Harcourt Brace Jovanovich, Inc.

HarperCollins Publishers: From *Spring Comes to the Ocean* by Jean Craighead George, cover illustration by John Wilson. Text and cover illustration copyright © 1965 by Jean Craighead George. Published by Thomas Y. Crowell. From pp. 69-84 in *Water Sky* by Jean Craighead George. Text and cover illustration copyright © 1987 by Jean Craighead George. Cover illustration from *The Riddle of the Rosetta Stone* by James Cross Giblin. Illustration © 1990 by HarperCollins Publishers. Published by Thomas Y. Crowell. Cover illustration by William Low from *Old Yeller* by Fred Gipson. Illustration copyright © 1989 by William Low. Cover illustration by Nancy Doniger from *Talk About English* by Janet Klausner. Illustration copyright © 1990 by Nancy Doniger. Published by Thomas Y. Crowell. Cover illustration by Jean Charlot from *. . . and now Miguel* by Joseph Krumgold. Copyright © 1953 by Joseph Krumgold. Cover illustration from *Harriet Tubman: Conductor on the Underground Railroad* by Ann Petry. Copyright 1955 by Ann Petry. Published by Thomas Y. Crowell. "Vergil, the Laid-back Dog" from *My Brother Louis Measures Worms* by Barbara Robinson. Text copyright © 1988 by Barbara Robinson. Cover illustration by David A. Carter from *How To Be an Ocean Scientist in Your Own Home* by Seymour Simon. Illustration copyright © 1988 by David A. Carter. Published by J.B. Lippincott. Cover

continued on page 623

HBJ TREASURY OF LITERATURE

Dear Reader,

    According to a character from the first story in this book, if you expect everything, the unexpected will never happen.

    This anthology includes stories about people who go beyond expectations by calling on a courage they didn't know they had. Phoebe Fraunces, a young African American girl, becomes a hero during the American Revolution. Members of a Danish family hide a Jewish girl from the Nazis during World War II. Frederick Douglass teaches himself to read, even though as a slave he is forbidden to do so.

    We invite you to go beyond the expected to discover other worlds. Storytellers will take you to Spain, Turkey, and ancient Egypt, where you'll find that these cultures can be different from ours, but also remarkably similar. Other writers will transport you to imaginary places and distant times, both past and future.

    We invite you to share the joy of watching others discover *our* world. Julia Alvarez learns to thrive in America after growing up in the Dominican Republic. Young people from Vietnam become students in American schools, learning the American way of life as their classmates learn about the heritage of the Vietnamese.

    You probably have expectations of what the coming year will bring. Now, as you read about worlds near and far, real and imaginary, we invite you to go *Beyond Expectations*.

Sincerely,
The Authors

BEYOND EXPECTATIONS

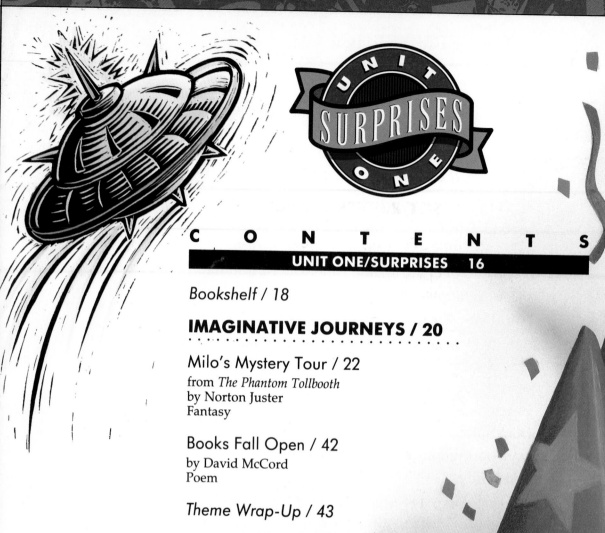

CONTENTS

UNIT ONE/SURPRISES 16

UNIT TWO/HEROES 96

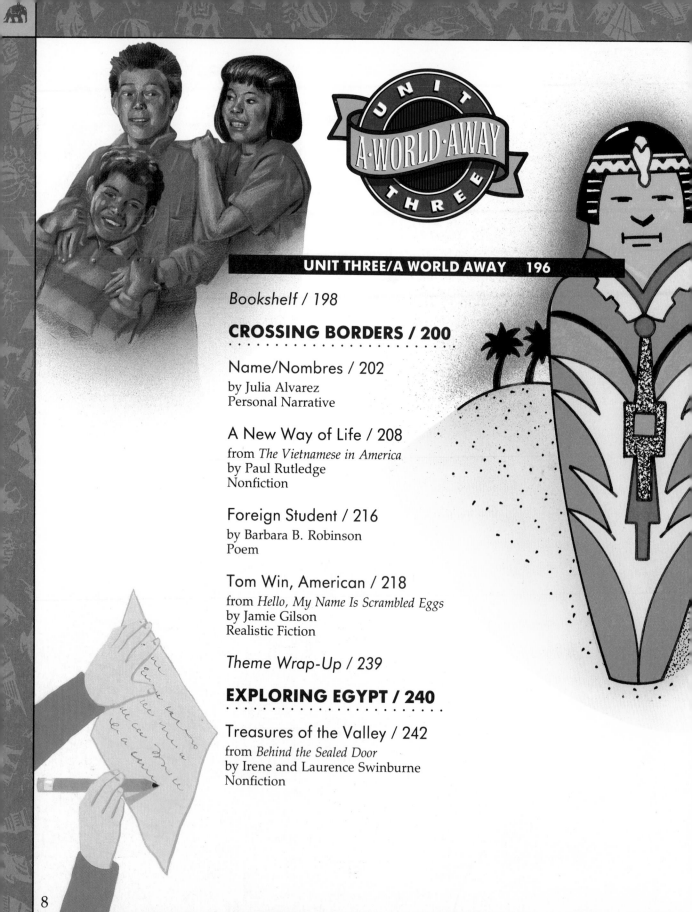

UNIT FOUR

LIGHT·MOMENTS

13

UNIT SIX/DAYS GONE BY 496

14

Maybe your mind is holding now
A marvelous new surprise!
Mary O'Neill

As the poet suggests, you never know where a surprise may come from. Books and stories are one good source of surprises. They take you to places you've never been—or bring other worlds to you! They even allow you to travel back through time and witness important moments in history, such as the meeting of the Aztecs and the Spanish. Wherever your adventures take you, watch out for the unexpected!

BOOKSHELF

great

THE WHIPPING BOY
BY SID FLEISCHMAN

The heir to the throne, known as "Prince Brat," must not be spanked, so street boy Jemmy is hired to be punished in his place. When the bored prince runs away from home, taking Jemmy, the adventures that follow change both boys forever. NEWBERY MEDAL, ALA NOTABLE BOOK, SCHOOL LIBRARY JOURNAL BEST BOOK

HBJ LIBRARY BOOK

Excellent

MRS. FRISBY AND THE RATS OF NIMH
BY ROBERT C. O'BRIEN

Mrs. Frisby, a widowed mouse with a sick child, seeks help from a strange group of ex-laboratory rats. Sworn to secrecy, she discovers some amazing truths, not only about the rats but about her late husband as well. NEWBERY MEDAL, ALA NOTABLE BOOK

INTENSE

TALK ABOUT ENGLISH
BY JANET KLAUSNER

Is a shirt related to a skirt? Does a secretary keep secrets? The author sees words as time travelers that have survived centuries of history. Her fascinating book traces the development of the English language.

THE WIND IN THE WILLOWS
BY KENNETH GRAHAME

This classic tale is filled with the adventures of Mole, Rat, Badger, and Toad. Wealthy Toad is always in hilarious trouble, while his friends spend much of their time trying to get him out of hot water.

JOURNEY TO THE PLANETS
BY PATRICIA LAUBER

This stunning book describes the nine planets of our solar system and their moons in scientific detail. Included are the most recent findings of *Voyager 2.* ALA NOTABLE BOOK, SCHOOL LIBRARY JOURNAL BEST BOOK

19

IMAGINATIVE JOURNEYS

Books can show you things you've already seen or heard about. But they can also take you to places you can know only in your imagination. In the following selections, you'll have encounters of the imaginative kind.

C O N T E N T S

MILO'S MYSTERY TOUR

from *The Phantom Tollbooth*

by NORTON JUSTER   illustrations by JULES FEIFFER

MILO

There was once a boy named Milo who didn't know what to do with himself—not just sometimes, but always.

When he was in school he longed to be out, and when he was out he longed to be in. On the way he thought about coming home, and coming home he thought about going. Wherever he was he wished he were somewhere else, and when he got there he wondered why he'd bothered. Nothing really interested him—least of all the things that should have.

"It seems to me that almost everything is a waste of time," he remarked one day as he walked dejectedly home from school. "I can't see the point in learning to solve useless problems, or subtracting turnips from turnips, or knowing where Ethiopia is or how to spell February." And, since no one bothered to explain otherwise, he regarded the process of seeking knowledge as the greatest waste of time of all.

As he and his unhappy thoughts hurried along (for while he was never anxious to be where he was going, he liked to get there as quickly as possible) it seemed a great wonder that the world, which was so large, could sometimes feel so small and empty.

"And worst of all," he continued sadly, "there's nothing for me to do, nowhere I'd care to go, and hardly anything worth seeing." He punctuated this last thought with such a deep sigh that a house sparrow singing nearby stopped and rushed home to be with his family.

Without stopping or looking up, he rushed past the buildings and busy shops that lined the street and in a few minutes reached home—dashed through the lobby—hopped onto the elevator—two, three, four, five, six, seven, eight, and off again—opened the apartment door—rushed into his room—flopped dejectedly into a chair, and grumbled softly, "Another long afternoon."

He looked glumly at all the things he owned. The books that were too much trouble to read, the tools he'd never learned to use, the small electric automobile he hadn't driven in months—or was it years?—and the hundreds of other games and toys, and bats and balls, and bits and pieces scattered around him. And then, to one side of the room, just next to the phonograph, he noticed something he had certainly never seen before.

Who could possibly have left such an enormous package and such a strange one? For, while it was not quite square, it was definitely not round, and for its size it was larger than almost any other big package of smaller dimension that he'd ever seen.

Attached to one side was a bright-blue envelope which said simply: "FOR MILO, WHO HAS PLENTY OF TIME."

Of course, if you've ever gotten a surprise package, you can imagine how puzzled and excited Milo was; and if you've never gotten one, pay close attention, because someday you might.

"I don't think it's my birthday," he puzzled, "and Christmas must be months away, and I haven't been outstandingly good, or even good at all." (He had to admit this even to himself.) "Most probably I won't like it anyway, but since I don't know where it came from, I can't possibly send it back." He thought about it for quite a while and then opened the envelope, but just to be polite.

"ONE GENUINE TURNPIKE TOLLBOOTH," it stated—and then it went on:

"EASILY ASSEMBLED AT HOME, AND FOR USE BY THOSE WHO HAVE NEVER TRAVELED IN LANDS BEYOND."

"Beyond what?" thought Milo as he continued to read.

"THIS PACKAGE CONTAINS THE FOLLOWING ITEMS:

"One (1) genuine turnpike tollbooth to be erected according to directions.

"Three (3) precautionary signs to be used in a precautionary fashion.

"Assorted coins for use in paying tolls.

"One (1) map, up to date and carefully drawn by master cartographers, depicting natural and man-made features.

"One (1) book of rules and traffic regulations, which may not be bent or broken."

And in smaller letters at the bottom it concluded:

"Results are not guaranteed, but if not perfectly satisfied, your wasted time will be refunded."

Following the instructions, which told him to cut here, lift there, and fold back all around, he soon had the tollbooth unpacked and set up on its stand. He fitted the windows in place and attached the roof, which extended out on both sides, and fastened on the coin box. It was very much like the tollbooths he'd seen many times on family trips, except of course it was much smaller and purple.

"What a strange present," he thought to himself. "The least they could have done was to send a highway with it, for it's terribly impractical without one." But since, at the time, there was nothing else he wanted to play with, he set up the three signs,

SLOW DOWN APPROACHING TOLLBOOTH

PLEASE HAVE YOUR FARE READY

HAVE YOUR DESTINATION IN MIND

and slowly unfolded the map.

As the announcement stated, it was a beautiful map, in many colors, showing principal roads, rivers and seas, towns and cities, mountains and valleys, intersections and detours, and sites of outstanding interest both beautiful and historic.

The only trouble was that Milo had never heard of any of the places it indicated, and even the names sounded most peculiar.

"I don't think there really is such a country," he concluded after studying it carefully. "Well, it doesn't matter anyway." And he closed his eyes and poked a finger at the map.

"Dictionopolis," read Milo slowly when he saw what his finger had chosen. "Oh, well, I might as well go there as anywhere."

He walked across the room and dusted the car off carefully. Then, taking the map and rule book with him, he hopped in and, for lack of anything better to do, drove slowly up to the tollbooth. As he deposited his coin and rolled past he remarked wistfully, "I do hope this is an interesting game, otherwise the afternoon will be so terribly dull."

BEYOND
EXPECTATIONS

Suddenly he found himself speeding along an unfamiliar country highway, and as he looked back over his shoulder neither the tollbooth nor his room nor even the house was anywhere in sight. What had started as make-believe was now very real.

"What a strange thing to have happen," he thought (just as you must be thinking right now). "This game is much more serious than I thought, for here I am riding on a road I've never seen, going to a place I've never heard of, and all because of a tollbooth which came from nowhere. I'm certainly glad that it's a nice day for a trip," he concluded hopefully, for, at the moment, this was the one thing he definitely knew.

The sun sparkled, the sky was clear, and all the colors he saw seemed to be richer and brighter than he could ever remember. The flowers shone as if they'd been cleaned and polished, and the tall trees that lined the road shimmered in silvery green.

"WELCOME TO EXPECTATIONS," said a carefully lettered sign on a small house at the side of the road.

INFORMATION, PREDICTIONS, AND ADVICE

CHEERFULLY OFFERED.

PARK HERE AND BLOW HORN.

With the first sound from the horn a little man in a long coat came rushing from the house, speaking as fast as he could and repeating everything several times:

"My, my, my, my, my, welcome, welcome, welcome, welcome to the land of Expectations, to the land of Expectations, to the land of Expectations. We don't get many travelers these days; we certainly don't get many travelers these days. Now what can I do for you? I'm the Whether Man."

"Is this the right road for Dictionopolis?" asked Milo, a little bowled over by the effusive greeting.

"Well now, well now, well now," he began again, "I don't know of any wrong road to Dictionopolis, so if this road goes to Dictionopolis at all it must be the right road, and if it doesn't it must be the right road to somewhere else, because there are no wrong roads to anywhere. Do you think it will rain?"

"I thought you were the Weather Man," said Milo, very confused.

"Oh no," said the little man, "I'm the Whether Man, not the Weather Man, for after all it's more important to know whether there will be weather than what the weather will be." And with that he released a dozen balloons that sailed off into the sky. "Must see which way the wind is blowing," he said, chuckling over his little joke and watching them disappear in all directions.

"What kind of a place is Expectations?" inquired Milo, unable to see the humor and feeling very doubtful of the little man's sanity.

"Good question, good question," he exclaimed. "Expectations is the place you must always go to before you get to where you're going. Of course, some people never go beyond Expectations, but my job is to hurry them along whether they like it or not. Now what else can I do for you?" And before Milo could reply he rushed into the house and reappeared a moment later with a new coat and an umbrella.

"I think I can find my own way," said Milo, not at all sure that he could. But, since he didn't understand the little man at all, he decided that he might as well move on—at least until he met someone whose sentences didn't always sound as if they would make as much sense backwards as forwards.

"Splendid, splendid, splendid," exclaimed the Whether Man. "Whether or not you find your own way, you're bound to find some way. If you happen to find my way, please return it, as it was lost years ago. I imagine by now it's quite rusty. You did say it was going to rain, didn't you?" And with that he opened the umbrella and walked with Milo to the car.

"I'm glad you made your own decision. I do so hate to make up my mind about anything, whether it's good or bad, up or down, in or out, rain or shine. Expect everything, I always say, and the unexpected never happens. Now please drive carefully; good-by, good-by, good-by, good . . ." His last good-by was drowned out by an enormous clap of thunder, and as Milo drove down the road in the bright sunshine he could see the Whether Man standing in the middle of a fierce cloudburst that seemed to be raining only on him.

The road dipped now into a broad green valley and stretched toward the horizon. The little car bounced along with very little effort, and Milo had hardly to touch the accelerator to go as fast as he wanted. He was glad to be on his way again.

"It's all very well to spend time in Expectations," he thought, "but talking to that strange man all day would certainly get me nowhere. He's the most peculiar person I've ever met," continued Milo—unaware of how many peculiar people he would shortly encounter.

As he drove along the peaceful highway he soon fell to daydreaming and paid less and less attention to where he was going. In a short time he wasn't paying any attention at all, and that is why, at a fork in the road, when a sign pointed to the left, Milo went to the right, along a route which looked suspiciously like the wrong way.

Things began to change as soon as he left the main highway. The sky became quite gray and, along with it, the whole countryside seemed to lose its color and assume the same monotonous tone. Everything was quiet, and even the air hung heavily. The birds sang only gray songs and the road wound back and forth in an endless series of climbing curves.

Mile after

mile after

mile after

mile he drove, and now, gradually the car went slower and slower, until it was hardly moving at all.

"It looks as though I'm getting nowhere," yawned Milo, becoming very drowsy and dull. "I hope I haven't taken a wrong turn."

Mile after

mile after

mile after

mile, and everything became grayer and more monotonous. Finally the car just stopped altogether, and, hard as he tried, it wouldn't budge another inch.

33

"I wonder where I am," said Milo in a very worried tone.

"You're . . . in . . . the . . . Dol . . . drums," wailed a voice that sounded far away.

He looked around quickly to see who had spoken. No one was there, and it was as quiet and still as one could imagine.

"Yes . . . the . . . Dol . . . drums," yawned another voice, but still he saw no one.

"WHAT ARE THE DOLDRUMS?" he cried loudly, and tried very hard to see who would answer this time.

"The Doldrums, my young friend, are where nothing ever happens and nothing ever changes."

This time the voice came from so close that Milo jumped with surprise, for, sitting on his right shoulder, so lightly that he hardly noticed, was a small creature exactly the color of his shirt.

"Allow me to introduce all of us," the creature went on. "We are the Lethargarians, at your service."

Milo looked around and, for the first time, noticed dozens of them—sitting on the car, standing in the road, and lying all over the trees and bushes. They were very difficult to see, because whatever they happened to be sitting on or near was exactly the color they happened to be. Each one looked very much like the other (except for the color, of course) and some looked even more like each other than they did like themselves.

"I'm very pleased to meet you," said Milo, not sure whether or not he was pleased at all. "I think I'm lost. Can you help me please?"

"Don't say 'think,'" said one sitting on his shoe, for the one on his shoulder had fallen asleep. "It's against the law." And he yawned and fell off to sleep, too.

"No one's allowed to think in the Doldrums," continued a third, beginning to doze off. And as each one spoke, he fell off to sleep and another picked up the conversation with hardly any interruption.

"Don't you have a rule book? It's local ordinance 175389-J."

Milo quickly pulled the rule book from his pocket, opened to the page, and read, "Ordinance 175389-J: It shall be unlawful, illegal, and unethical to think, think of thinking, surmise, presume, reason, meditate, or speculate while in the Doldrums. Anyone breaking this law shall be severely punished!"

"That's a ridiculous law," said Milo, quite indignantly. "Everybody thinks."

"We don't," shouted the Lethargarians all at once.

"And most of the time *you* don't," said a yellow one sitting in a daffodil. "That's why you're here. You weren't thinking, and you weren't paying attention either. People who don't pay attention often get stuck in the Doldrums." And with that he toppled out of the flower and fell snoring into the grass.

Milo couldn't help laughing at the little creature's strange behavior, even though he knew it might be rude.

"Stop that at once," ordered the plain one clinging to his stocking. "Laughing is against the law. Don't you have a rule book? It's local ordinance 574381-W."

Opening the book again, Milo found Ordinance 574381-W: "In the Doldrums, laughter is frowned upon and smiling is permitted only on alternate Thursdays. Violators shall be dealt with most harshly."

"Well, if you can't laugh or think, what can you do?" asked Milo.

"Anything as long as it's nothing, and everything as long as it isn't anything," explained another. "There's lots to do; we have a very busy schedule—

"At 8 o'clock we get up, and then we spend

"From 8 to 9 daydreaming.

"From 9 to 9:30 we take our early midmorning nap.

"From 9:30 to 10:30 we dawdle and delay.

"From 10:30 to 11:00 we take our late early morning nap.

"From 11:00 to 12:00 we bide our time and then eat lunch.

"From 1:00 to 2:00 we linger and loiter.

"From 2:00 to 2:30 we take our early afternoon nap.

"From 2:30 to 3:30 we put off for tomorrow what we could have done today.

"From 3:30 to 4:00 we take our early late afternoon nap.

"From 4:00 to 5:00 we loaf and lounge until dinner.

"From 6:00 to 7:00 we dillydally.

"From 7:00 to 8:00 we take our early evening nap, and then for an hour before we go to bed at 9:00 we waste time.

"As you can see, that leaves almost no time for brooding, lagging, plodding, or procrastinating, and if we stopped to think or laugh, we'd never get nothing done."

"You mean you'd never get anything done," corrected Milo.

"We don't want to get anything done," snapped another angrily; "we want to get nothing done, and we can do that without your help."

"You see," continued another in a more conciliatory tone, "it's really quite strenuous doing nothing all day, so once a week we take a holiday and go nowhere, which was just where we were going when you came along. Would you care to join us?"

"I might as well," thought Milo; "that's where I seem to be going anyway."

"Tell me," he yawned, for he felt ready for a nap now himself, "does everyone here do nothing?"

"Everyone but the terrible watchdog," said two of them, shuddering in chorus. "He's always sniffing around to see that nobody wastes time. A most unpleasant character."

"The watchdog?" said Milo quizzically.

"THE WATCHDOG," shouted another, fainting from fright, for racing down the road barking furiously and kicking up a great cloud of dust was the very dog of whom they had been speaking.

"RUN!"
"WAKE UP!"
"RUN!"
"HERE HE COMES!"
"THE WATCHDOG!"

Great shouts filled the air as the Lethargarians scattered in all directions and soon disappeared entirely.

"R-R-R-G-H-R-O-R-R-H-F-F," exclaimed the watchdog as he dashed up to the car, loudly puffing and panting.

Milo's eyes opened wide, for there in front of him was a large dog with a perfectly normal head, four feet, and a tail—and the body of a loudly ticking alarm clock.

"What are you doing here?" growled the watchdog.

"Just killing time," replied Milo apologetically. "You see—"

"KILLING TIME!" roared the dog—so furiously that his alarm went off. "It's bad enough wasting time without killing it." And he shuddered at the thought. "Why are you in the Doldrums anyway—don't you have anywhere to go?"

"I was on my way to Dictionopolis when I got stuck here," explained Milo. "Can you help me?"

"Help you! You must help yourself," the dog replied, carefully winding himself with his left hind leg. "I suppose you know why you got stuck."

"I guess I just wasn't thinking," said Milo.

"PRECISELY," shouted the dog as his alarm went off again. "Now you know what you must do."

"I'm afraid I don't," admitted Milo, feeling quite stupid.

"Well," continued the watchdog impatiently, "since you got here by not thinking, it seems reasonable to expect that, in order to get out, you must start thinking." And with that he hopped into the car.

"Do you mind if I get in? I love automobile rides."

Milo began to think as hard as he could (which was very difficult, since he wasn't used to it). He thought of birds that swim and fish that fly. He thought of yesterday's lunch and tomorrow's dinner. He thought of words that begin with J and numbers that end in 3. And, as he thought, the wheels began to turn.

"We're moving, we're moving," he shouted happily.

"Keep thinking," scolded the watchdog.

The little car started to go faster and faster as Milo's brain whirled with activity, and down the road they went. In a few moments they were out of the Doldrums and back on the main highway. All the colors had returned to their original brightness, and as they raced along the road Milo continued to think of all sorts of things; of the many detours and wrong turns that were so easy to take, of how fine it was to be moving along, and, most of all, of how much could be accomplished with just a little thought. And the dog, his nose in the wind, just sat back, watchfully ticking.

THINK IT OVER

1. *How well did this story live up to your expectations? Did it go beyond them?*

2. *What happens when Milo drives through the tollbooth?*

3. *One rule in Milo's rule book states that it is unlawful to think. What else does Milo learn he should not do in the Doldrums?*

4. *"In the doldrums" is a way of saying that someone is bored, sad, or dull. Why is it appropriate for Milo to wind up in a place called the Doldrums?*

5. *Why are the Lethargarians afraid of the watchdog?*

WRITE

The watchdog says that wasting time is bad enough without killing it. Write a paragraph or two explaining what you think the difference is between wasting time and killing it.

Books Fall Open

by David McCord

**illustrated by
Kevin Ghiglione**

Books fall open,
You fall in,
delighted where
you've never been;
hear voices not once
heard before,
reach world on world
through door on door;
find unexpected
keys to things
locked up beyond
imaginings.
What *might* you be,
perhaps *become*,
because one book
is somewhere? Some
wise delver into
wisdom, wit,
and wherewithal
has written it.
True books will venture,
dare you out,
whisper secrets,
maybe shout
across the gloom
to you in need,
who hanker for
a book to read.

AWARD-WINNING
POET

42

IMAGINATIVE JOURNEYS

How is traveling through the Phantom Tollbooth similar to "falling into a book"?

Does "Books Fall Open" describe the adventure of reading a story like "Milo's Mystery Tour"? Explain your answer.

WRITER'S WORKSHOP Imagine that you are an attendant who collects tolls at the Phantom Tollbooth. Think of several reasons why people should drive through to the other side. Organize your reasons in two or three paragraphs that might persuade someone to drive through the tollbooth.

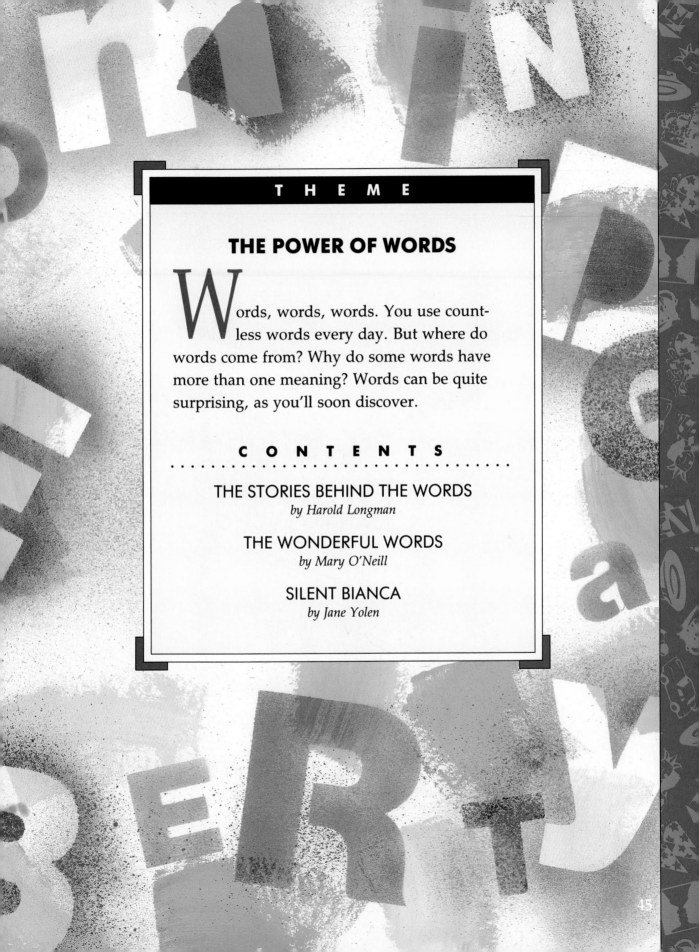

THE POWER OF WORDS

Words, words, words. You use countless words every day. But where do words come from? Why do some words have more than one meaning? Words can be quite surprising, as you'll soon discover.

CONTENTS

. . . .

OUR
LIVING
LANGUAGE

Each of the *Our Living Language* books deals with the origin of language. The books are intended to bring language alive for young people. These well-told and fascinating accounts of how certain familiar words came to be and their place in history will stimulate young people to use their language and communicate with more thought and real enjoyment.

What's Behind the
WORD?

OUR LIVING LANGUAGE SERIES

Longman

What's Behind the WORD?

BY HAROLD LONGMAN
Illustrated by Susan Perl

The Stories Behind the Words

from *What's Behind the Word?* by Harold Longman

illustrated by Rodica Prato

Every word we use has a story behind it. When we trace those stories, we learn a great deal about the people who have gone before us—their lives, their history, the way they thought.

For words are all we have to explain the world around us, to tell others what we want, what we think, or how we feel. You may not know what words you are going to use tomorrow, but one thing is sure. You will use words that have been used thousands of times before. Words are perhaps the oldest living things in the world. In some cases, they go back thousands of years to the dawn of civilized life.

Finding the story behind the word takes a bit of detective work. If we're lucky, we can find out exactly how a word came into our language. We're not always that lucky. Some words are total mysteries; their beginnings have never been discovered. There are other words we're almost sure of—but not quite. Some words we have to guess at—much as a scientist works on a theory until he can prove it.

In the following pages, you will find some of these different kinds of stories. And you will find something else: that stories about words are often as strange, interesting, and unexpected as the stories that words are used to tell.

The Honest Carpenter

SIN-CERE *adj.* 1. Being in reality as it is in appearance; real; genuine: *sincere* regret. 2. Free from hypocrisy; honest; faithful: a *sincere* friend.

The Roman patrician looked at the table critically and ran his finger along the grain of the wood, feeling for flaws. The surface felt perfectly smooth. It was a handsome table, well proportioned, and would look splendid in the place he had planned for it. He was greatly pleased; the table was his own design.

"It will do, I think," he said quite coolly. Enthusiasm, he had found, was likely to raise the price.

The cabinetmaker bowed obsequiously. "Your honor," he said, "I guarantee that the table is of the finest workmanship. The grain is most unusual; the wood is well-seasoned, sound, and *sine cera.*"

Sine cera, in Latin, meant without wax. It was the custom for Roman artisans to fill cracks or holes in furniture with colored wax, much as we might use plastic wood or putty. If the job was done skillfully, it would be hard to find the flaw. Since Roman carpenters were not about to throw away a good piece of wood because it had a small crack in it, there was

probably plenty of wax in most of the tables and benches. Only the best was *sine cera*—pure and without blemish.

The phrase was a handy one. Soon it became widely used among the Romans, not only for furniture but to describe anything that was whole and of sound workmanship. From that, it was an easy step to the more general meaning of pure, honest, straightforward, using the phrase not merely to describe work but to describe people and character.

The words, too, slid together to form *sincerus*. In this form, it was taken over into the Old French, and then into English.

Today we use the word much as the late Romans did, but in at least one way we've weakened it still further. It is unlikely that any Roman ever signed a letter he didn't want to write as "Yours sincerely."

The Gunpowder Plot

GUY *n.* 1. *Informal* A man or boy; fellow.

Early in November, 1605, a long-prepared plot to blow up King James I and all the members of the English Parliament was ready to be sprung. It was a devilish plot indeed.

The date was set for November 5, when the King was to address the opening session.

A mound of gunpowder, covered with dry sticks, was ready in the cellar, directly under the main chamber of the Parliament building.

One man, selected for his bravery, was stationed in the cellar, ready to fire the gunpowder. It was hoped that he could light the sticks with a slow fuse, run and escape before the explosion. The man's name was Guy Fawkes.

Guy Fawkes, though a brave man, was nothing but a tool. The plot was masterminded by Sir William Stanley, a traitor in the pay of the King of Spain.

The plot would probably have succeeded except for one thing. One of the conspirators was worried. His best friend was a member of Parliament and would be among those blown up. He thought he could save the man without upsetting the plot. So the conspirator wrote an unsigned note, urging his friend to stay away that evening and hinting mysteriously at the reason.

The friend, on receiving the note, immediately started an investigation. Late on the night of November 4, the plot was discovered. The discovery was kept a deep secret, but the King's men prepared to foil the plot.

When Guy Fawkes slipped into the cellar on November 5, he found the soldiers of the King waiting to arrest him.

Guy Fawkes was later tried along with some of his fellow conspirators. The others escaped, but all who were tried were hanged the following January.

Guy Fawkes Day—November 5— is celebrated in England much as Halloween is celebrated in America.

The earliest celebrations were torchlight parades, where the marchers, singing, carried ragged effigies of Guy Fawkes through the streets.

In time, anyone resembling those ragged effigies was called a *guy*—not a very complimentary term. But over the years the word has changed its meaning—so much so that we can now root for the good guys and hoot at the bad guys.

"Wolf Ho!"

TOWN *n.* 1. Any considerable collection of dwellings and other buildings larger than a village and constituting a geographical and political community unit, but not incorporated as a city.

In America, in states such as Iowa and Kansas, it is common enough to see vast stretches of farmland with only a lonely farmhouse breaking the horizon. The farm family often has no neighbors within miles. In many parts of Europe, things are quite different. There it is the custom for farmers to live together in little villages, with close-set houses. Each day they go out to tend their fields, which may be miles away.

The custom goes far back into the beginnings of history. For protection at night against wild animals and marauders, a man had to sleep within another man's hearing. In case of trouble, he could easily shout for help. It was not uncommon to hear a sudden cry in the night: "Wolf ho!" or "Wild dog!" or "Robbers!" Neighboring farmers would leap from their beds and run out with clubs or scythes to chase the intruder away.

In the Middle Ages, the villages often clustered around the lord's castle. The serfs supplied the lord with food; the lord, in turn, supplied protection. The communities were small and tightly knit; the farms radiated outward from the edge of the village in narrow strips. Each serf had one or more strips of land for his own, and there was a large open space, or common, where they could all graze their animals.

The system worked well; the feudal lords would have had a harder time protecting their people if the farmers had been widely scattered.

The best-kept villages were surrounded by a tightly grown hedge or fence to keep out wild animals or to make it harder for bands of robbers to get in. In Old England, this hedge was called a *tun* (pronounced "toon").

As time went on, a *tun* came to mean any kind of enclosure around a village, especially a good, sturdy wall. Still later, it came to mean the village within the wall.

Thus a *town*, as it came to be spelled in medieval times, was distinguished from a village, because it was sur-

rounded by a wall. As such, it was generally more prosperous, larger, and better organized than a village. The neighbors had taken enough pride in their town to do something about defending it.

Today, in parts of England, and especially in Scotland, the word *town* is still pronounced toon—as it was in the days when it meant no more than a hedge.

A One-Sided Love Story

ECH-O *n.* 1. The repetition of a sound by the reflection of sound waves from an opposing surface; also, the sound so produced. 2. The repetition or reproduction of the views, style, etc., of another. 3. One who imitates another or repeats his words.

In Greek mythology, Echo was the fairest of the wood nymphs. She was bright, pretty, and quick-witted. But she had one fault: she was too fond of talking.

This seems harmless enough, but it got Echo into dreadful trouble. It happened this way.

Hera, the Queen of the Gods,

was walking through the woods one day, and the chattering of Echo annoyed her. Quick to anger, Hera wasted no time in showing her displeasure.

"Chatter, chatter, chatter, will you? Silly nymph, you have offended my ears long enough. From this day on, you will use your tongue no more!"

The frightened nymph trembled before the mighty goddess, wanting to protest, but unable to utter a sound. Hera was struck with a sudden, wicked idea. "No, wait. You like to talk? Very well, talk you shall. But you will only repeat what is said to you." Then Hera smiled grimly, pleased with her own wit. "You will always have the last word—but never the first."

Majestically the goddess turned and walked away.

Poor Echo! She wandered through the woods, silent and unhappy. The light of the sun seemed dimmer now; the air, colder. She shuddered. Aimlessly she walked on, not caring where, knowing only that she wanted to avoid the other nymphs, her friends. She had not gone far when she came across a youth asleep in the forest. If Echo could have made a sound, she would have gasped, for this was the handsomest man she had ever seen. Simply looking at him, Echo fell deeply, hopelessly, in love.

The young man's name was Narcissus and he, poor fellow, was cursed in a curious way. He could love no one but himself. Many girls had been attracted to him, but he had ignored them all.

Echo knew none of this; she could only wonder how, without talking, she could make him pay attention to her. She stood, watching dreamily,

her troubles forgotten, but when he stirred in his sleep, she fled behind a tree so that he would not see her.

From that day on, Echo followed Narcissus everywhere but kept carefully hidden. She was sure her chance would come. She had only to be patient.

One day Narcissus, out hunting with another lad, missed his companion. He turned and called out, "Is anyone here?" Echo, watching as always, was sure that this was her opportunity.

"Here! Here!" she called out joyfully.

"Well then, come!" called Narcissus impatiently.

"Come!" she answered, and she stepped forth with her arms outstretched. Narcissus looked at her coldly and turned away. "I will die," he said, "before I give you power over me."

"I give you power over me," said Echo wistfully, but Narcissus was gone.

It was too much for Echo. Heartbroken, she fled to a cave. There she wasted away until only her voice was left.

Today, if you walk into a cave or a tunnel and call out, Echo will answer —but now as then, she can only repeat what you have said.

Off to America!

The dark, narrow streets of London were dangerous places for a lad to wander during the reign of Charles II (1660–1685). Roving bands of hoodlums, in the pay of unscrupulous ships' captains, were everywhere. Their job was to seize as many boys as they could find and carry them off to waiting ships in the harbor. Many a pale city lad would awake from a drugged sleep, or a blow on the head, to find himself on the high seas, bound for the New World. There he might become a farmhand, an apprentice, or perhaps a household servant.

Thousands of unsuspecting youths were abducted, never to return to the land of their birth. The traffic in young boys became, in time, a great public scandal, and this is the way it had come about.

America desperately needed colonists. At first, many had come willingly, lured by tales of quick wealth and unlimited opportunity. But once they arrived, they found it a far rougher place than they had imagined. True, there was opportunity, but hard work was needed to make it pay off. Many of the new colonists, hoping for easy fortunes, were not used to the rigors of hard manual labor. Even if they were, they could not manage large farms by themselves. They needed help of every sort: for planting, for harvesting, for building their houses. Some few skilled craftsmen had come and set up shop—blacksmiths, carpenters, wheelwrights and such—but they too needed help. Without apprentices and laborers, they could not possibly do all the work the colonists required.

To attract laborers, the shipowners, who also owned large parts of the colonies, first tried persuasion. They rounded up homeless boys from the slums of London with great promises of a golden future in America. But many were not so easily persuaded; perhaps they had heard stories of the hard labor required in the American wilderness. Or perhaps they did not want to leave home for an unknown country. The slums of London might be dreary, but they were at least familiar.

British shipowners offered free transportation to all who would come, in return for an agreement to work for seven years without wages. Thousands of immigrants, known as indentured servants, accepted the offer, for it was a way in which a poor man could in time become independent. After seven years of service, their master was required to give them a few farm implements, some clothing, some seed—and the colony usually gave them fifty acres of the public land. Then they were farmers in their own right—and needed help.

So, as the colonies became more prosperous, there was an increasing need for more workers. When the captains could not get colonists any other way, they hired toughs to seize any young boys they could find.

Over 100,000 youngsters were taken in this way. At the time, a new word was coined to describe the crime: *kidnap*, from *kid*, the slang word for child, and *nap*, which was thieves' slang for "steal." We have it with us yet, as "nab." Kidnapping became such an open scandal that in 1682 the London Council passed a law forbidding any person under fourteen to be bound into service without the knowledge and consent of his parents.

Today many a fine American family can perhaps trace its ancestry to a waif who was kidnapped one foggy night from the slums of London.

THINK IT OVER

1. Choose the word from this selection that you think has the most interesting or unexpected story behind it, and tell why you think so.

2. In England, why might someone say "toon" when referring to a town?

3. How can we learn about our past by studying the origins of words?

4. What are some ways a word can come into being?

WRITE

Some words, such as guy and echo, came originally from names. Using your own name, create a definition and write a short explanation of how your name could become an everyday word.

wriggle STORMY FRIEND

GULP roar

WARM HAPPY

lunar

juicy COOL

icy starlight

jump

scrawl dream

sweetest courage

lovely LAUGH

THE
WONDERFUL
WORDS

FROM *Words Words Words*
BY Mary O'Neill

Never let a thought shrivel and die
For want of a way to say it,
For English is a wonderful game
And all of you can play it.
All that you do is match the words
To the brightest thoughts in your head
So that they come out clear and true
And handsomely groomed and fed—
For many of the loveliest things
Have never yet been said.
Words are the food and dress of thought,
They give it its body and swing,
And everyone's longing today to hear
Some fresh and beautiful thing.
But only words can free a thought
From its prison behind your eyes.
Maybe your mind is holding now
A marvelous new surprise!

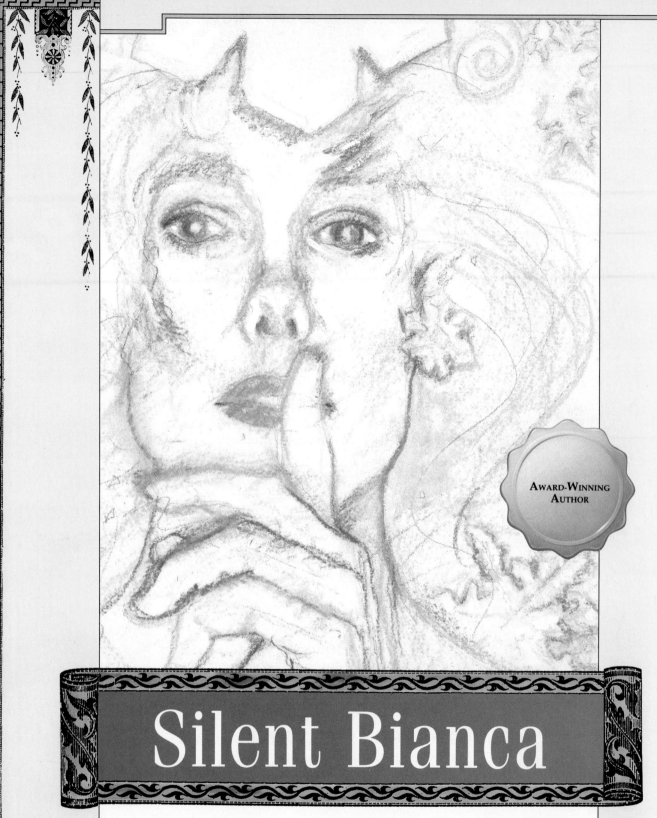

AWARD-WINNING
AUTHOR

Silent Bianca

by Jane Yolen   illustrated by Gil Ashby

from The Girl Who Cried Flowers and Other Tales

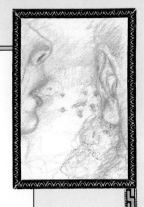

Once far to the North, where the world is lighted only by the softly flickering snow, a strange and beautiful child was born.

Her face was like crystal with the features etched in. And she was called Bianca, a name that means "white," for her face was pale as snow and her hair was white as a moonbeam.

As Bianca grew to be a young woman, she never spoke as others speak. Instead her words were formed soundlessly into tiny slivers of ice. And if a person wanted to know what she was saying, he had to pluck her sentences out of the air before they fell to the ground or were blown away by the chilling wind. Then each separate word had to be warmed by the hearthfire until at last the room was filled with the delicate sounds of Bianca's voice. They were strange sounds and as fragile as glass.

At first many people came to see the maiden and to catch her words. For it was said that she was not only beautiful but wise as well.

But the paths to her hut were few. For the frost cut cruelly at every step. And it took so long to talk with Bianca that after a while, no one came to visit her at all.

Now it happened that the king of the vast country where Bianca lived was seeking a wife who was both beautiful and wise. But when he asked his council how to find such a bride, the councilors scratched their heads and stroked their beards and managed to look full of questions and answers at the same time.

"Can you do such a thing?" asked one. "Can you not do such a thing?" asked another. "How is it possible?" asked a third. And they spent a full day looking up to the ceiling and down to the floor and answering each question with another.

At last the king said, "Enough of this useless noise. I will find a way and I will find a woman. And the one who will be my bride will be filled with silence and still speak more wisdom than any of you."

At that the councilors left off talking and began to laugh. For it was well known that wisdom was to be found in things said, not in silence. And it was also known that no one—not even the king—was as wise as the members of the king's council.

But the king sent his most trusted servant, a gentle old painter named Piers, to the corners of the kingdom. Piers was to talk with all the maidens of noble birth. Then he was to bring back portraits of the most beautiful of these from which the king might choose a bride.

Piers traveled many days and weeks. He wearied himself in the great halls and draughty palaces listening to the chattering, nattering maidens who wanted to marry the king. At last, his saddlebags filled with their portraits and his mind packed with their prattle, he started for home.

On his way home from the cold lands, Piers became lost in a fierce snowstorm. He was forced to seek shelter in a nearby hut. It was the hut where Bianca made her home. Piers meant to stay but a single day. But one day whitened into a second and then a third. It was soon a week that the old man had remained there, talking to Bianca and warming her few words by the fire. He never told her who he was or what his mission. If she guessed, she never said. Indeed, in *not* saying lay much of her wisdom.

At last the storm subsided and Piers returned to the king's castle. In his saddlebags he carried large portraits of the most beautiful noble maidens in the kingdom. But the old man carried on a chain around his neck a miniature portrait of Bianca. She had become like a daughter to him. The thought of her was like a calm, cool breeze in the warmer lands where he lived.

When the day came for the king to make his choice, all of

the king's council assembled in the Great Hall. Piers drew
the large portraits from his saddlebags one by one and
recalled what the maidens had spoken. The king and his
council looked at the pictures and heard the words. And one
by one they shook their heads.

As Piers bent to put the final portrait back into his pack,
the chain with the miniature slipped out of his doublet. The
king reached over and touched it. Then he held it up to the
light and looked at the picture.

"Who is this?" he asked. "And why is this portrait
smaller and set apart from the rest?"

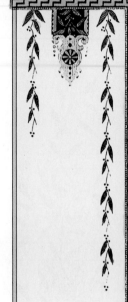

Piers answered, "It is a maiden known as Bianca. She
lives in the cold lands far to the North. She speaks in slivers
that cut through lies." And he told them about the storm and
how he had met the beautiful, silent girl and discovered her
great wisdom.

"This is the one I shall marry," said the king.

"It would be most improper," said the councilors
together. "She is not noble-born."

"How does one judge nobility?" asked the king. "How
does one measure it?"

The councilors scratched their heads and looked puzzled.
"Can you do such a thing?" asked one. "Can you not do
such a thing?" said another. "How is it possible?" asked a
third. And they continued this way for some time.

At last the king silenced them with his hand. "Enough of
this noise. I will make a measure. I will test the wisdom of
this Silent Bianca," he said. And under his breath, he added,
"And I will test *your* wisdom as well."

Then the king sent his council, with Piers to guide them,
off to the cold lands to bring Bianca back to the throne.

Piers and the councilors traveled twenty days and nights
until the stars fell like snow behind them and at last they
came to the chilly land where Bianca made her home.
There they packed up Bianca and her few belongings and
immediately started back to the king.

But when they reached the road that ran around the castle, strange to say, they found their way blocked by soldiers. Campfires blossomed like flowers on the plain. At every turning and every straightaway stood a guard. It seemed there was no place where they could pass.

"This is very odd," said Piers. "There have never been soldiers here before. Could some unknown enemy have captured the castle while we were away?"

The councilors tried to question the guards, but none would answer. Not even a single question. Unused to silence, the councilors fell to puzzling among themselves. Some said one thing and some said another. They talked until the sun burned out behind them, but they could figure out no way to get beyond the guards and so bring Bianca to the king.

The air grew cold. The dark drew close. The councilors, weary with wondering, slept.

Only Bianca, who had said nothing all this time, remained awake. When she was certain that all the councilors were asleep, and even Piers was snoring gently, Bianca arose. Slowly she walked along the road that circled around the castle. Now and then she opened her mouth as if to scream or speak or sigh. But of course no sounds came out of her mouth at all. Then she would close it again, kneeling humbly when challenged by a silent guard's upraised spear. For the guards still spoke not a word but remained closemouthed at their posts.

And so from path to path, from guard to guard, from

campfire to campfire, Bianca walked.

Just at dawn, she returned to the place where the councilors and Piers slept leaning on one another's shoulders like sticks stacked up ready for a fire.

As the sun flamed into the sky, a sudden strange babble was heard. At first it was like a single woman crying, calling, sobbing. Then, as the sun grew hotter and the morning cookfires were lit, it was as though a thousand women called to their men, wailing and sighing at each campfire and at every turning. It was the slivers of Bianca's voice which she had so carefully placed during her long night's walk; the slivers warmed and melted by the rising sun and the burning coals.

But the guards did not know this. And they looked around one way and another. Yet the only woman near them was Bianca, sitting silently, smiling, surrounded by Piers and the puzzled councilors.

And then, from somewhere beyond the guards, a chorus of women cried out. It was a cry like a single clear voice. "Come home, come home," called the women. "Leave off your soldiering. You need no arms but ours. Leave off your soldiering. No arms . . . no arms but ours."

The guards hesitantly at first, by ones and twos, and then joyfully by twenties and hundreds, threw down their weapons. Then they raced back home to their wives and sweethearts. For they were not really an unknown enemy at all but townsmen hired by the king to try the wisdom of the councilors and of Bianca.

When the councilors realized what Bianca had done, they brought her swiftly to the king. Instead of scratching their heads and looking puzzled, they spoke right out and said, "She is most certainly wise and more than fit for a king to marry."

The king, when he heard how Bianca had fooled the guards, laughed and laughed for he thought it a grand joke. And when he stopped laughing and considered the meaning of her words, he agreed she was indeed even wiser than old Piers had said.

So the king and Bianca were married.

And if the king had any problems thereafter, and his council could give him only questions instead of answers, he might be found at the royal hearthstone. There he could be seen warming his hands. But he was doing something more besides: He would be listening to the words that came from the fire and from the wise and loving heart of Silent Bianca, his queen.

THINK IT OVER

1. In what ways are the king's councilors and Bianca different?

2. How does Bianca get the guards to return to their homes?

WRITE

Do you think Bianca is happy to be the queen? Write a few paragraphs explaining your answer.

THE POWER OF WORDS

Poet Mary O'Neill wrote that "English is a wonderful game." How do the other selections show that this is true?

How are the stories of Echo and Bianca similar? How are they different?

WRITER'S WORKSHOP Bianca can speak only in slivers of ice, so she speaks very little. Imagine that you also must speak very little. A taxi driver needs directions from your home to school. In as few words as possible, give the driver directions. Be sure the directions are clear and accurate.

VISITORS FROM SPACE

Is that object in the sky a plane, a meteor, a very bright planet? Or is it something more surprising? The following selections explore our continuing fascination with unexpected flying objects.

C O N T E N T S

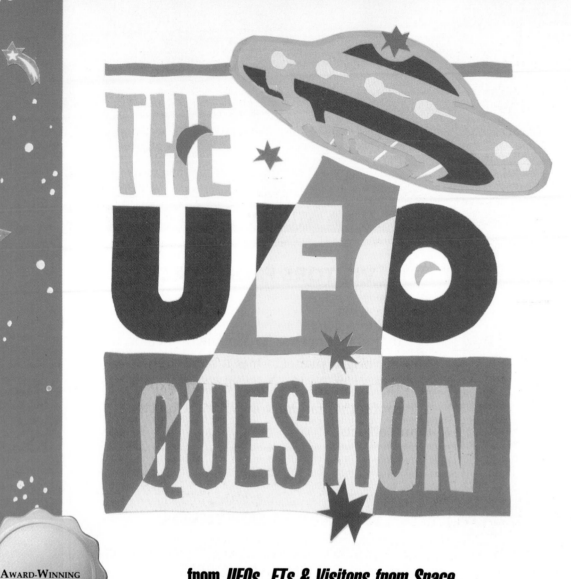

THE UFO QUESTION

from *UFOs, ETs & Visitors from Space*

by Melvin Berger   illustrations by Keith Gold

The radio announcer on the evening news program of October 31, 1938, kept telling his listeners to remain calm. He assured them that the authorities were on the scene. They were taking all steps necessary to prevent a catastrophe.

Although he tried to sound calm, there was a note of panic in his voice. His fright was not hard to understand. He was reporting that a spaceship from Mars had just landed in New Jersey. In vivid details he described how the Martians were spreading throughout the countryside, capturing or killing any humans who tried to stop them.

Terror spread like wildfire among those in New Jersey and nearby states who were tuned in to the program. As people learned what was happening, they bolted their doors and locked their windows. Others hid beneath beds or crawled into cellars. Nearly everyone wanted to escape the alien invaders. While thousands threw their most valuable belongings into bags and fled their homes by foot or car, many others, too frightened to move, stayed glued to their radio sets.

But very soon the facts came out. The newscast about the landing of Martians on Earth was nothing more than fiction—a realistic dramatization of H. G. Wells's book *War of the Worlds*. What was very real—and totally unexpected—was the reaction of the public. Almost everyone was fully prepared to believe in an invasion from Mars!

THE BELIEF IN LIFE ELSEWHERE

In our own day, with men on the moon and spaceships on Mars, the belief in life elsewhere is perhaps greater than ever. But what facts do we actually have about intelligent beings in space? Do they exist? If so, what are they like? And what are our chances of communicating or visiting with them?

For the longest time, writers of science fiction and fantasy were the only ones seeking answers to these questions. But more recently, scientists have begun researching the possibility of life on planets that revolve around other suns. Using the tools and methods of modern science, highly trained researchers are shedding new light on an old subject—one that has long been hidden behind a screen of rumors, half-truths and unreliable observations.

TWO FABLES FOR OUR TIME

One day, a newly hatched crow was looking at his feathers. "Are all crows black like me?" he asked his mother.

"Of course they are," his mother answered. "Every crow in our flock is black. All the crows in the fields and forests for miles around are black. Everyone knows that every crow is black."

When he was a little bigger, the young crow went flying off by himself. After a while he saw another bird. It looked like a crow. It said "Caw, caw" like a crow. But it wasn't black. It was white!

The young crow flew over to the other bird. "Are you a crow?" he asked.

"Yes, I am," the white bird answered.

"But you're white instead of black," said the young crow.

"I know," replied the white crow. "The other crows in my flock are black. My parents are black crows. So I'm a crow, too. But I'm white."

The young crow quickly flew back to his mother. "I just saw a white crow!" he shouted in great excitement.

"You made a mistake," she said very firmly. "It was probably a dove."

"I'm sure it was a crow," he insisted.

His mother grew angry. "I've seen hundreds and hundreds of crows. They're all black. Crows are black. And that's final!"

The young crow just smiled.

Moral: It takes just one exception to prove that there are exceptions.

Suzy Owl and Billy Owl were the two young children of the Owl family. One Christmas morning Suzy and Billy were opening their presents. "Here's a pretty skirt from Aunt Nancy!" Suzy cried.

"And here's a great book about monsters from Grandma Eleanor," Billy said.

They kept on unwrapping their presents and calling out the name of the person who had given them each gift. Then suddenly Suzy said, "Here's a doll. But I don't know who gave it to me."

A minute later Billy said, "And I don't know who gave me this baseball mitt."

The two children looked at each other. "It must be Santa Claus," Suzy decided.

"Of course!" Billy agreed. "After all, we know who gave us all the other presents. This proves there is a Santa Claus!"

Mom and Dad Owl started to laugh. "We bought you the doll and mitt," they confessed. "We didn't put cards in the boxes as a joke. But neither of us is Santa Claus!"

Moral: When something happens that seems hard to figure out, look first for a simple explanation.

These fables have two very different morals. They also illustrate two different ways of thinking about UFOs and ETs.

The first fable suggests that even one unexplained UFO sighting or ET contact is proof enough that such things exist. According to the second fable, though, even happenings that are surprising and unexpected may have simple explanations.

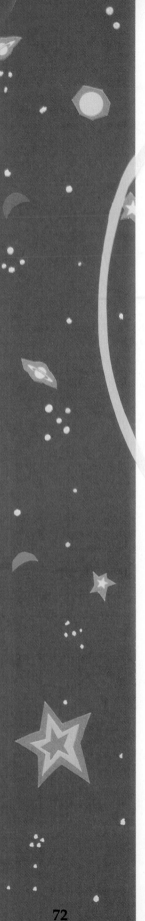

Over the years there have been thousands of reports of UFO sightings and ET contacts. Almost all the incidents have been explained in ordinary ways. Still, a few remain unaccounted for. That leaves it up to each of us to decide what to think. Do you believe that only one unexplained UFO or ET incident proves that UFOs and ETs exist? Or do you believe that even though a few incidents are hard to figure out, they offer no real proof of life in other worlds?

UFOs

UFOs: abbreviation of Unidentified Flying Objects. Objects seen in the air or on land but of unknown source or origin.

It was three o'clock on the afternoon of June 24, 1947. Kenneth Arnold, a 32-year-old salesman, was flying his private plane from Chehalis to Yakima, Washington, to call on a customer. Suddenly, off to his left, Ken saw a bright flash of light. He noticed nine strange-looking aircraft flying toward Mount Rainier.

"I could see their outline quite plainly against the snow as they approached the mountain," he later said. "They flew very close to the mountaintops, directly south to southeast, down the hog's back of the range, flying like geese in a diagonal line, as if they were linked together.

"They were approximately 20 or 25 miles away," Arnold also reported, "and I couldn't see a tail on them. I watched for about three minutes . . . a chain of saucerlike things at least 5 miles long, swerving in and out of the high mountain peaks. They were flat like a pie pan and so shiny they reflected the sun like a mirror."

The startled pilot estimated that each silvery craft was 45 to 50 feet long. They seemed to be flying at a height of about 9,500 feet. And he put their speed at 1,700 miles an hour—about three times swifter than any existing plane! "I never saw anything so fast," he said later.

As Arnold watched in amazement, the strange-looking aircraft dove, soared and scooted this way and that before disappearing out of sight. After locating the point on his map, he continued his flight to the Yakima airport.

Arnold's account of the mysterious sightings created an absolute sensation. Newspapers and magazines around the world rushed to print stories about what he had seen. Using the pilot's words, they reported that the unidentified craft looked "like a saucer would if you skipped it across the water." That name caught on, and soon everyone was talking about "flying saucers."

The news reached the ears of officials in the U.S. Air Force. Since it is their job to protect the United States from air attack, they decided to investigate. After all, the craft that Arnold saw might threaten the nation's security.

An expert in military intelligence questioned Arnold at great length. He reported: "It is the personal opinion of the interviewer that Mr. Arnold actually saw what he stated that he saw. It is difficult to believe that a man of Mr. Arnold's character and apparent integrity would state that he saw objects and write up a report to the extent that he did if he did not see them."

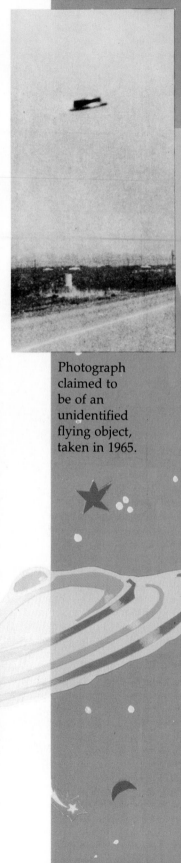

Photograph claimed to be of an unidentified flying object, taken in 1965.

In the little town of Maysville, Kentucky, on January 7, 1948, a number of people noted a strange-looking object in the sky overhead. Someone called the State Police. Several officers rushed out to look, and they, too, noticed something moving across the sky that they could not recognize. The police called the Godman Air Force Base near Louisville, Kentucky, for more information. The control tower could offer no explanation. But they agreed to help identify the flying object.

Meanwhile, other reports of the same craft began pouring in. People from many different locations described it in similar terms: It was round, between 250 and 300 feet in diameter, metallic in color and glowing brightly. Everyone also said that it was heading westward at great speed.

By now the top commanders at Godman were at the control tower. None of them could identify the object. But while they were trying to decide what to do next, a flight of four F-51 jets from the Air National Guard passed nearby on a routine training flight. Since these very fast planes were already in the air, the officers at Godman asked the lead pilot, Captain Thomas Mantell, to investigate.

Captain Mantell banked his plane south to look for the object. Very soon he radioed the control tower, "Object traveling at half my speed and directly ahead of me and above. I'm going to take a closer look. It appears metallic and tremendous in size. I'm going to 20,000 feet." Then silence.

At 3:20 P.M. the Godman control tower got word that Captain Mantell's plane had crashed. Based on first reports, some said that he had made contact with the mysterious object. Others suspected that the unidentified object had somehow caused his plane to go down.

On December 13, 1961, George E. Weber was walking across the parking lot of George Washington University in Washington, D.C., when a guard pointed out a strange-looking object in the sky. Meanwhile, William John Meyer, Jr., who was driving his car and waiting for a traffic light to change, also noted the same object overhead.

All three descriptions of the object were similar—dark gray in color, diamond-shaped, about 20 feet long and moving silently at a height of about 1,500 feet.

Edwin Aldrin on the moon with lunar module on *Apollo 11* mission.

Weber mentioned a light shining from the bottom of the object. Meyer told of an orange-brown glow from the center area. The craft had neither wings nor propellers and left no vapor trail in the air. The two men in the parking lot had it in view for about three minutes. Meyer could watch only for a minute before the beeping horns of the cars he was blocking forced him to move along with the traffic.

Launched on July 16, 1969, the Apollo 11 space shot had three astronauts on board—Neil Armstrong, Edwin Aldrin and Michael Collins. The historic flight was the first to place a human being on the moon.

After their return, certain stories began circulating about bizarre happenings on their trip. On the second day, when they were about halfway to the moon, it was said, the crew observed some shiny white objects flying alongside their ship and keeping pace with them. They supposedly photographed the objects. Two days later, they again saw the objects and again recorded the sighting on film.

According to some reports, the astronauts noted two objects flying together in close formation. At times they would come close together. Then they would separate. Both appeared to be emitting some sort of liquid. After watching their movements in space, the astronauts decided the objects were under intelligent control.

The report of astronaut sightings of unidentified objects was taken very seriously. Because astronauts are highly trained as pilots and scientists, they are considered very reliable observers. In this case, not only had they presumably sighted the objects, but they had also taken photos of them. It had long been expected that if there are intelligent beings elsewhere in the universe, they would be very interested in our space shots.

Colonel Osires Silva is a trained aeronautical engineer as well as the head of Brazil's state-owned oil company. Because of his background and position everyone listened very carefully to what he had to say when his private plane landed at the airport at São José dos Campos on May 19, 1986.

Silva told how he and his pilot had seen a strange light in the air. He described "a dancing point in the sky." The two observers estimated the object's speed at about 900 miles per hour.

On checking with the control tower, it was learned that some unidentified objects were also being picked up on the radar screen. The airport authorities quickly called the

Brazilian Defense Center. They sent up six of their fastest jets to locate and identify these mysterious lights.

Although all the pilots saw the lights, the planes they were flying could not catch up with the objects emitting them. After some three hours, the pilots lost sight of the lights entirely. They also disappeared from the radar screen. Even though the Brazilian Air Force investigated the incident, they never released their findings.

These have been among the best-known sightings of UFOs in recent years. At first, the accounts were generally accepted to be true. Like the black crow's finding the white crow in our first fable, many people believed it takes just one UFO sighting to prove that UFOs exist.

Later, however, a number of investigators tried to discover whether or not these reports were accurate. Like Suzy and Billy Owl in the second fable, they wanted to see if there were simple explanations of events that were hard to understand. Very often what they found was completely different from the original reports.

THE KENNETH ARNOLD CASE

This case proved to be one of the simplest to understand. Bright sunlight shining on clouds among mountain peaks frequently creates optical illusions, making things seem real that are not. One effect that has been noted often is the optical illusion of disks of light that seem to be floating in the air. There is every reason to believe that such round, flat, thin objects are what Arnold saw. The nine disks were merely a false impression of "flying saucers" caused by the particular relationship of the sun, clouds and mountains at the time.

THE CAPTAIN MANTELL CASE

Investigators of the Mantell incident found that the captain had been chasing a Skyhook balloon. The incident occurred, however, at a time when the Skyhook balloon was still a military secret. No one outside the program knew that it even existed.

The balloon, it was discovered, had a metallic surface, measured 100 feet across and carried various scientific measuring instruments. Captain Mantell did not crash because of any encounter with a UFO. The Air Force authorities said that he flew too high without oxygen and blacked out.

THE WEBER-MEYER SIGHTINGS

The 1961 Weber-Meyer sighting in Washington, D.C., is still listed as an unsolved case. After nearly thirty years, no one has been able to confirm it either as a known object, a natural event or a true encounter with a UFO.

THE APOLLO 11 INCIDENT

The Apollo 11 incident proved to be an out-and-out fake. When Neil Armstrong was asked about seeing UFOs, he answered, "We didn't see them, and with what we . . . are doing in space, that's a real wonder." NASA official Charles Redmond adds, "We don't have any UFO secrets."

One photograph of Earth taken from Apollo 11 did, however, show a bright white object floating in the air. But

Photograph taken from *Apollo 11* of an object in space. It proved to be a piece of metal that had broken off the spacecraft.

upon further investigation, it proved to be nothing more than a piece of metal that had broken off when the lunar module was released. In the same way, movie film shot from inside the spacecraft reveals a number of strange lights and shapes. All the experts agree, however, that they are simply reflections and glares in the window.

It now seems clear that the early reports of UFOs involving Apollo 11 were based on false quotes and transcripts of conversations between the crew and Mission Control. Also, it was discovered that someone had retouched the photos to make them look as though UFOs were present. Nevertheless, the desire to believe in UFOs is very strong in some people. Even when NASA released the original transcripts and the original photos, which did not show UFOs, some Americans continued to think that the Apollo 11 crew had seen UFOs. A few even charged that NASA was hiding the truth!

THE COLONEL SILVA SIGHTING

The results of the Brazilian Air Force investigation of the "dancing point of light" that Colonel Silva watched have never been made public. Nor have any other scientists been able to explain what the colonel, his pilot and the six pilots of the Air Force jets observed or what the radar screen showed that night.

James Oberg, a leading UFO researcher, points out that radar can be fooled by birds, insects or certain weather conditions. But neither he nor any of the others who have looked into the case has succeeded in identifying the mysterious lights. Colonel Silva's sighting, therefore, remains another significant case of an unsolved UFO encounter.

UFOs IN PERSPECTIVE

Sightings of UFOs are nothing new. As long ago as A.D. 98, a number of ancient Romans reported seeing a round burning shield flashing across the sky. Another sighting from around that time was of a giant globe, brighter than the sun, coming down to Earth and then flying off again. In fact, all through the Middle Ages people related tales about strange objects and unexplained lights that they saw in the sky—and sometimes on land as well.

What *is* new are the efforts of scientists to study UFOs. Soon after Kenneth Arnold reported seeing flying saucers in 1947, the U.S. Air Force set up an office to investigate all such sightings to make sure they were not part of a military attack or invasion. The inquiry was later given the name Project Blue Book. In 1969 the project was brought to a close when the Air Force concluded that UFOs did not threaten the nation's security.

Weather balloons, such as these, account for a large percentage of UFO sightings.

Besides the Air Force, many private organizations set up UFO investigations. Some of them are still in operation. Worldwide, reports on UFO sightings still pour in at the rate of about 100 a day!

To help in the study of UFOs, scientist J. Allen Hynek divided UFO sightings into six types.

The first three are distant observations:

1. Bright lights seen in the night sky.
2. Bright ovals or disks seen in the daytime sky.
3. Objects detected only by radar.

The final three are much closer and thus more exciting:

4. Close encounters of the first kind—sighting an unidentified object on Earth.
5. Close encounters of the second kind—sighting an unidentified object on Earth and tracing its physical effects on things or beings.
6. Close encounters of the third kind—sighting an unidentified object on Earth and making physical contact with the object or its occupants.

Most UFO reports fall into one of the first three of Dr. Hynek's categories. But experts find eventually that most of them, perhaps 90 percent or more, are not true UFOs. They are really IFOs—Identified Flying Objects.

According to these experts, people may be fooled into thinking they are making a Type One sighting when they catch an unusual or unexpected view of a plane, a meteor, the very bright planet Venus or one of the other planets. Weather balloons, particular cloud formations, artificial satellites, and blimps account for a large percentage of Type Two observations. False radar signals can come either from flocks of birds, swarms of insects or unexplained radar waves called "angels."

When Project Blue Book stopped operating, it had studied over 12,000 UFO sightings. Of the total number, the experts were able to explain well over 90 percent of the reported incidents. In over 2,000 of the cases, the observers were found to be seeing Venus or another planet, a particularly bright star or some other natural astronomical body or event. In another 1,500 cases, the object sighted proved to be an airplane. Nearly 800 more were glimpses of artificial satellites, and about 500 were balloons. A total of about 6,500 were false reports, posed or retouched photos, strange cloud formations, birds, insects and just plain human error.

When all was said and done, however, there remained about 700 events for which no explanation could be found, either natural or man-made. What do the experts say about these?

Major Hector Quintanilla, former director of Project Blue Book, insists that there are no UFOs. He cites the absence of even one fully confirmed report of a UFO sighting. Astronomer Carl Sagan concurs. A true sighting, he expects, would have many reliable witnesses all coming forward at the same time.

Other experts make these points: UFOs could not land and then take off without leaving significant evidence of the tremendous force needed to launch or slow down a spaceship. Since a spaceship would have to travel an immense distance to arrive on Earth, it would not just appear in a remote area, stay for a few minutes and then quickly fly away. Most likely it would stay for a period of time and make better contact with the earth's inhabitants. And with all the military air defense and civilian air traffic systems now operating, it is virtually impossible for any aircraft to enter the earth's air space without being detected.

Still, in a February 1987 Gallup poll, almost half of all Americans said they believe in UFOs. Some had had UFO experiences themselves and don't accept the scientists' explanations. Many more had read or seen very dramatic accounts of the most exciting of these encounters. For all these people, the unsolved, unexplained UFO events are enough to convince them that there are living beings that have come to Earth from the outer reaches of space in what we call UFOs.

THINK IT OVER

1. *After you read the explanations, what did you think about the UFO stories?*

2. *Why do the experts feel that there are no "real" UFOs?*

3. *What was Project Blue Book, and what were the final conclusions of this operation?*

4. *Do you think the people who reported these five sightings believed the scientific explanations? Consider each case.*

5. *According to Carl Sagan, a true sighting of a UFO would have many reliable witnesses. How does that opinion fit the sightings described in the selection?*

WRITE

Do you think Project Blue Book should be started again? Write a paragraph explaining your opinion.

THE DREADED SCUM BEINGS FIRE! SPACEMAN SPIFF IS *HIT!*

AWARD-WINNING CARTOONIST

IT NEVER FAILS. I JUST WASHED AND WAXED THIS THING.

OUR HERO, THE INTREPID SPACEMAN SPIFF, STRUGGLES WITH THE CONTROLS OF HIS DAMAGED SPACECRAFT!

THE FREEM PROPULSION BLASTERS ARE USELESS! SPIFF CRASHES ONTO THE SURFACE OF AN ALIEN PLANET!

UNSCATHED, THE FEARLESS SPACE EXPLORER EMERGES FROM THE SMOLDERING WRECKAGE! HE IS MAROONED ON A HOSTILE WORLD!

SCORCHED BY TWIN SUNS, THE PLANET IS NOTHING BUT BARREN ROCK AND METHANE! THERE'S NO HOPE OF FINDING FOOD OR WATER!

SPIFF COLLAPSES! OH NO, A HIDEOUS ALIEN SPOTS HIM! IN HIS WEAKENED STATE, SPIFF IS NO MATCH FOR THE MONSTER! *THIS COULD BE THE END!!*

LUNCHTIME! I BROUGHT YOU A SANDWICH AND SOME LEMONADE.

BRING THE DISHES BACK WHEN YOU'RE DONE, OK?

...OH WELL.

THANKS, MOM.

Calvin and Hobbes cartoon. Copyright 1985 by Universal Press Syndicate. Reprinted by permission of Universal Press Syndicate. All rights reserved.

84

WORDS ABOUT THE CARTOONIST

BILL WATTERSON

Bill Watterson likes his privacy. He doesn't like to have his picture taken or to have people ask him for his autograph. "I don't want to be more recognized than I am," he says. He thinks that people should be more interested in his cartoons than in him, and he believes that his drawing and writing are the important things about him. Obviously, he loves his work. He says doing his work is his best reward, better than money. "I wouldn't be doing this if I were just in it for the money," he once said. He

has wanted to be a cartoonist since he was a boy.

Bill Watterson was born in 1959 and grew up in Ohio, where his father was a lawyer. When he went to college, he studied political science, and after college he became a political cartoonist. He didn't stay with political cartooning very long, but he kept on drawing, trying many different ideas for comic strips. He even wrote science fiction comics, but these were not successful. One of his comics, called *Spaceman Spiff*, made fun of

AWARD-WINNING CARTOONIST

regular science fiction comics. In the *Calvin and Hobbes* strip, Calvin imagines himself as Spaceman Spiff from time to time.

Bill Watterson says of his creations that Calvin is "a little too intelligent for his age. The thing that I really enjoy about him is . . . he doesn't have the experience yet to know the things he shouldn't do. But I wouldn't want to be him, and I wouldn't want to have him in the house."

Hobbes is a stuffed tiger who is very much alive to Calvin. He is a little smarter and a little more careful than Calvin, and he often thinks ahead, which Calvin never does.

Bill Watterson's characters have a life of their own, and he lets them express themselves in their own ways. "One of the things that I don't think most people realize," he says, "is that I don't have any more idea of what these two are going to do next week than anybody else."

I had the evening watch that day, and when Burke relieved me at midnight he was absolutely normal. When I left he was settling down in the chief's chair with a detective story magazine. The CAA[1] frowns on that—the magazine, I mean, not the chief's chair—but most of us do read on duty, especially on the midnight watch, because ordinarily there is nothing to do at an intermediate landing field between midnight and eight but report the weather once an hour, and reading is about the only way to keep from getting sleepy. But once in a while things do happen, which is why they keep a twenty-four-hour watch at these places.

It must have been around one-twenty that things began to happen on this night. About that time Burke glanced up at the clock and decided it was time to start taking his weather—a job that wasn't likely to prove very interesting, since conditions had been "ceiling and visibility unlimited" all evening, and the forecasts stubbornly maintained that they would continue so—so he put aside his magazine and stepped outside to read the thermometers. It was while he was spinning the psychrometer crank and gazing around the sky for signs of cloudiness that he saw this plane coming in.

When he first saw it, he says, it was just a dot of light sliding slowly down the sky toward the field. The first thing that struck him as queer about this ship was that he couldn't hear the engines, even though it couldn't have been over half a mile from the west boundary. It seemed to be gliding in; this was a very silly thing to do with nothing but the boundary lights and beacon as a guide. Another thing, it was strange

---

[1] CAA: Civil Aviation Authority

that any plane at all would be landing here after dark, in good weather, since there was none based at our field, and it was only about once in a blue moon that we had a visitor. Burke wondered about that, but then he remembered that he had to get his weather in the sequence, so he ran inside and put it on the wire.

By the time he could get to the window for another look, the stranger was just landing. He could see it more plainly now in the flashes from the beacon, and if it was a plane, it was like none he'd ever seen or even heard of. It looked more like an airship—only not like an airship either. This may sound silly, but Burke says if you can imagine a flying submarine, that is just what it looked like, and he should know, being ex-Navy. He says it reminded him of the old gag the recruit instructors like to pull: If you were on guard and saw a battleship steaming across the parade ground, what would you do? It even had *U.S. Navy 1156* painted on its side in big black letters.

There was still no sound from the engines, but there was a faint blue exhaust from somewhere around its tail, and it was plain that the ship was under control—that is, if it really was there. When it was about thirty yards from the watchhouse, this exhaust stopped, and it settled gently to the ground on two broad skis that ran the length of the ship. It drifted down like a feather, but when the weight came on those skis they sank a good three inches into the unsurfaced runway. Burke began to wonder about secret Navy inventions, stratosphere planes, and stuff like that. Also he wondered whether he ought to call the chief, and decided not to since the chief is apt to be cranky when someone wakes him up in the middle of the night and makes him drive the six miles from his home to the field. Burke compromised by making an entry in the log that *Navy 1156* had landed at 0141. Then he walked out to the ship and waited for someone to get out. When he got close enough, just to satisfy his own curiosity, he gave one of the ski struts a good hearty kick. It was solid enough, all right. He almost broke his toe.

There was a glassed-in compartment in the upper part of the nose that looked like the control room, and through the glass Burke could see someone in a blue coverall and flight cap fussing with some instruments. He was so busy watching this fellow that he didn't notice the door open behind him until a voice spoke almost over his shoulder.

"Hey," the voice said, "what's the name of this place?"

Burke spun around and looked up at an open door in the side of the ship and another man in the same blue coverall and flight cap. This one wore a web pistol belt, though, and a funny, bulky-looking pistol in the holster. He had a lieutenant's stripes on his shoulder and Burke automatically saluted him.

"Parker, sir," he answered. "Parker, North Dakota."

The lieutenant turned and relayed this information to someone back in the ship. Then he and Burke stared at each other. Burke was on the point of mustering up courage to ask what the score was when another man came into view. This was the one who had been in the control room, and Burke saw that he was a commander. He, too, stared curiously at Burke.

"Can we get some water here?" he asked.

"Sure." Burke indicated the pump, visible in the light from the open watchhouse door. "Right over there."

The lieutenant eyed the pump doubtfully. "We might get it out of there in about a week," he said.

The commander jumped. "A week! We have a mission to perform. We can't stay around here for a week. We have to be out by morning."

"Yes, sir, I know, but we're going to need a lot of water. Those Jennies[2] will suck it up like a thousand-horse centrifugal[3] when we hit that warp, or whatever it is."

"About how much?"

The lieutenant said thoughtfully, "Well, we're almost dry now, and we'll need every drop we can carry. At least twenty-five thousand gallons."

---

[2] Jennies: generators
[3] thousand-horse centrifugal: a kind of engine

The commander turned back to Burke. "How about it?" he demanded. "Can we get that much water around here?"

Burke mentally pictured a five-hundred-gallon tank, multiplied by fifty. That was a lot of water. He found himself agreeing with the lieutenant that it would be hardly feasible to get it out of the watchhouse well, if a person was in a hurry.

"There's the river," he said, "but it'd be kind of hard to find in the dark."

"Never mind that. We'll pick it up in the visors. Which way?"

"South," Burke told him. "About five miles."

"Thanks."

For an instant longer they stared sharply at him, as if fascinated by his appearance, and he in turn began to realize that there was something obscurely alien about these people—nothing definite, just a hint of difference in the way they handled their words, a certain smooth precision in their movements. It made him vaguely uneasy, and he felt a distinct sense of relief when the commander turned and spoke to the lieutenant.

"Come on," he said. "Let's get her up."

The two officers disappeared into the ship. A seaman stepped into view and threw a switch and the door began silently to close. Burke suddenly remembered there were questions he wanted to ask.

"Hey," he shouted. "Wait a minute."

The door slid open a foot and the seaman's head popped

out. "Stand clear," he warned. "If you're caught in the field when we start to go up, you'll go with us."

Before Burke could open his mouth to speak the face disappeared and the door closed again. Burke prudently retired to the watchhouse porch.

Presently the ship lifted into the air, the exhaust flared out softly, and she spun on her tail and headed southward. Burke watched until the blue glow had faded out into the starry sky, then went inside and looked thoughtfully at the log. There are no regulations covering the landing of submarines at intermediate fields, and the CAA does not approve of unorthodox use of its facilities.

Finally he came to a decision and sat down to the typewriter.

"0152," he wrote. "*Navy 1156* took off."

THINK IT OVER

1. *Do you think Burke writes enough in the logbook after the strange ship leaves? Explain your answer.*

2. *What does the crew of the ship need from Burke, and how does he help them?*

3. *What is it about the ship that puzzles Burke?*

4. *What does Burke see? Use evidence from the story to support your answer.*

WRITE

Write three questions you would have asked the crew if you had seen the strange ship.

VISITORS FROM SPACE

What do you think UFO researchers would say to Burke if he told them about his encounter?

· ·

How does Burke's description of the object he saw compare with the descriptions of objects in "The UFO Question"?

· ·

WRITER'S WORKSHOP In "The UFO Question," the author says that about one hundred UFO sightings are reported each day worldwide. Imagine that you are part of the team that handles these reports. Refer to the examples from the selection as you make up a case in which someone reports seeing a UFO. Write a description of the sighting, including all important details. Then use your scientific understanding of UFOs to write a possible explanation for the sighting.

CONNECTIONS

THE VALLEY OF MEXICO

Imagine how surprised you would be to encounter a civilization unlike any you had ever seen before. That's what happened in 1519, when Spanish troops under Hernando Cortés landed in Mexico.

For native Mexicans, it was almost as if aliens from space had arrived. The Spaniards had pale skin, wore suits of armor, and carried guns. They also rode horses, animals that were unknown in the Americas.

The Spaniards were equally surprised when they crossed a mountain pass and looked down on the Valley of Mexico. Below them lay the Aztec capital of Tenochtitlán, set on an island in a shimmering lake. Tenochtitlán was larger and more splendid than any European city of the time. One Spaniard wrote, "The soldiers asked whether it was not all a dream."

■ *Imagine that you have come upon a fabulous city and civilization. Where is it located, and what is it like? Share your ideas in a class brainstorming session.*

Aztec calendar

DESIGN A CITY

Working with a partner, design a city based on ideas from your brainstorming session. Make a drawing of the city (top view and side view), and give your city a name. Display your drawings, and discuss them with classmates.

ANCIENT MODERN CITIES

Mexico City is built on the site of old Tenochtitlán, and signs of its ancient past can still be seen. Research Mexico City or another modern city with an ancient history, such as Cuzco, Peru; Athens, Greece; or Beijing, China. Write a report on the city, using an outline like the one below to organize your information.

Old and new Beijing, China

(CITY, COUNTRY)
I. Geography (location/land/climate) A. B.
II. Population (size/social groups) A. B.
III. History A. B.
IV. Old and New Features A. B.

95

UNIT TWO

HEROES

In my opinion, those who turn out to be heroes are people who respond in particular ways to their circumstances.

Lois Lowry

How do you recognize a hero? True heroes come in all sizes and shapes and from every land. Heroes such as Mohandas Gandhi and Martin Luther King, Jr., though leaders in their own countries, belong to the world. What makes someone a hero? Is it courage? Determination? Action? Consider what makes a hero as you read the next selections.

THEMES

EVERYDAY HEROES

COURAGE AND KINDNESS

REVOLUTIONARY HEROES

BOOKSHELF

ZEELY

BY VIRGINIA HAMILTON

Elizabeth changes her name to Geeder for the summer and is ready for something unusual to happen. When she meets the elegant Zeely, Geeder is sure she is in the presence of royalty. ALA NOTABLE BOOK

HBJ LIBRARY BOOK

ISLAND OF THE BLUE DOLPHINS

BY SCOTT O'DELL

A young Native American girl is stranded on an island off the coast of California. This book tells of her long and lonely struggle to survive. NEWBERY MEDAL, ALA NOTABLE BOOK

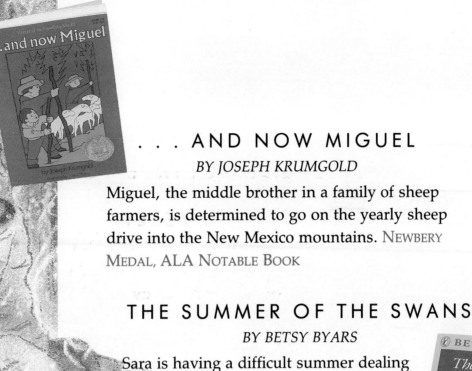

. . . AND NOW MIGUEL

BY JOSEPH KRUMGOLD

Miguel, the middle brother in a family of sheep farmers, is determined to go on the yearly sheep drive into the New Mexico mountains. NEWBERY MEDAL, ALA NOTABLE BOOK

THE SUMMER OF THE SWANS

BY BETSY BYARS

Sara is having a difficult summer dealing with the emotions involved in growing up. Then her life is further complicated by the disappearance of her younger brother. NEWBERY MEDAL, ALA NOTABLE BOOK

GEORGE WASHINGTON

BY MARY POPE OSBORNE

Here is the life story of an American hero who, although a distinguished leader, preferred the quiet life of a Virginia farmer. AWARD-WINNING AUTHOR

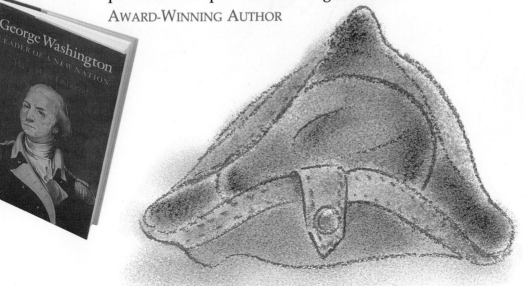

EVERYDAY HEROES

When you think of a hero, who comes to mind? Do you think of your best friend, a stranger who saves a life, or a basketball player? The next selections may make you reconsider your ideas about heroes.

CONTENTS

Dana Parker is busy enough just trying to adjust to life at junior high. Imagine her surprise when she becomes a heroine!

102

Mystery Girl Saves Tot's Life

from *COURAGE, DANA* by Susan Beth Pfeffer

AWARD-WINNING
AUTHOR

illustrated by Michael Garland

I got to the corner of Main and North streets, just in time to miss the traffic light. I swear they run that thing just for pedestrians to have to stand there. It's a busy corner, and unless you're really feeling daring, you don't cross against the light. That's the sort of dumb thing Charlie might do, but not me. I wasn't in that big a hurry to get home and work on my book report.

I half noticed the people who were waiting for the light with me, the way you half notice things when you really aren't thinking about anything special, just waiting to cross the street. There was a woman carrying a bag, and a man in a business suit who looked a little like my father, and a mother with a half dozen packages in one hand, trying to control her little kid with the other. The kid was two or maybe three. I don't have that much experience with little kids, so it's hard for me to tell how old they are, or if they're boys or girls. This one was just a wriggling kid in overalls and a blue shirt.

But then the kid managed to wriggle away from its mother. And before she even had a chance to notice, the kid had run smack into the middle of Main and North streets, with a big blue car coming right at it.

The funny thing is I didn't even think. If I'd taken one second to think, I never would have moved. I would have stood there frozen and watched the car hit the kid. It couldn't possibly have stopped in time. I couldn't even be sure if the driver would see the kid, it was so little.

Not that any of that really registered. Instead, I ran into the street, right into the path of that big blue car, and pushed the kid out of the way. The momentum of pushing kept me going, and I stumbled along, half holding the hysterical kid and half holding my school books.

I knew the car could hit us. It was roaring at us like a blue giant. But the funny thing was I felt like a giant too, an all-powerful one, like even if the car hit us, it wouldn't hurt us because I was made of steel, too. Like Superman. And as long as I was there, the kid was safe. I moved my giant steel legs and lifted the kid with my giant steel arms, and in what couldn't have been more than ten seconds, but felt more like ten years, I pushed both of us out of the path of the car.

By the time I'd gotten to the other side of the street with the kid, the blue car's brakes were screeching it to a halt. But over that noise, and the noise of the kid crying, I could hear its mother screaming from way across the street. It was amazing how far off she looked.

I really wanted to lean against the lamppost, but I wasn't going to let go of that kid. I'd already lost most of my books, since I wasn't about to go to the middle of the street and pick them up where I'd dropped them. So I stood there, holding on to the kid with my grip getting weaker and weaker as I started to realize just what I'd done, and just what the car could have done to the kid and me.

The man in the business suit stood in the middle of the street, holding his hand up to stop the cars, and picked up my books for me. The kid's mother, still screaming, crossed the street, walked over to where we were, and started weeping. She was shaking pretty hard, too, but nowhere near as hard as I was. The kid ran to its mother, and the two of them hugged and sobbed. That left me free to grab onto the lamppost, which I did, with both arms.

"I couldn't see, I didn't see," the driver of the blue car cried at us. I guess she pulled her car over to the side of the street, because I watched her join us. She seemed like a nice lady, too, not the sort that drove blue giant monster cars and aimed them at kids. "I have two of my own. I never would have . . ."

"He just got away from me," the kid's mother said. "I was holding his hand, and then he just broke away from me. . . ."

"Here are your books," the businessman said, handing them to me. That meant I had to give up the lamppost, which I did reluctantly. That car could have killed me. I risked my life for some little kid—I didn't even know if it was a boy or a girl. I could have been killed trying to save some strange kid's life.

"I have to go home now," I said, trying to sound conversational. Nobody was paying any attention to me anyway. I grabbed my books and took about a half dozen steps away from the corner of Main and North streets before my legs gave way, and I practically sank onto the sidewalk.

"I'll drive you home," the woman with the bag said. "My car is right here."

I ignored all the warnings about taking lifts from strangers, and gratefully followed the woman into her car. She didn't say anything to me, except to ask where I lived. A couple of times, though, she patted me on the hand, as if to say things were going to be all right.

"Here," I said when we got to our house. What a beautiful house, too. I'd never noticed just how beautiful it was before. The grass was mowed, and there were marigolds blooming in the front garden. Marigolds. If that car had hit me, I might never have seen marigolds again.

"There's no car in the driveway," the woman said. "Are you sure your parents are home?"

"Oh, no, they aren't," I said. "They both work."

"I won't leave you here alone," she said.

"That's okay," I said. "My older sister should be in." I

fumbled around, got the key from my pocket and unlocked the front door. The woman followed me in, to make sure Jean really was there.

She was in the living room, sprawled on the sofa, watching TV and eating an apple. I wanted to hug her.

"You see?" I said instead. "She's here."

"If you want, I'll stay until your parents come," the woman said.

"No, really," I said. "I'm okay."

"Dana?" Jean asked, turning around to face us. "What's the matter? What's going on?"

"You should be very proud of your younger sister," the woman said. "She saved a little boy's life. She's quite a heroine."

And that was the first I realized that I really was one.

The next morning at the breakfast table, I was trying to finish my math homework. I hadn't felt like working the night before, and I'd had to tell the story of what happened with the kid to Jean and Mom and Dad so often that I almost believed it had happened. But I didn't think the math teacher would accept it as an excuse for my homework not being done. Jean was nibbling on her toast, and Mom was drinking her orange juice and reading the paper. Dad was upstairs shaving.

"Good grief!" Mom exclaimed, and nearly choked on her juice.

"What?" Jean asked. I didn't even look up.

"There's an article here about Dana," she said.

That was enough to arouse my attention. So I put aside the math, and got up to see what Mom was talking about.

Sure enough, the *Herald* had an article on page 28, all about what had happened. "Mystery Girl Saves Tot's Life" the headline read.

I tried skimming the article, but it wasn't easy with Mom calling to Dad to come downstairs, and Jean reading it out loud.

"Listen to this," Jean said. "'I'd know her anywhere. She was about fourteen years old, and she was wearing a red shirt.' Fourteen."

"Do I really look fourteen?" I asked.

"No," Mom said. "The woman was in a state of shock. Bill! Come down here!"

"If Dana looks fourteen, I must look sixteen," Jean said. "That's only fair."

"I wasn't wearing a red shirt," I said. "But it's got to be me."

"Of course it's you," Mom said.

"What's all the excitement?" Dad asked. He still had lather over half his face.

"Look at this," Mom said, and she took the paper away from me before I had a chance to finish it. I didn't think that was fair, since it was about me, but Dad started reading the article before I had a chance to protest. "Would you look at that," he said. "You're famous, Dana."

"She isn't famous yet," Jean said. "Nobody knows Dana's the one who saved that kid."

"Can I tell the lady?" I asked.

"I don't see why not," Mom said. "I'm sure she wants to thank you in person."

"That's what the article says," Jean said. "'I owe my child's life to this girl. I won't be happy until I can thank her personally.'"

"We wouldn't want her to be unhappy forever," Dad said. "I think Dana should go to the paper after school and let them know. They can contact this woman."

"Why can't I go before school?" I asked. What a great excuse not to finish my math.

"Because school is more important," Mom said. "This can wait. Now, finish your homework, and then you'd better get going."

"Do you think they'll put my picture in the paper?" I asked.

"They might," Dad said. "I guess we'd better prepare ourselves for life with a celebrity."

"All I did was . . ." I started to say. But then I realized what I did was save that kid's life. Who knows? The kid might grow up to be president. Or cure cancer. And it would all be thanks to me. I smiled.

"I think the next few days are going to be absolutely unbearable," Jean said, looking at me. "Anybody mind if I change my name?"

"No teasing," Dad said. "Face it, Jean, you're as proud of Dana as the rest of us."

"I guess," she said, and then she smiled at me. "Sure, why not? My sister, the heroine."

I have to admit I liked the sound of it.

It wasn't easy making it to lunch without telling Sharon the whole story, but every spare minute I had until then I spent on my homework. It was hard concentrating on homework when I knew I was going to go to the paper after school and become famous. The little Dutch boy with his finger in the dike probably didn't have to do his homework for a week after he'd saved Holland. But there were no such breaks for me.

"Did you see that article in the paper?" I asked Sharon as soon as we sat down with our trays.

"What article?" Sharon asked.

"This one," I said, pulling it out of my schoolbag. It hadn't been easy getting Mom and Dad to agree that I should have the one copy of it. But they decided they could buy more on their way to work, so they let me take mine to school.

Sharon skimmed the article. I practically knew it by heart. Another reason my homework hadn't gotten done. "What about it?" she asked.

"That's me," I said. "I'm the fourteen-year-old who saved that kid's life."

"What are you talking about?" she asked, and then she read the article more carefully. "You're not fourteen, Dana. And you were wearing an orange shirt yesterday, not red. How can it be you?"

"It was me," I said, grabbing the article back from her. "It was after we had our ice cream cones. There are witnesses and everything."

Sharon looked at me and laughed. "You're crazy," she said.

"I am not crazy!" I cried. "That's me they're writing about. And Mom and Dad said I could go to the paper after school and let them know it was me. They might even run my picture in the paper."

"Dana, you're my best friend," Sharon said. "I've known you forever. You would never do anything that brave. I'm sorry, but you just wouldn't."

"What are you talking about?" I asked. I was too upset to start eating lunch, even though it was chili, my favorite. Instead, I fingered the article and tried not to pout.

"Dana, you're afraid of your own shadow," Sharon said. "I remember when you wet your pants just because of a little lightning."

"I was in kindergarten then," I said. "And it wasn't just the lightning. I was too scared to ask where the bathroom was."

"See what I mean?" she said. "You were too scared to ask where a bathroom was, and you expect me to believe you ran in front of a car and saved some kid's life? Really, Dana."

"But I did," I said. "Besides, I wasn't scared to ask about the bathroom. More like shy. Embarrassed. And I really did save the kid's life. I didn't think about it. I just did it. And if that kid cures cancer someday, it's going to be because of me."

"I think you've gone crazy," Sharon said, then started eating her chili. "So did you work on your book report?"

"I didn't work on anything!" I shouted. "Listen to me, Sharon. I'm the person they're looking for. I saved that kid's life. That seemed a little more important than some dumb book report. And I don't understand why you won't believe me. Have I ever lied to you before?"

"No," Sharon said. She stopped eating her chili and looked me over thoughtfully. "You're not a liar."

"Thank you," I said.

"It's just hard to believe, that's all," Sharon said, and went back to her chili.

"I'm going to the paper after school," I said. "I was going to ask you if you wanted to come with me, but since you don't believe me, I guess there isn't any point."

"You're really going?" Sharon asked.

"Of course I am," I said. "I told you my parents said I could."

"That's an awfully long walk for a practical joke," she said.

"Don't come," I said. "Don't see a mother's grateful tears." That had been my favorite phrase in the whole article.

"If I go with you, will you really go through with it?" Sharon asked.

"If it isn't true, I'll treat you to ice cream," I said. "A sundae. Deal?"

"Deal," Sharon said.

I didn't much like the idea that Sharon believed in ice cream more than she believed in me, but I was glad to have company when I went to the paper. I could have asked Jean,

but she was fourteen, and looked enough like me that I was afraid the woman might think Jean was the one who saved the kid's life. Sharon doesn't look anything like me.

School that afternoon was even harder to concentrate on than school that morning. I thought I would scream when the clock only moved one second at a time. Fortunately none of my teachers called on me, so I didn't have to let everybody know I didn't have the slightest idea what was going on. If Sharon hadn't believed me, I doubted anybody else would accept my explanation.

When the final bell rang, I jumped up, grabbed my books and Sharon, and practically pushed her out of the building.

"What's the hurry?" she asked. "You'll be just as much a heroine three minutes from now."

"I want to get it over with," I said. The truth was, the longer the day had gone, the more uncertain I'd gotten. Maybe two kids' lives had been saved the day before. Maybe the lady wouldn't recognize me. The longer I waited, the more her memory would fade. I just wanted to have it done with.

So I forced Sharon to keep pace with me, and I half ran to the paper. I knew where it was, but hadn't been inside it since our class trip in second grade.

"We're going to die of heart attacks before we ever get there," Sharon said, puffing by my side. I'm in better shape than she is.

"It's only four blocks more," I said. "Come on, you can do it."

"I want to live!" she screeched at me, but I ignored her. I had my moment of destiny waiting for me four blocks away. If she couldn't make it, that was her problem.

We were both panting pretty hard by the time we got to the newspaper building. I didn't protest when Sharon raised her hand up to stop me from going in until we both caught our breath. She took out a comb and combed her hair, then offered it to me. I combed mine as well. If they were going to take a picture of me, I wanted to look neat.

"Come on," I said, and walked into the building. I straightened myself as best I could and tried to look fourteen. But my stomach was hurting and my heart was beating, and all of a sudden I started worrying that I'd dreamed the whole thing up.

"Yes?" the receptionist asked.

"I'm the person in the paper," I said. "I mean that article about the mystery girl who saved the tot's life. That's me."

"Oh," the receptionist said, raising her eyebrows. She

didn't look like she believed me, and she didn't even know me.

"She really is," Sharon said. "Honest."

I turned around to face her. "Why do you believe me now?" I whispered at her.

"You're not crazy enough to do this if you didn't really do it," she whispered back.

The receptionist looked at both of us, but then she pressed a few buttons and said, "Mrs. Marsh, there's a girl here who claims she's the one who saved that child's life."

I stood there, not even breathing.

"All right," the receptionist said, and hung up. "Girls, Mrs. Marsh would like you to go to the city room and talk with her. She's waiting for you. Straight down the hallway and then it's the first left."

"Okay," I said, and Sharon and I started walking that way. Sure enough, the city room was easy enough to recognize, and Mrs. Marsh was standing there by the door. She'd written the article about me. I'd never met a reporter before, and I felt even more nervous. But Mrs. Marsh didn't look scary. Actually, she sort of looked like my mother.

"Which one of you?" she asked.

"Me," I said. "I mean I. My name is Dana Alison Parker, and I saved that kid's life."

"Come on over here," Mrs. Marsh said, leading Sharon and me to her desk. "Could you tell me a few details about what happened yesterday, Dana? Just to make sure we're talking about the same thing."

"Sure," I said, and I told her the whole story. I'd told it often enough the day before. I made sure to mention the businessman who picked up my books from the street, and the woman who'd been driving the car and had two of her own, and the woman with the bag who'd taken me home. "The kid was wearing overalls," I said. "And a blue shirt, but I didn't know if it was a boy or a girl. It's hard to tell sometimes."

"You certainly sound like you were there," Mrs. Marsh said. "A lot of what you told me wasn't in my article."

"Dana wouldn't lie," Sharon said. "Are you going to call the lady and let her know?"

"Yes, I think I will," Mrs. Marsh said, and sure enough, she dialed a number. Before I knew it, Mrs. Marsh was saying, "Mrs. McKay, I think we've found your heroine. Would you like to come down to the paper and meet her? Fine. We'll expect you here in ten minutes." She hung up the phone and smiled at me. "Can I get you something?" she asked us. "A soft drink, maybe?"

"No, thank you," I said, and Sharon shook her head.

"Wait here," Mrs. Marsh said. "We're going to want some photographs." She got up and went to the other end of the room.

"Do you think there'll be a reward?" Sharon asked me.

"A reward?" I asked.

"Well, you did save that kid's life," she said. "And he might cure cancer, just like you said."

"A reward," I said. What would I do with a reward? And how much might it be?

But I didn't like the way my mind was going. I didn't save that kid's life just to get some money. I didn't even do it to get my name in the paper, or to earn the respect of everybody I knew. I still wasn't sure why I did it, but it wasn't for any sort of profit.

Of course thinking about a reward made the minutes go a lot faster. Mrs. Marsh came back with a photographer, who was holding an awfully big camera with a huge flash attachment. He winked at me, but I started getting nervous again. Mrs. McKay might not recognize me. I couldn't be sure I'd recognize her, and I'd been a lot less upset than she was.

But then Mrs. Marsh started walking toward the door, and I recognized Mrs. McKay all right, and her little boy. Sharon and I both stood up, and I had this horrible thought that Mrs. McKay would walk over to Sharon and thank her by mistake.

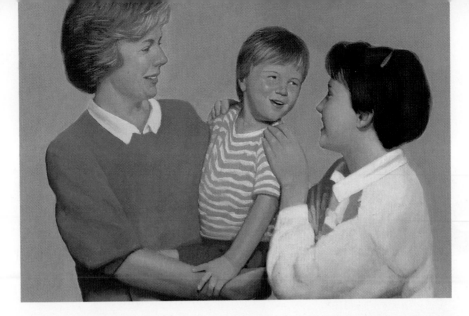

But I didn't have to worry. With the photographer clicking and flashing away, Mrs. McKay swooped up her boy and ran to me. "It's her!" she cried as she got closer to me. "Oh, how can I ever thank you?" And soon she was hugging me and the little boy, and the photographer was going crazy, and Mrs. Marsh was taking notes, and Sharon was looking at me almost respectfully. "Oh, thank you, thank you, thank you."

And I swear she cried grateful tears right on me.

THINK IT OVER

1. *About saving the boy, Dana says, "I still wasn't sure why I did it, but it wasn't for any sort of profit." Why do you think she saved the boy?*

2. *Why doesn't Dana's friend Sharon believe that Dana is the girl who saved the boy's life?*

3. *Compare the way Dana feels the day she rescues the boy with the way she feels the following day. How do her feelings change?*

4. *Do you think Dana should have been celebrated as a hero for rescuing the boy?*

WRITE

Write your own definition for the word hero. *Then write a paragraph explaining whether or not Dana fits your definition.*

BASKETBALL PLAYERS

by Lillian Morrison

illustrated by Clarence Porter

When we're happy,
we jump for joy.
Basketball players
jump as ploy
to get the ball
or net the ball.
Jump! Slamdunk!
Come down, splatSPLAT.
They get *their* joy
out of that.
And they like the sound,
as well as the soaring,
as they pound down the floor,
of the crowd roaring.

"It's possible for a player to jump because he's happy, but it's more likely that he's happy because he's jumping." —Bill Russell in *Second Wind*

B-BALL
THE TEAM THAT NEVER LOST A GAME

FROM *B-BALL: THE TEAM THAT NEVER LOST A GAME*
BY **RON JONES**   ILLUSTRATED BY **CLARENCE PORTER**

Coach Ron Jones has a very unusual basketball team. Every player on his San Francisco Special Olympic squad has a physical or mental handicap. However, they all play the game with great enthusiasm. Their spirit is contagious. It quickly spreads to their fans, to their pep band (the Talking Conga Corps), and even to the opposing teams. To everyone who watches them play, these heroic athletes show what it truly means to be a winner.

Finding a local team that wanted to play against a Special Olympic team wasn't as easy as I thought. All the high school coaches were busy within their own leagues, and an extra game counted against the total allotment of games they were allowed to play. So when I described my team's peculiarities, there was usually a sigh, followed by an apology. I knew that once one of these teams played us they would experience the "beginner's joy" my players brought to the game and it would be a positive experience for all. The problem was finding a team that would take that risk.

One solution was to look for teams in trouble. I brazenly challenged the local professional team. The Golden State Warriors were in last place and their promotion department was giving away tickets. The Warriors responded by sending their center, Clifford Ray, to one of our practice sessions. He was a great one-man success story, but still it was not a game. I did accept his offer to have several San Francisco Special Olympic athletes attend a Warriors game and conduct a half-time demonstration of our shooting skills.

It didn't quite work out as expected. A network sportscaster wanted to interview us. That seemed all right. Michael and Leonette were in full uniform and their socks matched, and they were very excited. Leonette's Statue of Liberty shot was going in, Joey was running around a lot, and to the crowd's delight, Michael was launching his half-court shots.

The problem came when the network switched on the television lights. Undaunted by sudden blindness, Michael unleashed a shot into the fourth row of surprised spectators. Having decided that Michael's long shot shouldn't make national news, the suave sportscaster turned his lights and microphone to Leonette. Before he could even ask a question, she flashed her Magic Johnson look and raced off the floor toward a corner exit.

Without missing a beat, the announcer turned and pointed the microphone at Joey Asaro. "And tell me, sir, how many years have you been playing Special Olympic basketball?" Joey just smiled. The man asked impatiently, "Do you have a favorite shot that your coach here has taught you?" Once again Joey smiled.

Mr. Sports thrust the microphone closer to Joey as if that might help him speak. Joey responded the best way he could—he opened and closed his hand, and by putting his hands in the shape of a bowl and flinging them upward, he could mime his shot. Delighted by his answer, Joey drooled into the waving microphone and grunted.

The announcer pulled the microphone away from Joey and back in front of his face, but he had run out of things to say. His first story had thrown the ball into the crowd. His backup story suddenly ran off. And then he tried to interview a man who grunts. Mr. Sports just stood there with a frozen smile on his face.

Although our national television debut wasn't quite what the network or the Warriors' front office had expected, it did provide a moment of glory. Not sure what to do next, the commentator pivoted the camera back to Joey. With twenty million basketball fans wondering about the identity of the strange-looking player with the two-hand scoop shot, Joey Asaro calmly eyed the rim, tiptoed forward, and sprung his arms and body upward. The ball left his hands as it had thousands of times before. Only this time something special happened—the ball swished into the waiting basket!

With both hands flailing into the air, Joey let out a guttural cry. On his tiptoes he spun around and then seemed to levitate in a bubble of yelps. At center court Michael caught up to Joey and they exchanged high fives, low fives, all the in-between fives. With a grin that split the universe, Joey caught my eye. He roared and pointed to the basket. I knew what he meant. With an arena of fans watching and television replaying the shot in slow motion, Joey Asaro had made his first basket. It was a shot that had traveled seven years before finally dropping into the net!

Leonette ran back to the center circle and the three of them began running, hopping, skipping, jumping, laughing, and crying in an infectious display of athletic success. In a blur of arms, legs, and hugs, I joined the celebration. The crowd knew something important had happened, and the noise got louder and louder, then pitched into a wild scream as members of the Warriors and '76ers stood at courtside and joined in the applause. This was a spontaneous tribute not to the best basket ever made or the last basket in a big game—this was a party for the first basket and a player named Asaro.

Then suddenly the television crews realized that this nationally televised game was being delayed by accolades for a disabled athlete. They angrily pointed to their watches, then at Joey, then at the lineup of applauding athletes. This wasn't what their sponsors wanted the world to see.

The arena announcer blared, "Ladies and gentlemen, please take your seats for the second half of today's game."

When a gang of red-vested courtside ushers tried to waltz Joey off the floor, the crowd booed the dance into a stalemate, then gave a tumultuous uproar when the red vests retreated to the sidelines. In the confusion, fans started screaming for Joey to shoot again. Other fans started picking up the chant. *Oh, no*, I thought. *They don't know what they're asking for. It could take another seven years for Joey to make a basket.*

I was trying to get Joey, Michael, and Leonette off the floor

as the Warriors' coach sauntered toward us. His mere presence prompted a roar of approval that quickly subsided as the bulky figure of a man flapped his hands at his sides for silence. I didn't know what to expect.

The coach sensed my concern and calmed it with his baritone voice and sideways glance toward the network TV people. "It's all right, they just pay the light bill," he said. Then he took Joey's wobbling hand and tantalized us with an offer we couldn't refuse. "You got quite a shooter here. You want to play for us?"

Joey nodded yes. So did Michael and Leonette.

"How much?" I joked. The coach's eyes glistened and his face spread with a laugh that sounded like a car having trouble getting started.

"Give you a Rolls and a condominium in Oakland."

I whispered in Joey's ear. "Take it." Joey grinned and shook the coach's hand.

"Okay, man, you're on the team!" As the coach spoke he swiped a Warriors warm-up jacket off the scorers' table and gently spread it over Joey's shoulders like a matador's cape. The crowd went crazy. They were satisfied. For just a moment the game was theirs again. Every basket counted. There were no commercial interruptions. And Joey Asaro was a member of the Warriors—forever.

Yin Ling is here! During the past five years the mystery voice of Yin Ling has telephoned a thousand times to announce, "This is Yin Ling. I'm coming right away!" Click. In trying to find his address or telephone number, I discovered there was no Yin Ling on any Recreation Center roster—click—city telephone directory list—click—and the members of the Talking Conga Corps shrugged at the mention of this mystery name. Perhaps it was a hoax, but more likely every Thursday somewhere in the city, someone named Yin Ling traveled by bus searching for the elusive basketball practice.

During practice I regularly caught myself glancing toward the closed gymnasium door. I realized I was watching, waiting, and hoping for the resplendent entrance of someone named Yin Ling. I'd heard his dreams so often, that hyperactive signal, "Hello, this is Yin Ling, you know me, I'm coming to practice today!" Click. No matter what I said, or how hard I tried to stem this rush of excitement, the result was always the same: click.

So when the gym door opened and a young Chinese man walked confidently toward me, I knew at once it was Yin Ling! He was dressed just as I expected—hightops and bright-red sweats. I couldn't contain myself. "Hey, Yin Ling, you've made it all right!" The visitor turned away from my greeting and faced the closing door. Before it could click shut, in walked another Yin Ling. And another. And then a dozen Yin Lings. They were all dressed alike, all about the same height. They clustered nervously at the entrance as my look-alike from the Chinese consulate, Jian-She Cao, entered and with a beaming smile proclaimed, "Mr. Coach, we're ready to play you and your Special Olympic team like you said!"

Mr. Jian was brimming with pleasure. I was stunned.

"But you didn't telephone, or tell me you were coming, and this is just a practice—" I swept my hand in the air toward my team that was gathering around me in awe of the red-sweat invasion. Mr. Jian swept his hand in a similar fashion toward his team.

"We are anxious to play you. You are the first to invite us to your gym, so we are here!"

The red-sweat team methodically began to warm up. They attacked the basketball with whiplike intensity. Each player charged the hoop and hooked the ball into the target. A rebounder snapped the ball from the basket and fired it to the next attacking player. Jian stood at courtside with his feet spread apart, his arms crossed over his chest, and the look of victory on his face. I wondered if I looked like that. Then I realized I was standing in the same posture watching my team. Only my team wasn't cutting to the basket. They looked like telephone poles cemented to the floor, immobilized by the red storm buzzing around the other basket.

Of course, some of my best players weren't available. Daniel had found a girlfriend and showed up only for scheduled games. Gary stood at courtside with his basketball that never left his arms. I was tempted to let Louie Louie play, but he preferred his congas.

The Talking Conga Corps sensed the drama of this titanic struggle, and they began hammering out a rhythmic crescendo. It got faster and faster, louder and louder. Our opponents seemed impervious to the noise, and worst of all, they seemed intent on playing—and winning.

The contest began with Michael, Joey, and Leonette watching a Chinese player receive the tip-off and race for a basket. And then another Chinese player raced for a basket. And another . . . and another. I called time out.

Taking Joey by the hand, I approached the huddled opponents. "Hey, you," I said, grabbing the flinching hand of their tallest, fastest player. Mr. Jian's eyes were wide as saucers. "Here's what we do here. I'm going to trade you our best player—Joey here—for your best player!" As I pulled the Chinese player from their huddle, Joey started giving his new teammates high fives. They didn't know what he was doing. Three of them simultaneously ducked.

I tried to explain. "It's a trade. We'll give your tall player here ten thousand dollars and throw in Joey Asaro. You get Joey, we get your center."

Jian was besieged with Chinese and he tried to explain in Chinese and English, "Ten thousand—trade—no, no—traitor—ten thousand dollars?" The tall Chinese player stubbornly refused to move as three of his comrades grabbed his jersey in defense.

I smiled and let go of the potential star. "U.S. Special Olympic team fails in its effort to abduct star Chinese athlete." Joey grunted agreement and joined the red team. He was grinning among his new comrades, clapping his good hand against his curled wrist. "You guys don't know it, but you've got our best player," I said as I walked back to our bench.

Jian followed me with questions. "We don't understand, is this Joey, is he ours?" I didn't answer. Jian continued to worry out loud. "What do we do with him?" I didn't answer. I was buried in thoughts about how to get the Chinese to slow down and just enjoy the game, how to have fun—they were so grim, so fearful of losing. Jian continued his inquiry. "Do you play without a clock, do you play a ten-minute quarter, and where is our score, do you mark down our score?"

Jian's concerns followed me as I entered the gym closet and grabbed the electric scoreboard. Back on the gym floor, Jian watched with an approving nod as I plugged in the board. Like a miniature carnival the tiny colored lights twinkled to life declaring "HOME"—"VISITOR"—"TIME." Jian tapped the light box and asked. "What is our score today?"

"You won the first game!"

"We won!"

"Yeah, you won. Now let's try to play another game, and this time let's try to get everyone to play and this time everyone can have a chance to win."

"Everyone?" Jian asked quizzically. "You let everyone play, even the impaired?"

"Everyone." I grinned. "Even the coach." I looked Jian in the eyes and repeated the Chinese sports anthem, "Friendship first—competition second."

He grinned. "Teacher, coach—friendship first, yes."

Before the second game could commence, I put the team under Michael's tutelage and chased around the Center looking for staff who wanted to play with us against the Chinese Communist consulate team. Several women from the pool staff joined our cause. Two janitors gladly put aside their brooms for the epic conflict. One of our van drivers put on his tennis shoes, and our music and drama specialist, a red-haired woman who played a saxophone, heard the call. Even the Talking Conga Corps put down their drums. I placed Larry Mason, the only Special Olympic athlete to attend school, on the scoreboard. This was war!

The red tide once again readied for the tip-off. Only this time they apprehensively bounced up and down and stared in wonder at the players surrounding them. They didn't know why Joey was cheering for them or why we had women in the game playing in bathing suits and no shoes. Two of our players were speaking frenetic Spanish, and our conga drummer in the wheelchair was talking to a basketball.

With the Talking Basketball's being thrown into the air, the second game began. Once again the red team swept down the floor and scored. This didn't stop us. We continued to press on, looking for a shot. The Chinese scored again. We sent in more players. They scored. We threw in an extra basketball. They scored. We struggled to get the Kid with the Talking Basketball into a position where he could drop the ball into the closest ash can. They scored. We were wearing them down. They scored.

I blew a whistle and yelled, "Foul!" Everything came to a halt. "Two shots against the red team 'cause they're wearing red!" Half the red team giggled. The other half told them to be quiet. I gently handed the ball to the Kid in the wheelchair and pushed him over to a garbage can. The janitor proudly held the can at an angle, the kid trickled the ball into the trash. "Ya hoo!" We scored. They called time out. Our music teacher, who had brought along her saxophone, revved into "On, Wisconsin!"

Jian's team was in a state of shock. "What are you doing?" he asked, pointing to the trash can, the woman saxophone player, the scantily clad aquatics staff, the sight of Joey clapping for the red team only to fall over and require the Chinese to help him up. Jian settled his attention on the scoreboard. "Look, it's still moving! The numbers keep changing, your man there just sits turning the dials, one moment there are two minutes to play, then suddenly twenty-two minutes!"

"Oh, that's Larry," I offered without apology. Jian took a deep breath. "How do you know who's winning?"

I smiled, "I don't!"

"Don't?" he implored.

"I don't know who's winning—it's more important to note who's playing!" Jian studied me and then without saying a word, retreated to his team and clutched them into a tight circle. From the center of this red bundle, he stuck out his head and motioned for Joey to join them. Joey Asaro became the first Special Olympic athlete to play basketball for the People's Republic of China.

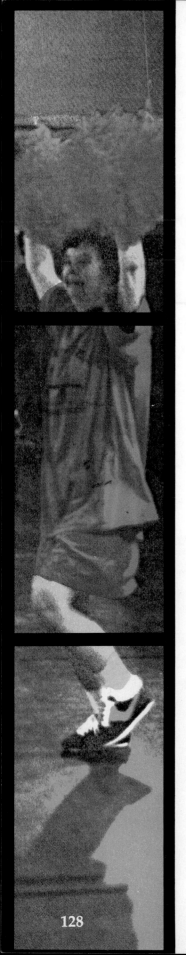

Everyone felt alive and part of the game. There was still the opportunity to race up and down the floor and *take* a shot—but now there was also the opportunity and obligation to *give* a shot.

The scoreboard never did signal the end of the game or even the accurate totals of points. The contest came to a natural conclusion when we gathered around the center circle and counted in at least three languages, "Ten, nine, eight . . ." By the end of our countdown all the players were hugging each other, trading T-shirts, and shaking with joy. Jian uncharacteristically threw his arm around me. "You have a great team here, they are real heroes. They are heroes of the heart!"

THINK IT OVER

1. *Does the second game with the Chinese team turn out the way you thought it would?*

2. *According to Coach Jones, what is more important than knowing who's winning the game?*

3. *Explain what Coach Jones means when he says his team brings "beginner's joy" to the game.*

4. *Explain why the San Francisco Special Olympic team never lost a game.*

WRITE

Write a paragraph explaining what you think makes the Special Olympic athletes "heroes of the heart."

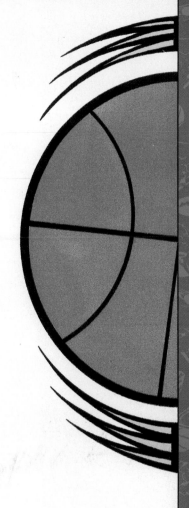

THEME WRAP-UP

EVERYDAY HEROES

Are the basketball players and Dana the same kind of heroes? Explain your answer.

. . . .

Think of any games you have witnessed or participated in that were similar to the basketball games played in "B-Ball: The Team That Never Lost a Game." Describe the similarities and the differences.

. . . .

WRITER'S WORKSHOP There are both advantages and disadvantages to playing sports after school. Write a few paragraphs explaining what you think are the advantages and disadvantages of playing after-school sports. Be sure to explain each point clearly.

COURAGE AND KINDNESS

Both of the following selections were written by the same author, Lois Lowry. But the stories are about very different heroes.

C O N T E N T S

· ·

131

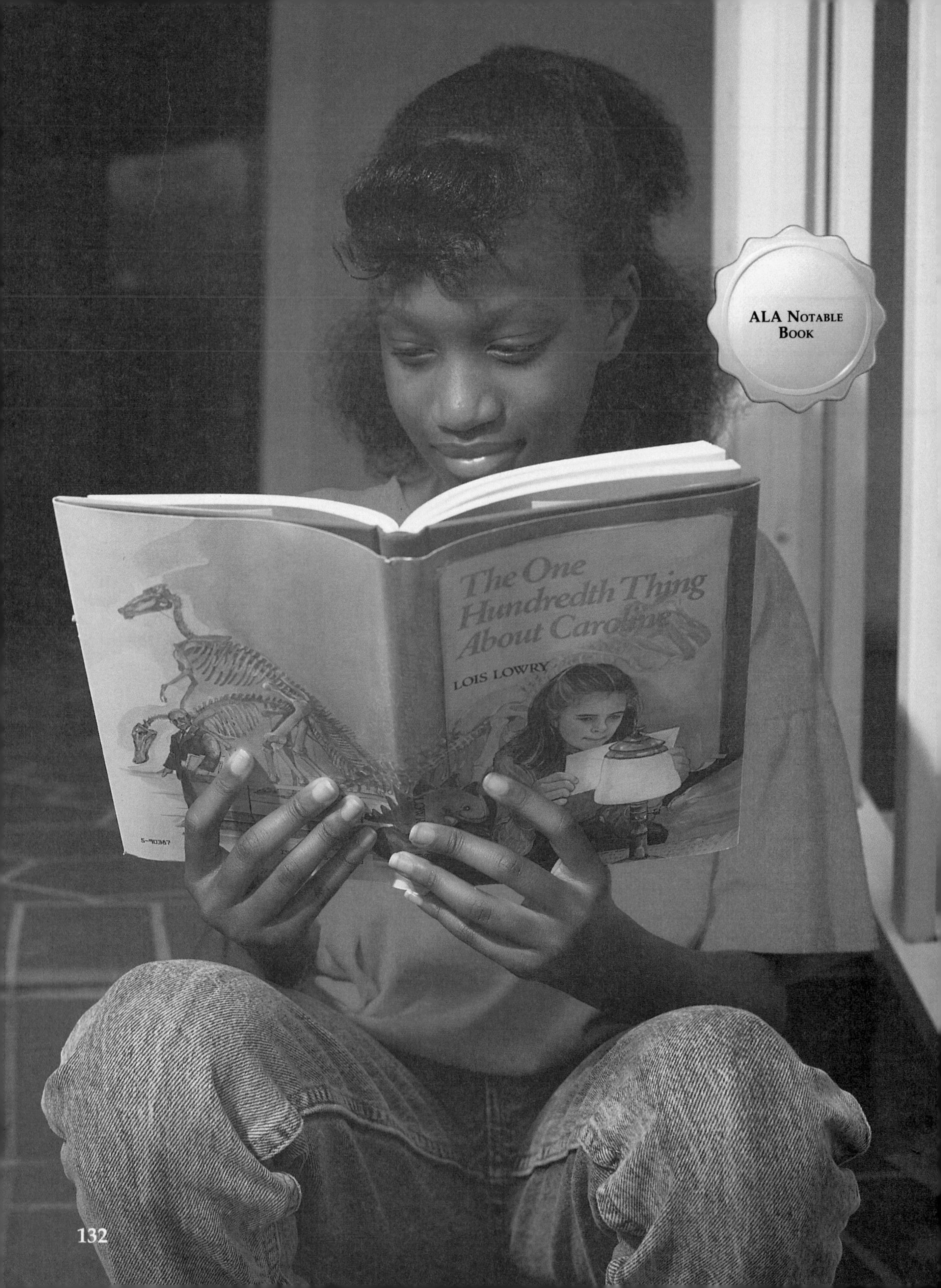

ALA NOTABLE BOOK

Caroline's Hero

from *The One Hundredth Thing About Caroline*

by Lois Lowry ■ illustrated by Charles Pyle

Eleven-year-old Caroline Tate lives with her mother and J.P., her older brother, in New York City. J.P., who loves taking apart toasters, alarm clocks, and mixers, is an electronics genius. Caroline's best friend, Stacy, is a future investigative reporter. Ever since becoming a member of the Museum of Natural History, Caroline has wanted to be a paleontologist. On a rainy Saturday she pays a visit to her favorite museum.

The museum wasn't a long walk. Caroline headed east to Central Park, and then south to 79th Street, where the enormous building covered the entire block.

In front of the museum, next to the huge statue of Theodore Roosevelt, a boy was unwrapping a candy bar. He dropped the wrapper on the museum steps.

"Excuse me," Caroline said to him politely and pointed to the nearby sign: LITTERING IS FILTHY AND SELFISH. SO DON'T DO IT.

The boy looked at her for a moment. Then very carefully he reached into his pocket, removed a wadded-up tissue, and dropped it ostentatiously next to his candy wrapper. He grinned nastily and sauntered off.

Caroline looked around for a policeman. But there were only two nuns, a taxi driver leaning against his parked cab, and a couple of mothers with a troop of Brownies.

She thought about making a citizen's arrest. But the boy was bigger than she—he looked at least fifteen—and besides, he was already down at the corner of 78th Street.

She sighed and picked up his trash with two fingers. It was almost as bad as touching parsnips. She dropped it into a trash can angrily and headed up the steps into the museum.

"Hello, Mr. Erwitt," she called into the office inside the front door. Mr. Erwitt looked up from his desk and waved.

"Hello there, Caroline," he called back. "Great exhibit in Meteorites, Minerals, and Gems this afternoon!"

"Thanks anyway, Mr. Erwitt," she said. "I have work to do on the fourth floor."

She showed her membership card to the woman at the admissions booth, took the little blue button that indicated she hadn't sneaked in, and attached it to her raincoat. Then she walked past the postcard counter and the gift shop, down the hall to the elevator.

The fourth floor was absolutely her favorite place in the entire museum. No question. Biology of Invertebrates, on the first floor, was okay; and so was Small Mammals. On the second floor, African Mammals was kind of interesting because of the stuffed elephants and the gorilla who looked like King Kong and had a leaf sticking out of his mouth to indicate that he was a harmless plant-eater. Primates, on the third floor, wasn't too bad.

But the fourth floor was heaven. The Hall of Early Dinosaurs even had blue walls, which was what Caroline had always supposed heaven had.

She went into the blue-walled Early Dinosaur room and stood there, awed, as she always was. There, in the center, were the Stegosaurus, the Allosaurus, and the gigantic Brontosaurus—only their bones, of course—standing in their huge, awkward poses.

"Hi, you guys," said Caroline. She thought of them as old buddies. She always came in to say "Hi," even when she was going to the Late Dinosaur exhibit, as she was today.

They all smiled their toothy smiles at her. Even Allosaurus, a fierce flesh-eater, looked sweet and happy and a little embarrassed, standing there without his skin, quite helpless.

Then she went over to say "Hi" to the mummified Anatosaurus in his glass case. They had found him in Wyoming, of all places, with his skin still on. Sometimes Caroline wished her father had moved to Wyoming instead of Des Moines; she would be tempted to visit him more often if he had. There might be a mummified Anatosaurus buried in his backyard.

Finally, she walked to the end of the huge room and said, "Greetings, Jaws," to the jaws of the giant extinct shark that hung at the entrance to the room of Fossil Fishes.

The jaws just hung there, wide open, as if they were waiting for a dentist to say "Spit."

Caroline wasn't all that crazy about the shark jaws. They gave her the creeps. But she always said "Greetings" to them, politely, before she left the Hall of Early Dinosaurs. She did it for the same reason that she was always very nice to Marcia-Anne Hennessy, the worst bully in her class at school.

She didn't want the giant shark jaws, or Marcia-Anne Hennessy, ever to take a dislike to her.

Then Caroline took out her notebook and headed to her destination: Late Dinosaurs. That room was just as big, though the walls were green. And in the center, dominating the Triceratops and the two Trachodonts next to him, stood the hideous, monstrous Tyrannosaurus Rex. Even without his skin, quite naked and with all his bones exposed, he was horrifying. It made Caroline shiver just to look at him. It also gave her a stiff neck, because he was so tall that she almost had to do a backbend to see his face towering above her, looking down, with his sharp teeth exposed. If ever, by magic, he should come to life, Caroline thought a little nervously, he would only have to bend his mammoth neck, snap his jaws, and in one bite he could consume a whole Scout troop.

"Boo!"

Caroline jumped and dropped her pencil.

"Sorry, Caroline," said the man behind her. "I didn't mean to scare you, really."

Caroline smiled sheepishly. "That's okay, Mr. Keretsky. You just startled me. How are you?"

Gregor Keretsky was Caroline's hero. Stacy had two heroes:

135

Woodward and Bernstein, the journalists who had broken the Watergate story in the *Washington Post*. And J.P.'s hero was Guglielmo Marconi, the Italian electrical engineer who had invented the wireless receiver. Caroline could drive her brother into a screaming rage whenever she wanted to just by referring to Goo-goo Macaroni.

But she did that only when she was driven to desperation, because she knew how sacred people's heroes were. She was lucky that her hero was right here, in the Museum of Natural History, and that he was one of her best friends. Gregor Keretsky was a vertebrate paleontologist, one of the world's experts on dinosaurs. His office was on the fourth floor of the museum, and sometimes he invited Caroline to have a cup of tea with him. She loved his office; it had bookcases filled with every book that had ever been written about dinosaurs, and some of them had been written by Gregor Keretsky himself.

"I'm fine"—her hero grinned—"and I've been looking for you. I knew my little paleontologist friend would be here, because it is Saturday. And I need your help once again, Caroline."

Caroline sighed. Poor Mr. Keretsky. He had this problem that she helped him with from time to time.

"Neckties?" she asked.

He nodded, embarrassed. "Tomorrow I fly to London. There is a conference there on Monday morning."

"Let's take a look," said Caroline, and she followed him to his office.

He closed the door, because this was a very private consultation. Then he took a bag marked "Brooks Brothers" out of a desk drawer. He took three neckties out of the bag and laid them on the top of the desk.

"What do you think?" he asked helplessly.

Poor Mr. Keretsky was colorblind. No one knew, not even his secretary. And he had no wife. Caroline was the only person in the world to whom he had confided his secret problem since 1946. In 1946, when he had left Europe and come to live in the United States, the Department of Motor Vehicles had refused him a driver's license because he couldn't tell a red light from a green.

His suits were all gray, and his shirts were all white. So those were not a problem. But neckties, he said, made him crazy. He desperately needed help with neckties.

"These two," said Caroline decisively after looking them over. "Keep these two. But take this one back." She wrinkled her nose and handed him the third tie. "It's purple and brown. Really ugly, Mr. Keretsky. Very severely ugly."

"Are you sure?" he asked sadly. "I do like the pattern on this one. It has a—what would you say?—a pleasant geometric order to it."

"Nope," said Caroline firmly. "Take it back."

"The woman at the store said that it was very, very attractive," Mr. Keretsky pointed out.

"What did it cost?"

He turned it over and looked at the price tag. "$22.50," he said.

Caroline groaned. "No *wonder* she said it was very, very attractive. She conned you, Mr. Keretsky. She sold you the ugliest necktie in New York City, for a ridiculously high price. Don't trust her again, under any circumstances."

"All right," he said, sighing, and put the tie back into the bag. "But the others, they are not ugly? You are certain?"

"The others are fine. The striped one's gray and dark green, with a little yellow. And the paisley's some nice shades of blue. They'll look nice on you."

"Caroline," said Gregor Keretsky, "you have once again preserved my dignity. Come to the cafeteria with me and I will buy you a big ice cream."

Caroline fingered her notebook. She really didn't want to miss a chance to talk to one of the world's most famous vertebrate paleontologists. But she had planned to work on a drawing of Tyrannosaurus Rex.

She compromised. "Okay," she said. "I'll go to the cafeteria. But would you do me a favor? Would you tell me everything you know about Tyrannosaurus Rex?"

Gregor Keretsky began to laugh. "Caroline," he said, "that would take me days, I think!"

She laughed, too. She knew he was right. "Well," she said, "tell me a *little* about him, then, over some ice cream."

"By the way," she whispered, as they waited for the elevator. "I wouldn't wear those cuff links to London if I were you."

"These?" Mr. Keretsky held up one wrist. "Why not? These I just bought. There is something wrong with them?"

"Mr. Keretsky," Caroline said as tactfully as she could, "they're *pink*."

THINK IT OVER

1. *Are you surprised at Caroline's choice of a hero? Explain your answer.*

2. *Do you agree with Caroline that people's heroes are sacred? Explain your answer.*

WRITE

Caroline has been to the museum many times, but she is still awed by what she sees in the Hall of Early Dinosaurs. Write a few sentences telling why.

An Interview with:
Lois Lowry

Writer Ilene Cooper spoke with Lois Lowry about how she came to write her Newbery Award–winning novel, **Number the Stars.** *This interview tells how Lois Lowry thinks people become heroes and how Mr. Keretsky in* **The One Hundredth Thing About Caroline** *is a different kind of hero from the Danish heroes in* **Number the Stars.**

AWARD-WINNING
AUTHOR

COOPER: *Many people, children and adults, who read* Number the Stars *come away from it wondering if they could be heroes. What do you think makes a hero?*

LOWRY: Although we can't pick the circumstances in which we find ourselves, we can and do choose the way we respond to situations. In my opinion, those who turn out to be heroes are people who respond in particular ways to their circumstances. They respond in a way that may put them at personal risk or call upon them to make sacrifices, without any idea of personal gain.

COOPER: *Who are some of today's heroes?*

LOWRY: First let me say I think the word *hero* is often misused. What we often call a hero today is really an idol. Sports figures or movie stars aren't heroes. They are idols and that's okay, but different. They are successful, and kids admire and respect them, but a baseball player or a rock singer doesn't take any risks or make any sacrifices or set aside any ambitions. My personal heroes are

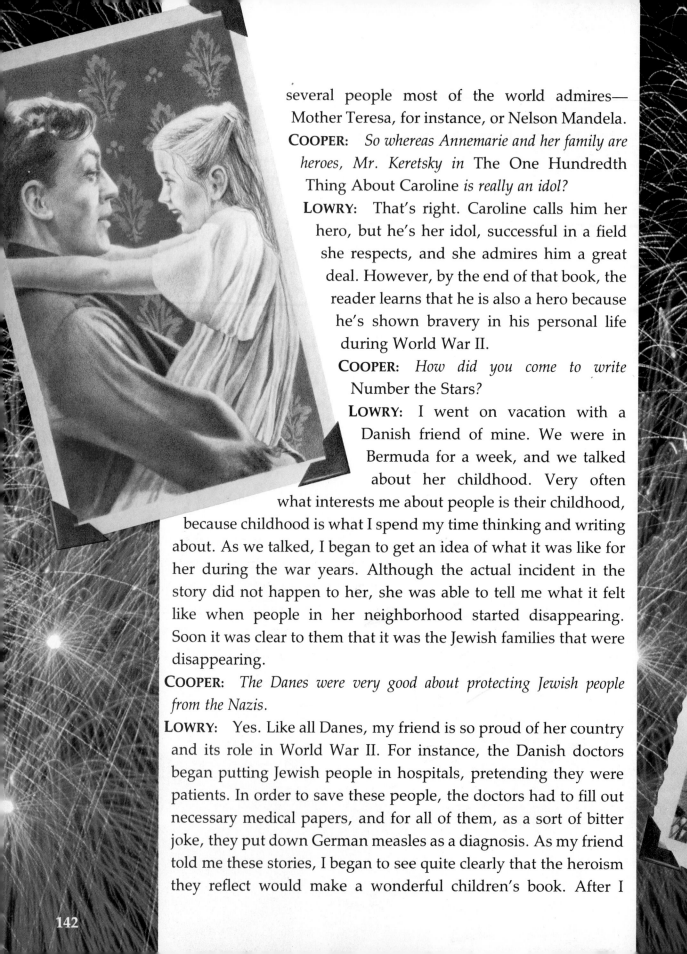

several people most of the world admires—
Mother Teresa, for instance, or Nelson Mandela.

COOPER: *So whereas Annemarie and her family are heroes, Mr. Keretsky in* The One Hundredth Thing About Caroline *is really an idol?*

LOWRY: That's right. Caroline calls him her hero, but he's her idol, successful in a field she respects, and she admires him a great deal. However, by the end of that book, the reader learns that he is also a hero because he's shown bravery in his personal life during World War II.

COOPER: *How did you come to write* Number the Stars?

LOWRY: I went on vacation with a Danish friend of mine. We were in Bermuda for a week, and we talked about her childhood. Very often what interests me about people is their childhood, because childhood is what I spend my time thinking and writing about. As we talked, I began to get an idea of what it was like for her during the war years. Although the actual incident in the story did not happen to her, she was able to tell me what it felt like when people in her neighborhood started disappearing. Soon it was clear to them that it was the Jewish families that were disappearing.

COOPER: *The Danes were very good about protecting Jewish people from the Nazis.*

LOWRY: Yes. Like all Danes, my friend is so proud of her country and its role in World War II. For instance, the Danish doctors began putting Jewish people in hospitals, pretending they were patients. In order to save these people, the doctors had to fill out necessary medical papers, and for all of them, as a sort of bitter joke, they put down German measles as a diagnosis. As my friend told me these stories, I began to see quite clearly that the heroism they reflect would make a wonderful children's book. After I

142

started writing, I saw that I would need to do a great deal of research on the story, and I eventually went to Denmark. I spoke to people who had been alive during the war. I went to the Holocaust Museum, which is dedicated to the role of Denmark during the Holocaust. That was where I saw the shoes of fish skin that I used in my story.

COOPER: *Unlike* Number the Stars, *most of your stories take place today. Your Anastasia Krupnik books are especially popular. Why do you keep coming back to her?*

LOWRY: I hadn't intended to write books about the same character, but I did because kids liked them so well. Anastasia is an old friend by now. I know her family, their neighborhood. I can see them in my head so clearly. There's a familiarity about the Krupniks that makes them easy to write about.

COOPER: *Is it more difficult to find heroes today because the newspapers and television tell us so much about people's everyday lives?*

LOWRY: It's true that we do find out more about our heroes than we ever did in the past, but that doesn't have to deter us from having heroes. After all, heroes are human too. It's in those extraordinary circumstances that I spoke of where they rise to more than human stature.

NUMBER THE STARS

a novel by Lois Lowry

NEWBERY MEDAL

ALA NOTABLE
BOOK

A TEST OF COURAGE

FROM *NUMBER THE STARS* BY *LOIS LOWRY*

ILLUSTRATED BY *David Wilgus*

By 1943, German troops had occupied Denmark for about a year. Annemarie Johansen; her little sister, Kirsti; and her best friend, Ellen, could remember when there was plenty of food and when the tall German soldier, "the Giraffe," and his partner didn't stand watch on the street corner near the school. These soldiers had stopped the three girls one day when they were running home from school. Annemarie's older sister, Lise, had died in an accident two weeks before she was to be married; but Peter, her sister's fiancé, still visited the Johansens to bring news of the Danish Resistance and to offer gifts to the family. Ellen's family, the Rosens, lived in the same building as the Johansens. On many afternoons, Mrs. Rosen would have "coffee," hot water with herbs, with Annemarie's mother.

The days of September passed, one after the other, much the same. Annemarie and Ellen walked to school together, and home again, always now taking the longer way, avoiding the tall soldier and his partner. Kirsti dawdled just behind them or scampered ahead, never out of their sight.

The two mothers still had their "coffee" together in the afternoons. They began to knit mittens as the days grew slightly shorter and the first leaves began to fall from the trees, because another winter was coming. Everyone remembered the last one. There was no fuel now for the homes and apartments in Copenhagen, and the winter nights were terribly cold.

Like the other families in their building, the Johansens had opened the old chimney and installed a little stove to use for heat when they could find coal to burn. Mama used it too, sometimes, for cooking, because electricity was rationed now. At night they used candles for light. Sometimes Ellen's father, a teacher, complained in frustration because he couldn't see in the dim light to correct his students' papers.

"Soon we will have to add another blanket to your bed," Mama said one morning as she and Annemarie tidied the bedroom.

"Kirsti and I are lucky to have each other for warmth in the winter," Annemarie said. "Poor Ellen, to have no sisters."

"She will have to snuggle in with her mama and papa when it gets cold," Mama said, smiling.

"I remember when Kirsti slept between you and Papa. She was supposed to stay in her crib, but in the middle of the night she would climb out and get in with you," Annemarie said, smoothing the pillows on the bed. Then she hesitated and glanced at her mother, fearful that she had said the wrong thing, the thing that would bring the pained look to her mother's face. The days when little Kirsti slept in Mama and Papa's room were the days when Lise and Annemarie shared this bed.

But Mama was laughing quietly. "I remember, too," she said. "Sometimes she wet the bed in the middle of the night!"

"I did not!" Kirsti said haughtily from the bedroom doorway. "I never, *ever* did that!"

Mama, still laughing, knelt and kissed Kirsti on the cheek. "Time to leave for school, girls," she said. She began to button Kirsti's jacket. "Oh, dear," she said, suddenly. "Look. This button has broken right in half. Annemarie, take Kirsti with you, after school, to the little shop where Mrs. Hirsch sells thread and buttons. See if you can buy just one, to match the others on her jacket. I'll give you some kroner—it shouldn't cost very much."

But after school, when the girls stopped at the shop, which had been there as long as Annemarie could remember, they found it closed. There was a new padlock on the door, and a sign. But the sign was in German. They couldn't read the words.

"I wonder if Mrs. Hirsch is sick," Annemarie said as they walked away.

"I saw her Saturday," Ellen said. "She was with her husband and their son. They all looked just fine. Or at least the *parents* looked just fine—the son *always* looks like a horror." She giggled.

Annemarie made a face. The Hirsch family lived in the neighborhood, so they had seen the boy, Samuel, often. He was a tall teenager with thick glasses, stooped shoulders, and unruly hair. He rode a bicycle to school, leaning forward and squinting, wrinkling his nose to nudge his glasses into place. His bicycle had wooden wheels, now that rubber tires weren't available, and it creaked and clattered on the street.

"I think the Hirsches all went on a vacation to the seashore," Kirsti announced.

"And I suppose they took a big basket of pink-frosted cupcakes with them," Annemarie said sarcastically to her sister.

"Yes, I suppose they did," Kirsti replied.

Annemarie and Ellen exchanged looks that meant: Kirsti is so *dumb*. No one in Copenhagen had taken a vacation at the seashore since the war began. There *were* no pink-frosted cupcakes; there hadn't been for months.

Still, Annemarie thought, looking back at the shop before they turned the corner, where was Mrs. Hirsch? The Hirsch family had gone *somewhere*. Why else would they close the shop?

Mama was troubled when she heard the news. "Are you sure?" she asked several times.

"We can find another button someplace," Annemarie reassured her. "Or we can take one from the bottom of the jacket and move it up. It won't show very much."

But it didn't seem to be the jacket that worried Mama. "Are you sure the sign was in German?" she asked. "Maybe you didn't look carefully."

"Mama, it had a swastika on it."

Her mother turned away with a distracted look. "Annemarie, watch your sister for a few moments. And begin to peel the potatoes for dinner. I'll be right back."

"Where are you going?" Annemarie asked as her mother started for the door.

"I want to talk to Mrs. Rosen."

Puzzled, Annemarie watched her mother leave the apartment. She went to the kitchen and opened the door to the cupboard where the potatoes were kept. Every night, now, it seemed, they had potatoes for dinner. And very little else.

Annemarie was almost asleep when there was a light knock on the bedroom door. Candlelight appeared as the door opened, and her mother stepped in.

"Are you asleep, Annemarie?"

"No. Why? Is something wrong?"

"Nothing's wrong. But I'd like you to get up and come out to the living room. Peter's here. Papa and I want to talk to you."

Annemarie jumped out of bed, and Kirsti grunted in her sleep. Peter! She hadn't seen him in a long time. There was something frightening about his being here at night. Copenhagen had a curfew, and no citizens were allowed out after eight o'clock. It was very dangerous, she knew, for Peter to visit at this time. But she was delighted that he was here. Though his visits were always hurried—they almost seemed secret, somehow, in a way she couldn't quite put her finger on—still, it was a treat to see Peter. It brought back memories of happier times. And her parents loved Peter, too. They said he was like a son.

Barefoot, she ran to the living room and into Peter's arms. He grinned, kissed her cheek, and ruffled her hair.

"You've grown taller since I saw you last," he told her. "You're all legs!"

Annemarie laughed. "I won the girls' footrace last Friday at school," she told him proudly. "Where have you been? We've missed you!"

"My work takes me all over," Peter explained. "Look, I brought you something. One for Kirsti, too." He reached into his pocket and handed her two seashells.

Annemarie put the smaller one on the table to save it for her sister. She held the other in her hands, turning it in the light, looking at the ridged, pearly surface. It was so like Peter, to bring just the right gift.

Papa became more serious. "Annemarie," he said, "Peter tells us that the Germans have issued orders closing many stores run by Jews."

"Jews?" Annemarie repeated. "Is Mrs. Hirsch Jewish? Is that why the button shop is closed? Why have they done that?"

149

Peter leaned forward. "It is their way of tormenting. For some reason, they want to torment Jewish people. It has happened in other countries. They have taken their time here—have let us relax a little. But now it seems to be starting."

"But why the button shop? What harm is a button shop? Mrs. Hirsch is such a nice lady. Even Samuel—he's a dope, but he would never harm anyone. How could he—he can't even see, with his thick glasses!"

Then Annemarie thought of something else. "If they can't sell their buttons, how will they earn a living?"

"Friends will take care of them," Mama said gently. "That's what friends do."

Annemarie nodded. Mama was right, of course. Friends and neighbors would go to the home of the Hirsch family, would take them fish and potatoes and bread and herbs for making tea. They would be comfortable until their shop was allowed to open again.

Then, suddenly, she sat upright, her eyes wide. "Mama!" she said. "Papa! The Rosens are Jewish, too!"

Her parents nodded, their faces serious and drawn. "I talked to Sophy Rosen this afternoon, after you told me about the button shop," Mama said. "She knows what is happening. But she doesn't think that it will affect them."

Annemarie thought, and understood. She relaxed. "Mr. Rosen doesn't have a shop. He's a teacher. They can't close a whole school!" She looked at Peter with the question in her eyes. "Can they?"

"I think the Rosens will be all right," he said. "But you keep an eye on your friend Ellen. And stay away from the soldiers. Your mother told me what happened on Østerbrogade."

Annemarie shrugged. She had almost forgotten the incident. "It was nothing. They were only bored and looking for someone to talk to, I think."

She turned to her father. "Papa, do you remember what you heard the boy say to the soldier? That all of Denmark would be the king's bodyguard?"

Her father smiled. "I have never forgotten it," he said.

"Well," Annemarie said slowly, "now I think that all of Denmark must be bodyguard for the Jews, as well."

"So we shall be," Papa replied.

Peter stood. "I must go," he said. "And you, Longlegs, it is way past your bedtime now." He hugged Annemarie again.

Later, once more in her bed beside the warm cocoon of her sister, Annemarie remembered how her father had said, three years before, that he would die to protect the king. That her mother would, too. And Annemarie, seven years old, had announced proudly that she also would.

Now she was ten, with long legs and no more silly dreams of pink-frosted cupcakes. And now she—and all the Danes—were to be bodyguard for Ellen, and Ellen's parents, and all of Denmark's Jews.

Would she die to protect them? *Truly?* Annemarie was honest enough to admit, there in the darkness, to herself, that she wasn't sure.

For a moment she felt frightened. But she pulled the blanket up higher around her neck and relaxed. It was all imaginary, anyway—not real. It was only in the fairy tales that people were called upon to be so brave, to die for one another. Not in real-life Denmark. Oh, there were the soldiers; that was true. And the courageous Resistance leaders, who sometimes lost their lives; that was true, too.

But ordinary people like the Rosens and the Johansens? Annemarie admitted to herself, snuggling there in the quiet dark, that she was glad to be an ordinary person who would never be called upon for courage.

Alone in the apartment while Mama was out shopping with Kirsti, Annemarie and Ellen were sprawled on the living room floor playing with paper dolls. They had cut the dolls from Mama's magazines, old ones she had saved from past years. The paper ladies had old-fashioned hair styles and clothes, and the girls had given them names from Mama's favorite book. Mama had told Annemarie and Ellen the entire story of *Gone With the Wind*, and the girls thought it much more interesting and romantic than the king-and-queen tales that Kirsti loved.

"Come, Melanie," Annemarie said, walking her doll across the edge of the rug. "Let's dress for the ball."

"All right, Scarlett, I'm coming," Ellen replied in a sophisticated voice. She was a talented performer; she often played the leading roles in school dramatics. Games of the imagination were always fun when Ellen played.

The door opened and Kirsti stomped in, her face tear-stained and glowering. Mama followed her with an exasperated look and set a package down on the table.

"I won't!" Kirsti sputtered. "I won't ever, *ever* wear them! Not if you chain me in a prison and beat me with sticks!"

Annemarie giggled and looked questioningly at her mother. Mrs. Johansen sighed. "I bought Kirsti some new shoes," she explained. "She's outgrown her old ones."

"Goodness, Kirsti," Ellen said, "I wish my mother would get *me* some new shoes. I love new things, and it's so hard to find them in the stores."

"Not if you go to a *fish* store!" Kirsti bellowed. "But most mothers wouldn't make their daughters wear ugly *fish* shoes!"

"Kirsten," Mama said soothingly, "you know it wasn't a fish store. And we were lucky to find shoes at all."

Kirsti sniffed. "Show them," she commanded. "Show Annemarie and Ellen how ugly they are."

Mama opened the package and took out a pair of little girl's shoes. She held them up, and Kirsti looked away in disgust.

"You know there's no leather anymore," Mama explained. "But they've found a way to make shoes out of fish skin. I don't think these are too ugly."

Annemarie and Ellen looked at the fish skin shoes. Annemarie took one in her hand and examined it. It was odd-looking; the fish scales were visible. But it was a shoe, and her sister needed shoes.

"It's not so bad, Kirsti," she said, lying a little.

Ellen turned the other one over in her hand. "You know," she said, "it's only the color that's ugly."

"Green!" Kirsti wailed. "I will never, *ever* wear green shoes!"

"In our apartment," Ellen told her, "my father has a jar of black, black ink. Would you like these shoes better if they were black?"

Kirsti frowned. "Maybe I would," she said, finally.

"Well, then," Ellen told her, "tonight, if your mama doesn't mind, I'll take the shoes home and ask my father to make them black for you, with his ink."

Mama laughed. "I think that would be a fine improvement. What do you think, Kirsti?"

Kirsti pondered. "Could he make them shiny?" she asked. "I want them shiny."

Ellen nodded. "I think he could. I think they'll be quite pretty, black and shiny."

Kirsti nodded. "All right, then," she said. "But you mustn't tell anyone that they're *fish*. I don't want anyone to know." She took her new shoes, holding them disdainfully, and put them on a chair. Then she looked with interest at the paper dolls.

"Can I play, too?" Kirsti asked. "Can I have a doll?" She squatted beside Annemarie and Ellen on the floor.

Sometimes, Annemarie thought, Kirsti was such a pest, always butting in. But the apartment was small. There was no other place for Kirsti to play. And if they told her to go away, Mama would scold.

"Here," Annemarie said, and handed her sister a cut-out little girl doll. "We're playing *Gone With the Wind*. Melanie and Scarlett are going to a ball. You can be Bonnie. She's Scarlett's daughter."

Kirsti danced her doll up and down happily. "I'm going to the ball!" she announced in a high, pretend voice.

Ellen giggled. "A little girl wouldn't go to a ball. Let's make them go someplace else. Let's make them go to Tivoli!"

"Tivoli!" Annemarie began to laugh. "That's in Copenhagen! *Gone With the Wind* is in America!"

"Tivoli, Tivoli, Tivoli," little Kirsti sang, twirling her doll in a circle.

"It doesn't matter, because it's only a game anyway," Ellen pointed out. "Tivoli can be over there, by that chair. 'Come, Scarlett,'" she said, using her doll voice, "'we shall go to Tivoli to dance and watch the fireworks, and maybe there will be some handsome men there! Bring your silly daughter, Bonnie, and she can ride on the carousel.'"

Annemarie grinned and walked her Scarlett toward the chair that Ellen had designated as Tivoli. She loved Tivoli Gardens, in the heart of Copenhagen; her parents had taken her there, often, when she was a little girl. She remembered the music and the brightly colored lights, the carousel and ice cream and especially the magnificent fireworks in the evenings; the huge colored splashes and bursts of lights in the evening sky.

"I remember the fireworks best of all," she commented to Ellen.

"Me too," Kirsti said. "I remember the fireworks."

"Silly," Annemarie scoffed. "You never saw the fireworks." Tivoli Gardens was closed now. The German occupation forces had burned part of it, perhaps as a way of punishing the fun-loving Danes for their lighthearted pleasures.

Kirsti drew herself up, her small shoulders stiff. "I did too," she said belligerently. "It was my birthday. I woke up in the night and I could hear the booms. And there were lights in the sky. Mama said it was fireworks for my birthday!"

Then Annemarie remembered. Kirsti's birthday was late in August. And that night, only a month before, she, too, had been awakened and frightened by the sound of explosions. Kirsti was right—the sky in the southeast had been ablaze, and Mama had comforted her by calling it a birthday celebration. "Imagine, such fireworks for a little girl five years old!" Mama had said, sitting on their bed, holding the dark curtain aside to look through the window at the lighted sky.

The next evening's newspaper had told the sad truth. The Danes had destroyed their own naval fleet, blowing up the vessels one by one, as the Germans approached to take over the ships for their own use.

"How sad the king must be," Annemarie had heard Mama say to Papa when they read the news.

"How proud," Papa had replied.

It had made Annemarie feel sad and proud, too, to picture the tall, aging king, perhaps with tears in his blue eyes, as he looked at the remains of his small navy, which now lay submerged and broken in the harbor.

"I don't want to play anymore, Ellen," she said suddenly, and put her paper doll on the table.

"I have to go home, anyway," Ellen said. "I have to help Mama with the housecleaning. Thursday is our New Year. Did you know that?"

"Why is it yours?" asked Kirsti. "Isn't it our New Year, too?"

"No. It's the Jewish New Year. That's just for us. But if you want, Kirsti, you can come that night and watch Mama light the candles."

Annemarie and Kirsti had often been invited to watch Mrs. Rosen light the Sabbath candles on Friday evenings. She covered her head with a cloth and said a special prayer in Hebrew as she did so. Annemarie always stood very quietly, awed, to watch; even Kirsti, usually such a chatterbox, was always still at that time. They didn't understand the words or the meaning, but they could feel what a special time it was for the Rosens.

"Yes," Kirsti agreed happily. "I'll come and watch your mama light the candles, and I'll wear my new black shoes."

But this time was to be different. Leaving for school on Thursday with her sister, Annemarie saw the Rosens walking to the synagogue early in the morning, dressed in their best clothes. She waved to Ellen, who waved happily back.

"Lucky Ellen," Annemarie said to Kirsti. "She doesn't have to go to school today."

"But she probably has to sit very, very still, like we do in church," Kirsti pointed out. "*That's* no fun."

That afternoon, Mrs. Rosen knocked at their door but didn't come inside. Instead, she spoke for a long time in a hurried, tense voice to Annemarie's mother in the hall. When Mama returned, her face was worried, but her voice was cheerful.

"Girls," she said, "we have a nice surprise. Tonight Ellen will be coming to stay overnight and to be our guest for a few days! It isn't often we have a visitor."

Kirsti clapped her hands in delight.

"But, Mama," Annemarie said, in dismay, "it's their New Year. They were going to have a celebration at home! Ellen told me that her mother managed to get a chicken someplace, and she was going to roast it—their first roast chicken in a year or more!"

"Their plans have changed," Mama said briskly. "Mr. and Mrs. Rosen have been called away to visit some relatives. So Ellen will stay with us. Now, let's get busy and put clean sheets on your bed. Kirsti, you may sleep with Mama and Papa tonight, and we'll let the big girls giggle together by themselves."

Kirsti pouted, and it was clear that she was about to argue. "Mama will tell you a special story tonight," her mother said. "One just for you."

"About a king?" Kirsti asked dubiously.

"About a king, if you wish," Mama replied.

"All right, then. But there must be a queen, too," Kirsti said.

Though Mrs. Rosen had sent her chicken to the Johansens, and Mama made a lovely dinner large enough for second helpings all around, it was not an evening of laughter and talk. Ellen was silent at dinner. She looked frightened. Mama and Papa tried to speak of cheerful things, but it was clear that they were worried, and it made Annemarie worry, too. Only Kirsti was unaware of the quiet tension in the room. Swinging her feet in their newly blackened and shiny shoes, she chattered and giggled during dinner.

"Early bedtime tonight, little one," Mama announced after the dishes were washed. "We need extra time for the long

story I promised, about the king and queen." She disappeared with Kirsti into the bedroom.

"What's happening?" Annemarie asked when she and Ellen were alone with Papa in the living room. "Something's wrong. What is it?"

Papa's face was troubled. "I wish that I could protect you children from this knowledge," he said quietly. "Ellen, you already know. Now we must tell Annemarie."

He turned to her and stroked her hair with his gentle hand. "This morning, at the synagogue, the rabbi told his congregation that the Nazis have taken the synagogue lists of all the Jews. Where they live, what their names are. Of course the Rosens were on that list, along with many others."

"Why? Why did they want those names?"

"They plan to arrest all the Danish Jews. They plan to take them away. And we have been told that they may come tonight."

"I don't understand! Take them where?"

Her father shook his head. "We don't know where, and we don't really know why. They call it 'relocation.' We don't even know what that means. We only know that it is wrong, and it is dangerous, and we must help."

Annemarie was stunned. She looked at Ellen and saw that her best friend was crying silently.

"Where are Ellen's parents? We must help them, too!"

"We couldn't take all three of them. If the Germans came to search our apartment, it would be clear that the Rosens were here. One person we can hide. Not three. So Peter has helped Ellen's parents to go elsewhere. We don't know where. Ellen doesn't know either. But they are safe."

Ellen sobbed aloud, and put her face in her hands. Papa put his arm around her. "They are safe, Ellen. I promise you that. You will see them again quite soon. Can you try hard to believe my promise?"

Ellen hesitated, nodded, and wiped her eyes with her hand.

"But, Papa," Annemarie said, looking around the small apartment, with its few pieces of furniture: the fat stuffed sofa, the table and chairs, the small bookcase against the wall. "You said that we would hide her. How can we do that? Where can she hide?"

Papa smiled. "That part is easy. It will be as your mama said: you two will sleep together in your bed, and you may giggle and talk and tell secrets to each other. And if anyone comes—"

Ellen interrupted him. "Who might come? Will it be soldiers? Like the ones on the corners?" Annemarie remembered how terrified Ellen had looked the day when the soldier had questioned them on the corner.

"I really don't think anyone will. But it never hurts to be prepared. If anyone should come, even soldiers, you two will be sisters. You are together so much, it will be easy for you to pretend that you are sisters."

He rose and walked to the window. He pulled the lace curtain aside and looked down into the street. Outside, it was beginning to grow dark. Soon they would have to draw the black curtains that all Danes had on their windows; the entire city had to be completely darkened at night. In a nearby tree, a bird was singing; otherwise it was quiet. It was the last night of September.

"Go, now, and get into your nightgowns. It will be a long night."

Annemarie and Ellen got to their feet. Papa suddenly crossed the room and put his arms around them both. He kissed the top of each head: Annemarie's blond one, which reached to his shoulder, and Ellen's dark hair, the thick curls braided as always into pigtails.

"Don't be frightened," he said to them softly. "Once I had three daughters. Tonight I am proud to have three daughters again."

"Do you really think anyone will come?" Ellen asked nervously, turning to Annemarie in the bedroom. "Your father doesn't think so."

"Of course not. They're always threatening stuff. They just like to scare people." Annemarie took her nightgown from a hook in the closet.

"Anyway, if they did, it would give me a chance to practice acting. I'd just pretend to be Lise. I wish I were taller, though." Ellen stood on tiptoe, trying to make herself tall. She laughed at herself, and her voice was more relaxed.

"You were great as the Dark Queen in the school play last year," Annemarie told her. "You should be an actress when you grow up."

"My father wants me to be a teacher. He wants *everyone* to be a teacher, like him. But maybe I could convince him that I should go to acting school." Ellen stood on tiptoe again, and made an imperious gesture with her arm. "I am the Dark Queen," she intoned dramatically. "I have come to command the night!"

"You should try saying, 'I am Lise Johansen!'" Annemarie said, grinning. "If you told the Nazis that you were the Dark Queen, they'd haul you off to a mental institution."

Ellen dropped her actress pose and sat down, with her legs curled under her, on the bed. "They won't really come here, do you think?" she asked again.

Annemarie shook her head. "Not in a million years." She picked up her hairbrush.

The girls found themselves whispering as they got ready for bed. There was no need, really, to whisper; they were, after all, supposed to be normal sisters, and Papa had said they could giggle and talk. The bedroom door was closed.

But the night did seem, somehow, different from a normal night. And so they whispered.

"How did your sister die, Annemarie?" Ellen asked suddenly. "I remember when it happened. And I remember the funeral—it was the only time I have ever been in a Lutheran church. But I never knew just what happened."

"I don't know *exactly*," Annemarie confessed. "She and Peter were out somewhere together, and then there was a telephone call, that there had been an accident. Mama and Papa rushed to the hospital—remember, your mother came and stayed with me and Kirsti? Kirsti was already asleep and she slept right through everything, she was so little then. But I stayed up, and I was with your mother in the living room when my parents came home in the middle of the night. And they told me Lise had died."

"I remember it was raining," Ellen said sadly. "It was still raining the next morning when Mama told me. Mama was crying, and the rain made it seem as if the whole *world* was crying."

Annemarie finished brushing her long hair and handed her hairbrush to her best friend. Ellen undid her braids, lifted her dark hair away from the thin gold chain she wore around her neck—the chain that held the Star of David—and began to brush her thick curls.

"I think it was partly because of the rain. They said she was hit by a car. I suppose the streets were slippery, and it was getting dark, and maybe the driver just couldn't see," Annemarie went on, remembering. "Papa looked so angry. He made one hand into a fist, and he kept pounding it into the other hand. I remember the noise of it: slam, slam, slam."

Together they got into the wide bed and pulled up the covers. Annemarie blew out the candle and drew the dark curtains aside so that the open window near the bed let in some air. "See that blue trunk in the corner?" she said, pointing through the darkness. "Lots of Lise's things are in there. Even her wedding dress. Mama and Papa have never looked at those things, not since the day they packed them away."

Ellen sighed. "She would have looked so beautiful in her wedding dress. She had such a pretty smile. I used to pretend that she was *my* sister, too."

"She would have liked that," Annemarie told her. "She loved you."

"That's the worst thing in the world," Ellen whispered. "To be dead so young. I wouldn't want the Germans to take my family away—to make us live someplace else. But still, it wouldn't be as bad as being dead."

Annemarie leaned over and hugged her. "They won't take you away," she said. "Not your parents, either. Papa promised that they were safe, and he always keeps his promises. And you are quite safe, here with us."

For a while they continued to murmur in the dark, but the murmurs were interrupted by yawns. Then Ellen's voice stopped, she turned over, and in a minute her breathing was quiet and slow.

Annemarie stared at the window where the sky was outlined and a tree branch moved slightly in the breeze. Everything seemed very familiar, very comforting. Dangers were no more than odd imaginings, like ghost stories that children made up to frighten one another: things that couldn't possibly happen. Annemarie felt completely safe here in her own home, with her parents in the next room and her best friend asleep beside her. She yawned contentedly and closed her eyes.

It was hours later, but still dark, when she was awakened abruptly by the pounding on the apartment door.

Annemarie eased the bedroom door open quietly, only a crack, and peeked out. Behind her, Ellen was sitting up, her eyes wide.

She could see Mama and Papa in their nightclothes, moving about. Mama held a lighted candle, but as Annemarie watched, she went to a lamp and switched it on. It was so long a time since they had dared to use the strictly rationed electricity after dark that the light in the room seemed startling to Annemarie, watching through the slightly opened bedroom door. She saw her mother look automatically to the blackout curtains, making certain that they were tightly drawn.

Papa opened the front door to the soldiers.

"This is the Johansen apartment?" A deep voice asked the question loudly, in terribly accented Danish.

"Our name is on the door, and I see you have a flashlight," Papa answered. "What do you want? Is something wrong?"

"I understand you are a friend of your neighbors the Rosens, Mrs. Johansen," the soldier said angrily.

"Sophy Rosen is my friend, that is true," Mama said quietly. "Please, could you speak more softly? My children are asleep."

"Then you will be so kind as to tell me where the Rosens are." He made no effort to lower his voice.

"I assume they are at home, sleeping. It is four in the morning, after all," Mama said.

Annemarie heard the soldier stalk across the living room toward the kitchen. From her hiding place in the narrow sliver of open doorway, she could see the heavy uniformed man, a holstered pistol at his waist, in the entrance to the kitchen, peering in toward the sink.

Another German voice said, "The Rosens' apartment is empty. We are wondering if they might be visiting their good friends the Johansens."

"Well," said Papa, moving slightly so that he was standing in front of Annemarie's bedroom door, and she could see nothing except the dark blur of his back, "as you see, you are mistaken. There is no one here but my family."

"You will not object if we look around." The voice was harsh, and it was not a question.

"It seems we have no choice," Papa replied.

"Please don't wake my children," Mama requested again. "There is no need to frighten little ones."

The heavy, booted feet moved across the floor again and into the other bedroom. A closet door opened and closed with a bang.

Annemarie eased her bedroom door closed silently. She stumbled through the darkness to the bed.

"Ellen," she whispered urgently, "take your necklace off!"

Ellen's hands flew to her neck. Desperately she began trying to unhook the tiny clasp. Outside the bedroom door, the harsh voices and heavy footsteps continued.

"I can't get it open!" Ellen said frantically. "I never take it off—I can't even remember how to open it!"

Annemarie heard a voice just outside the door. "What is here?"

"Shhh," her mother replied. "My daughters' bedroom. They are sound asleep."

"Hold still," Annemarie commanded. "This will hurt." She grabbed the little gold chain, yanked with all her strength, and broke it. As the door opened and light flooded into the bedroom, she crumpled it into her hand and closed her fingers tightly.

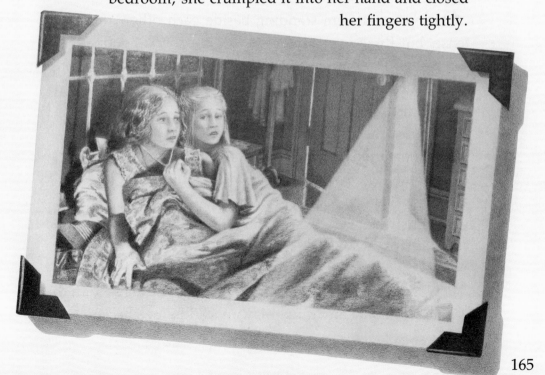

Terrified, both girls looked up at the three Nazi officers who entered the room.

One of the men aimed a flashlight around the bedroom. He went to the closet and looked inside. Then with a sweep of his gloved hand he pushed to the floor several coats and a bathrobe that hung from pegs on the wall.

There was nothing else in the room except a chest of drawers, the blue decorated trunk in the corner, and a heap of Kirsti's dolls piled in a small rocking chair. The flashlight beam touched each thing in turn. Angrily the officer turned toward the bed.

"Get up!" he ordered. "Come out here!"

Trembling, the two girls rose from the bed and followed him, brushing past the two remaining officers in the doorway, to the living room.

Annemarie looked around. These three uniformed men were different from the ones on the street corners. The street soldiers were often young, sometimes ill at ease, and Annemarie remembered how the Giraffe had, for a moment, let his harsh pose slip and had smiled at Kirsti.

But these men were older and their faces were set with anger.

Her parents were standing beside each other, their faces tense, but Kirsti was nowhere in sight. Thank goodness that Kirsti slept through almost everything. If they had wakened her, she would be wailing—or worse, she would be angry, and her fists would fly.

"Your names?" the officer barked.

"Annemarie Johansen. And this is my sister—"

"Quiet! Let her speak for herself. Your name?" He was glaring at Ellen.

Ellen swallowed. "Lise," she said, and cleared her throat. "Lise Johansen."

The officer stared at them grimly.

"Now," Mama said in a strong voice, "you have seen that we are not hiding anything. May my children go back to bed?"

The officer ignored her. Suddenly he grabbed a handful of Ellen's hair. Ellen winced.

He laughed scornfully. "You have a blond child sleeping in the other room. And you have this blond daughter—" He gestured towards Annemarie with his head. "Where did you get the dark-haired one?" He twisted the lock of Ellen's hair. "From a different father? From the milkman?"

Papa stepped forward. "Don't speak to my wife in such a way. Let go of my daughter or I will report you for such treatment."

"Or maybe you got her someplace else?" the officer continued with a sneer. "From the Rosens?"

For a moment no one spoke. Then Annemarie, watching in panic, saw her father move swiftly to the small bookcase and take out a book. She saw that he was holding the family photograph album. Very quickly he searched through its pages, found what he was looking for, and tore out three pictures from three separate pages.

He handed them to the German officer, who released Ellen's hair.

"You will see each of my daughters, each with her name written on the photograph," Papa said.

Annemarie knew instantly which photographs he had chosen. The album had many snapshots—all the poorly focused pictures of school events and birthday parties. But it also contained a portrait, taken by a photographer, of each girl as a tiny infant. Mama had written, in her delicate handwriting, the name of each baby daughter across the bottom of those photographs.

She realized too, with an icy feeling, why Papa had torn them from the book. At the bottom of each page, below the photograph itself, was written the date. And the real Lise Johansen had been born twenty-one years earlier.

"Kirsten Elisabeth," the officer read, looking at Kirsti's baby picture. He let the photograph fall to the floor.

"Annemarie," he read next, glanced at her, and dropped the second photograph.

"Lise Margrete," he read finally, and stared at Ellen for a long, unwavering moment. In her mind, Annemarie pictured the photograph that he held: the baby, wide-eyed, propped against a pillow, her tiny hand holding a silver teething ring, her bare feet visible against the hem of an embroidered dress. The wispy curls. Dark.

The officer tore the photograph in half and dropped the pieces on the floor. Then he turned, the heels of his shiny boots grinding into the pictures, and left the apartment. Without a word, the other two officers followed. Papa stepped forward and closed the door behind him.

Annemarie relaxed the clenched fingers of her right hand, which still clutched Ellen's necklace. She looked down, and saw that she had imprinted the Star of David into her palm.

THINK IT OVER

1. Would you call Annemarie and her family heroes? Explain your answer.

2. How does Mr. Johansen intend to hide Ellen from the Germans?

3. Who is the dark-haired girl in the photograph that Mr. Johansen shows to the soldiers?

4. The characters in this story face many hardships. Which hardship do you think would be the most difficult to face? Explain your answer.

5. Why does Annemarie yank the Star of David necklace off Ellen's neck?

WRITE

Annemarie says that all of Denmark must be bodyguard for the Jews. Write a paragraph explaining how the characters in the story act as bodyguards.

THEME WRAP-UP

COURAGE AND KINDNESS

Compare the heroes in each story. How are they similar? How are they different?

· ·

Why do you think writers choose to inform readers about history through stories about fictional characters?

· ·

WRITER'S WORKSHOP Imagine that in "A Test of Courage," Papa does not have the photographs to show the soldiers. Think of other ways that Papa could convince the soldiers that Ellen is his daughter. Then write a new ending for the story.

169

REVOLUTIONARY HEROES

George Washington is famous. Phoebe Fraunces is not. Find out why they are both Revolutionary War heroes.

PHOEBE and the GENERAL

by Judith Berry Griffin ★ illustrated by Margot Tomes

★ ★ ★ ★ ★ ★

*I*n 1776, the year Phoebe Fraunces was thirteen years old, her father gave her a very dangerous job. Phoebe was going to be a spy.

At that time most black people in New York were slaves. But Phoebe and her family had always been free. Phoebe's father, Samuel Fraunces, owned the Queen's Head Tavern. The Queen's Head was a popular eating and meeting place. George Washington (who was now General George Washington, commander in chief of the American Army) had dinner there when he visited New York. So did John Adams.

Many people met there because they knew it was a safe place to talk. In 1776 the war had begun, and there could be trouble if a person were caught talking against the king. But the Patriots knew that Samuel Fraunces could be trusted. So they held meetings at his tavern and discussed their secret plans, and Sam Fraunces never let on that he knew any of them.

One morning in April, 1776, Sam and his daughter Phoebe were sitting side by side in the long dining room of the Queen's Head. There was to be a big dinner that night, and they were getting the room ready—polishing the pewter plates and candlesticks and laying out fresh candles.

Phoebe loved the Queen's Head from its broad front steps all the way up to its bright red-tiled roof. But this room —called the Long Room—was the room she loved best, with its neat tables and chairs, its fireplaces and its big windows. From the window seat where she sat she could see clear to the harbor. The water was dotted with big white-sailed ships, their tall masts pointing at the sky like fingers.

"Phoebe," her father began.

"Yes, sir," Phoebe answered. Her father did not respond, and Phoebe looked up at him, smiling. She thought him very handsome, with his curly hair powdered and drawn back and his smooth brown skin and dark eyes.

"Phoebe, I've something important to say to you this day," he said. "It's a bad time in this country."

Phoebe stopped smiling when she saw he was so serious.

"It's hard to find a person you can trust with a secret—especially a dangerous secret," he went on. "I'm glad to know I can trust you. Young as you are, you've learned from your father how to listen well and talk little."

Something in her father's voice made Phoebe put down the candlestick she was holding. She sat quite still, waiting for him to go on, watching the polishing cloth in his hands go around and around.

"I have a great fear in me," he said slowly, "that our General Washington is in dread, dread danger. It is he who is keeping the colonies together. But there are those who'd like to see the colonies separated and so ruled more easily by the king. And if something were to happen to the general, it would be a hard, hard job to find another such as he, to pull the colonies together and throw off the king. Indeed, such a man might not be found at all, and the king would rule on."

There was silence for a time. The sunlight, stronger now, pushed warm fingers through the windows, glittering against the candlesticks.

"New York is full of soldiers," he continued. "Some are only out for money. To them it makes no difference what side they're on. They'd even take money from the enemy and do anything they'd ask. Some such scoundrel might be paid to kill the general. I heard something."

Phoebe closed her eyes, seeing her father moving like a shadow among his guests, gracious, smiling, pouring cider and exchanging greetings. It was so easy for him to hear secrets without seeming to listen!

"What I heard could cost my life, Daughter, and the general's as well," her father said quietly. "Phoebe, I need your help."

Phoebe opened her mouth to speak, but her voice would only whisper. "What must I do?" she asked.

Her father put down the candlestick and took her hand in his. "I want you to do a big job, Phoebe," he said gravely. "General Washington has let me know he's arriving in New York with his household in seven days' time. He's to move into Mortier House on Richmond Hill, and I promised to find him a housekeeper. I want you to live there and be his housekeeper, Phoebe. I know you will be a good one. But your real job will be to watch—to listen—to spy out every bit of information you can. I want you to find out if there is someone planning to kill him and how he plans to do it. Your real job will be to save General Washington's life."

Phoebe was very frightened. General Washington was a great soldier! How could she save his life, if his whole army could not? She wouldn't know who to look for. She was not even strong enough to fight anyone! And what if she failed?

Her father spoke again, as if he had read her thoughts. "I'm asking only that you try, Daughter," he said. "I have no proof of a plot against the general's life. I know only what I heard. If I tell, his enemies would only hide themselves and wait for a safer time."

Phoebe shook her head. Could this really be happening? But her father's voice was real. "You'll tell no one who you are. You'll listen as you serve the officers of the Army. You must watch for a member of General Washington's bodyguard—someone whose name begins with T. It is this man who is supposed to carry out the plan. Every day you and I will meet down by the market, and you can tell me what news you have.

"Now hear me well, Phoebe. You are to do nothing by yourself—nothing that would put you in danger. You are only to listen and tell me what you hear. Trust no one. No one." He picked up his candlestick and began to polish it once more. When he spoke this time, his voice sounded sad, but Phoebe heard more than sadness. Her father was angry.

"You know, Phoebe," he said, "'tis a strange freedom we're fighting for, alongside George Washington."

Phoebe nodded. She knew what her father meant. How could a man lead an army to win freedom if he himself owned slaves? For General Washington did own slaves. It was said he treated them well. But still, they were slaves.

"And 'tis stranger yet that you and I will save him," Samuel went on. "And those like us will have no share in that freedom he's fighting for!"

"But maybe," Phoebe said, "when the Patriots win their freedom, they'll let the slaves go free, too. Maybe then everyone will be free!"

Samuel shook his head. "I think not, Daughter," he said. "But maybe, one day. . . ." Then he looked at Phoebe and smiled. "Here, now! Get on with your polishing! It won't do to have tonight's dinner set off by dull candlesticks!"

And so it was that a few days later Phoebe packed two clean aprons and a bottle of her father's best cider into a bundle, said good-bye to her family, and set off to save George Washington's life.

Mortier House was just a few blocks from the Queen's Head, but Phoebe felt as if she were going miles and miles away from home as she slowly made her way through the narrow, winding, crowded streets. A cold, damp wind blew in off the harbor. Everywhere, it seemed, men were pushing carts. They rattled over the cobblestones, loaded with guns and ammunition. Soldiers were everywhere, shouting orders. War was in the air.

Mortier House sat high on a hill, with a carpet of grass around it that reached away to the large, beautiful trees beyond. There was a small storage house to one side, with a hen house and yard where several chickens pecked and scratched contentedly. Phoebe followed the long drive to the back of the house, wondering how soon she would meet someone whose name began with T and what she would do when she did. Mortier House was quiet and calm, quite a change from the busy street, but here, too, war was in the air.

A tall, thin woman opened the back door. She looked very surprised when Phoebe told her who she was. "Why, you're nothin' but a child!" she said. "How are you going to take care of this big place?"

"I'm strong," replied Phoebe, standing as tall as she could. "And I work hard. I'll have no trouble."

The woman looked at her doubtfully. "Well," she said, "leastways you talk right up. I'm Mary. I cook. This here's Pompey," she continued as a boy about eight appeared from behind her. "He's my boy. He'll be a help to you—bringing in firewood and such like that."

She led Phoebe through room after room of beautiful, shining furniture, up stairs and more stairs, across carpeted floors—all silent and waiting. Finally, on the top floor of the house, they stopped before a door that Mary opened into a tiny room. It contained a small window and a narrow cot. "This is yours," she said. "I'm in the kitchen should you need me."

As soon as the door closed, Phoebe sank down on the cot. Already she missed the Queen's Head and her father. If she were home now, she'd be helping him ready the tables for dinner. At the thought of her father Phoebe rocked back and forth on the cot in despair, still clutching her bundle. How could she take care of this big, quiet, unfriendly house, with its gleaming floors and stiff furniture? And take care of General Washington, too? She could not do it. Her father had asked too much.

After a while she stood up and walked toward the window. She could see out over much of the city. Over there was the fort. Here were the harbor and the tall spire of Trinity Church. And could it be—she looked harder—yes, it was! There, among all the dark-brown and black roofs of the other buildings, was the bright red-tiled roof of the Queen's Head! It stood out like a flag, almost like a signal! And suddenly, Phoebe did not feel so hopeless. She wasn't so far from home, after all. She would see her father every day. And she was to do nothing by herself—he had said so. His words came back to her: "I only want you to try, Daughter." Phoebe sighed and began to untie her bundle.

Phoebe soon settled into her job. The work wasn't as hard as she thought it would be. Mrs. Washington had brought her own quilts and feather beds. It was Phoebe's job to air and turn these every morning, as well as to see to the buying of food and the serving of meals. She had to keep the silver cleaned and shining and the furniture dusted and polished. She did not have any special jobs to do for General Washington, except to see that his meals were served on time. He was very particular about having dinner served promptly at four o'clock, and Phoebe sometimes had a hard time getting everything finished by then.

General Washington never said very much. He was tall, with a quiet voice. He looked like the kind of man who could win a war. Mrs. Washington was to have a fresh egg each day, and Pompey, who was a lot of company to Phoebe even though he was only eight years old, helped by visiting the hen house early every morning. When dinner was over, he and Phoebe often stood on the kitchen steps and fed the hens leftover scraps of bread from the table.

Phoebe was a good housekeeper. But she did not forget why she was there. Day after day she watched, and waited, and listened. General Washington came and went. The house was full of people all the time—officers of the Army, friends, members of the bodyguard. Phoebe slipped among them silent as a shadow, as her father had taught her. Whenever she saw anyone talking softly, she stopped to poke the fire, fill their glasses, light new candles. But still she saw nothing, heard nothing.

Each day at noon she took a basket and went down to the waterfront to do the day's marketing. When she was finished, she would make her way to the edge of the harbor and stand looking out over the ocean. No one took any notice of her, in her clean white apron and cap, a shawl thrown across her shoulders. Nor did anyone particularly notice the man who always came to stand beside her, his curly hair powdered and pulled back, his brown face plump and smiling.

The two of them would stand together for a few moments, seeming to talk of nothing important. Sometimes Phoebe would throw out a few crumbs to the gulls, which would gather noisily at their feet. After a time they would move off in different directions—Phoebe back to Mortier House, Sam Fraunces back to the Queen's Head.

Phoebe never had anything to report. She was particularly careful to watch every member of the general's bodyguard who came to the house. None was called by a name starting with T. They all seemed to be truly fond of the general and laughed and joked with him. Two members of the bodyguard did stand out from the others. One was especially nice. Mr. Hickey was his name. He smiled at Phoebe while she was serving and often came into the kitchen to joke with her and Mary while Mary was preparing the meals.

Phoebe was the youngest servant in the house except for Pompey. When the others were talking, she often felt left out. She was glad to have someone to talk to. Hickey seemed much younger than the other men—not much older, in fact, than Phoebe herself. And he seemed glad to talk to her, too. Like Phoebe, he seemed not to have many friends. Phoebe often saw him sitting by himself at the edge of the woods.

Mr. Green was another member of General Washington's bodyguard who kept to himself, but he was not like Hickey. He never spoke to Phoebe at all, even when he saw her in the yard. Phoebe would always say, "Evening, sir," but he never so much as looked at her. From what she could tell, he didn't say much to anyone, even at dinnertime when everyone did a lot of talking. Though his name didn't begin with T, Phoebe made up her mind to watch him very carefully. There was something about him she didn't like.

One day, when Hickey came to the kitchen, he had a small cloth bag with him. He handed it to Phoebe. "Here," he said. "It's some seed for your precious chickens."

Phoebe was surprised. She didn't know anyone had noticed that she fed them. She opened the bag. "But it's good seed, sir!" she protested. "It's too good to feed the chickens!"

Hickey laughed. "It's only the king's true men who'll be missing it," he said. "Let's see if your chickens will get fatter from British grain than from American bread crumbs!"

Phoebe smiled. She didn't ask him how he had got the seed. But he began to bring it home to her often. Sometimes he would bring it himself. Other times she would find a bag lying on the table when she came into the kitchen. Sometimes there would be a bright ribbon tied around it. Then Hickey would say, "The ribbon's for you, pretty Phoebe. Compliments of King George III!" Sometimes there would be a stick of candy inside—always, he said, stolen from those loyal to the King of England.

Soon she was looking forward to his visits every day. And as the days went by and Phoebe still could find no one who seemed to be plotting to take General Washington's life, she thought about asking Mr. Hickey for help. Her father had told her to trust no one. Still . . . perhaps she could trust him. She would wait and see.

Weeks went by. The beautiful house, once so strange to her, was now like a good friend. Phoebe enjoyed using the fine china plates and crystal glasses. She enjoyed serving Mary's deliciously prepared meals to General Washington and his important guests, while Pompey followed solemnly behind with the salt cellar and pepper mill.

She knew she was there to save General Washington's life. But as the days went by and she still heard nothing, she began to wonder if perhaps her father was mistaken. No one seemed to be plotting anything, and it was now the beginning of June. Phoebe had been at Mortier House almost two months.

Then one day, when she went to the market, her father wasn't there. Phoebe stood by the water a long time, waiting and wondering. Should she go to the Queen's Head? Or back to Mortier House? As she was trying to decide, she saw her father hurrying toward her. He looked very worried. For the first time he seemed not to care that people might notice them. He held her by the shoulders and looked into her face.

"Phoebe," he said urgently, "I have heard that General Washington will be leaving Mortier House in a very few days. The person known as T will act before that time. You must find out who it is!"

Phoebe's mind was whirling as she hurried back toward the house. She was frightened, but she was also determined. She *would* save General Washington! She had long ago figured that he would likely be shot. During dinner he always sat in a chair by the window. He would make an easy target for anyone waiting outside.

If only she could get him to change his place, away from that window! His good friend General Gates would be a dinner guest at the house this evening. Everyone else was part of the family or a member of the bodyguard. Over and over she said their names. No one's name began with T.

As she reached the kitchen door, she saw Hickey sitting on the steps. "Why are you so solemn, pretty Phoebe?" he asked.

182

"Oh, Mr. Hickey, sir," said Phoebe breathlessly. "I'm so worried. . . ." She paused. She did need help! Should she tell him? Maybe he knew something, had seen something that had escaped her notice. After all, he was a member of the bodyguard—it was his job to protect General Washington. Her father's words came back to her. "Trust no one," he had said. "No one." She sighed. She'd have to keep trying alone.

"Well," said Hickey after a moment. "I've something to bring a smile back to that pretty face. Fresh June peas for the general's dinner—first of the season! His favorite and mine—and enough for us both! Some friends of the king will be mighty hungry tonight!" He handed her a large sack, filled to the brim with pea pods. Phoebe smiled in spite of herself.

"Grown men—soldiers of the American Army—stealing peas!" she said.

Hickey pretended to be hurt. "All right," he said, snatching the sack from her and holding it over his head. "I'll just throw them out to your chickens—"

"No, no, Mr. Hickey." Phoebe laughed. "Here—I'll fix them myself."

Hickey handed her the sack. "I'll be here to fill my plate at dinnertime," he promised.

All afternoon, as she went about her chores, Phoebe worried. *How* could she get the general's chair away from that window? She would have to stand in front of it, blocking the view from outside. But then, would someone shoot her? By the time dinnertime arrived she was almost sick with fear. She was in the kitchen with Pompey getting ready to serve the plates when a voice behind her made her jump. It was Hickey.

"I've come for my peas," he said softly.

"Oh! Mr. Hickey, sir!" she said. "You gave me such a start! I was—" She stopped and looked at him, even more startled. He looked ill? frightened? She couldn't tell which.

"Which is my plate, and which is General Washington's?" he

said. "It wouldn't do for him to have more than me." He spoke quickly, without smiling this time.

"I never heard of such carryings on over a pile of peas!" Phoebe said. "This is the general's plate, and this is yours!" She turned away to fill Pompey's salt cellar and turned back just in time to see Hickey's hand move quickly away from General Washington's plate and slide into his pocket. Something winked for a second in the light—something shiny, like glass.

"What are you doing to General Washington's plate?" she said. "I told you yours is here!" She picked up the plate. Was it her

imagination, or was there something grainy, like sugar, on the peas? Phoebe looked more closely, but as she looked, whatever it was seemed to have disappeared. An instant later she wasn't sure—had she seen anything at all? She thought of the window again and forgot about the peas. She had to serve General Washington.

Leaving Hickey standing in the kitchen, Phoebe nervously entered the dining room, Pompey following with the salt. As she walked toward the general, Phoebe looked at every face around the table. Some of the guests were talking, some merely smiling. None seemed nervous or frightened.

And then she noticed the empty chair. Who was missing? But even as she asked herself the question, she knew. It was Mr. Green. Was he outside the house, with a gun, waiting? General Washington was sitting by the window, as she had feared. He sat back easily in his chair, listening to something General Gates was saying. The window was open! As she went past, Phoebe looked outside anxiously. There was not a sound, not a shadow, not a movement. The green grass was smooth and unruffled. Even the leaves in the trees beyond were still.

"Well, Phoebe!" General Washington exclaimed as she stopped beside the chair. "June peas! How did you get them so early in the season?"

"It wasn't me, sir," replied Phoebe, looking past him out the window. "It was your Mr. Hickey brought them in, fresh today. He says they're your favorite."

"And mine as well!" said General Gates. "Where is Mr. Thomas Hickey? I want to thank him!"

Phoebe started to put the plate down in front of General Washington. Then, in a flash, it came to her who she was looking for. Mr. Green was not hiding outside the window to shoot at the general. The person who was trying to kill him was here—in the kitchen! Phoebe stood like a stone, the plate still in her hands. She saw Hickey again—Thomas Hickey—laughing and teasing, bringing her candy and ribbons and seed for her chickens. And then bringing June peas for the general and sprinkling them with poison! T was for Thomas, member of General Washington's bodyguard!

Still holding the plate, she whirled around. Pompey was waiting behind her. "Run!" she screamed. "Run! Get my father!"

Everyone stopped talking. Pompey looked at her in amazement. "Y-your father?" he stammered.

"Sam Fraunces! At the Queen's Head! Go!" And she stamped her foot. Pompey had never heard Phoebe sound like that before. He dropped the salt cellar and ran through the kitchen door.

Everyone in the dining room sat frozen. All eyes were on Phoebe. "General Washington!" she cried. "Mr. Hickey has put poison in your dinner! I saw him!" There was a gasp from the table.

"What jest is this?" roared General Gates, getting up from his place and reaching for the plate. But before he could take it from her, Phoebe ran to the open window and threw the whole plate out into the yard.

Now the dining room was in an uproar. Chairs overturned; cider spilled as the men jumped to their feet in confusion. Some ran toward the window where Phoebe was standing, as if they feared she might try to escape. Others started for the

kitchen. Some ran to surround General Washington. No one knew what to do.

It was General Gates who first noticed the chickens in the yard. "Look!" he shouted, pointing out the window.

Three of Phoebe's chickens had come to peck at the peas she had thrown outside. Two had already fallen dead. The third was still moving its wings, but as they watched, it, too, grew still. The poison, meant for General Washington, had killed the chickens instead.

"Get Hickey!" bellowed General Gates, and members of the bodyguard rushed to obey. Minutes later Thomas Hickey was dragged in from the yard, his face white with terror. He had not been able to escape. Minutes after that, Sam Fraunces burst into the room. Phoebe was still standing by the window, shaking. He ran to her and held her tightly. Phoebe clung to him, burying her face in his shoulder.

"Well done, Daughter," Samuel Fraunces said quietly. "Well done."

After the excitement had died down and Hickey had been taken away, General Washington came to speak to Phoebe and her father. "It's nice to know people whom I can trust," he said simply. "Thank you."

General Washington went on to lead the American Army to victory, and the United States was born. So freedom did come to some Americans, but not all. In 1783, when the war was won, General Washington chose to give his victory party at Fraunces' Queen's Head Tavern, and there he said good-bye to the leaders of his army. And when he became the first President of the United States, he invited Sam Fraunces to become his official steward. Fraunces held that job until 1796.

Thomas Hickey was tried and convicted of trying to kill George Washington. Seven days later he was hanged. As was usual in those days, everyone turned out to watch. No one knows whether Phoebe was there. No one knows what happened to Phoebe after that. But we do know that she was a good spy.

Postscript from the Author

The story of Phoebe Fraunces is essentially historically accurate. Samuel Fraunces did indeed allow his restaurant to serve as a meeting place for the Patriots. He was so steadfast in his loyalty to the revolutionary cause that after the war ended he was voted the sum of £200 by Congress, as a reward. Soon after that Fraunces changed the name of the Queen's Head to the name by which it is still known today—Fraunces Tavern. The tavern is still standing, at the corner of Broad and Pearl streets in New York City. Part of it is a museum, but the bottom floor still operates as a restaurant. It looks very much as it did when Samuel Fraunces and his family lived there, except that it no longer has its red-tiled roof.

SAMUEL FRAUNCES

THINK IT OVER

1. *Did you think that Phoebe's story was remarkable? Explain what you thought of this young hero.*

2. *Why couldn't Phoebe discover anyone whose name began with the letter T?*

3. *When did Phoebe finally suspect Mr. Hickey?*

4. *Do you think Phoebe's father should have turned to his daughter for help? What else do you think he might have done?*

5. *Explain why no one suspected Phoebe of being a spy.*

WRITE

How would you rate Phoebe's spying skills? Choose one of the following ratings, and write an explanation for your choice.

**** Excellent   *** Good   ** Fair   * Poor

Judith Berry Griffin wrote *Phoebe and the General* as a way to help celebrate the bicentennial of the American Revolution. After she became aware of the story of how Phoebe Fraunces saved George Washington's life, Ms. Griffin did further research on Phoebe and her father, and she visited the Fraunces Tavern in New York City. She walked through the tavern, imagining what it was like to live there during the American Revolution.

Judith Berry Griffin is also the author of other books, including *Nat Turner* and *The Magic Mirrors*, an original African folktale. She was born and raised in Chicago, Illinois, and received her bachelor's and master's degrees in psychology from the University of Chicago and a master's degree in special education from Columbia University's Teachers College. She has been a third-grade teacher in North White Plains, New York, and was an elementary-school principal in Hartsdale, New York. One of her strongest interests is in ensuring that all children have access to the finest education possible. She currently lives in Massachusetts.

Words About the Author:

Judith Berry Griffin

Washington's
FAREWELL TO HIS OFFICERS

from *The American Revolutionaries:*
A History in Their Own Words   1750–1800

edited by Milton Meltzer

The world conflict known as the American Revolution was over. On December 4, 1783, General Washington bid farewell to his officers in New York at the Fraunces Tavern. Colonel Benjamin Tallmadge wrote this description of that final meeting:

We had been assembled but a few moments when His Excellency entered the room. His emotion, too strong to be concealed, seemed to be reciprocated by every officer present.

After partaking of a slight refreshment, in almost breathless silence, the general said, "With a heart full of love and gratitude, I now take leave of you. I most devoutly wish that your latter days may be as prosperous and happy as your former ones have been glorious and honorable.

"I cannot come to each of you, but shall feel obliged if each of you will come and take me by the hand."

General Knox, being nearest to him, turned to the commander in chief, who, suffused in tears, was incapable of utterance, but grasped his hand, when they embraced each other in silence. In the same affectionate manner, every officer in the room marched up to, kissed, and parted with his general in chief.

Such a scene of sorrow and weeping I had never before witnessed, and hope I may never be called upon to witness again. . . . Not a word was uttered to break the solemn silence . . . or to interrupt the tenderness of the . . . scene. The simple thought that we were then about to part from the man who had conducted us through a long and bloody war, and under whose conduct the glory and independence of our country had been achieved, and that we should see his face no more in this world, seemed to me utterly insupportable.

But the time of separation had come, and waving his hand to his grieving children around him, he left the room, and passing through a corps of light infantry who were paraded to receive him, he walked silently on to Whitehall, where a barge was in waiting. We all followed in mournful silence to the wharf, where a prodigious crowd had assembled to witness the departure of the man who, under God, had been the great agent in establishing the glory and independence of these United States. As soon as he was seated, the barge put off into the river, and when out in the stream, our great and beloved General waved his hat and bid us a silent adieu.

From *Memoir*, Benjamin Tallmadge, 1904.

REVOLUTIONARY HEROES

Sam and Phoebe Fraunces are on the same side of the war as General Washington. Does an American victory mean the same thing to all of them? Explain your answer.

. . . .

"Washington's Farewell to His Officers" was written by Benjamin Tallmadge, an eyewitness to the events. As a modern writer, Judith Berry Griffin had to rely on research and her imagination to write about that same time period. As a reader, do you prefer eyewitness accounts or well-researched fiction about the past? Explain your preference.

. . . .

WRITER'S WORKSHOP   At the end of *Phoebe and the General,* General Washington went on to lead the Americans to victory. Afterward, he held a celebration at the Queen's Head Tavern. Imagine that General Washington gave a speech about heroes of the war during this celebration. What might he have said about two unusual heroes, Sam and Phoebe Fraunces? Write the speech that General Washington might have delivered.

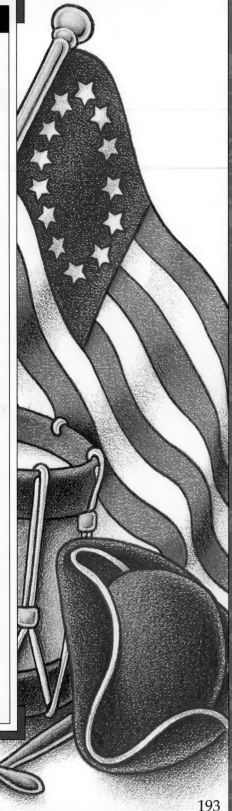

CONNECTIONS

HERO OF INDIA—AND THE WORLD

One of the great heroes of the twentieth century was Mohandas Gandhi (1869–1948) of India. Gandhi was the father of Indian independence. The story of his life continues to inspire people everywhere who are struggling for human rights and freedom.

Gandhi gained fame for his use of nonviolent protest in the movement to free India from British rule. Under Gandhi's leadership, millions of Indians simply refused to obey their British rulers. Gandhi was jailed repeatedly, but his popular support was so great that the British always released him. Finally, after three decades of struggle, India won its independence in 1947. Gandhi's ideas about nonviolence influenced Dr. Martin Luther King, Jr., and other leaders in all parts of the world.

■ *Have a "great heroes" discussion with your classmates. Think of women and men who have worked to improve conditions for people. Compare and contrast these heroes and their achievements.*

Mohandas Gandhi

194

GREAT HERO PROFILE

Write a biographical sketch of one of the heroes mentioned in your discussion. Be sure to explain what it was that made that man or woman a hero. Include a picture of your subject, if possible, and present an oral report to your classmates.

Lech Walesa

LANGUAGE ARTS CONNECTION

DRAMATIC MOMENTS

With a partner or a group of classmates, write a scene for a play about one of the heroes you have studied. Your scene should capture an important moment in that hero's life. Be sure to use correct play format. Add stage directions where they are necessary. You might enjoy rehearsing the scene and presenting it to your classmates.

(TITLE OF PLAY)
Characters:
Setting:
Character 1:
Character 2:
Character 1:

Rosa Parks (left)

Dr. Martin Luther King, Jr., on Selma march, 1965

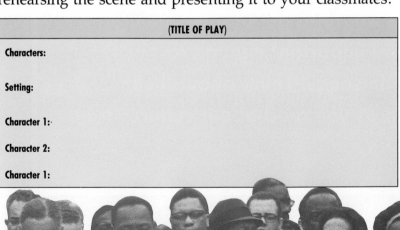

195

A·WORLD·AWAY

Our culture includes not only traditions from within our borders but also those brought here by people from around the world. How important is it to preserve all those traditions? The griots of West Africa, whom you will read about later, thought their history important enough to memorize in songs. Think about their dedication as you read about cultures from near and far.

THEMES

CROSSING BORDERS
. . . .
200

EXPLORING EGYPT
. . . .
240

ACROSS THE SEA
. . . .
274

BOOKSHELF

A JAR OF DREAMS
BY YOSHIKO UCHIDA

When Rinko is snubbed at school and in the street, she almost wishes she were not Japanese. Then Aunt Waka visits from Japan, and the whole family finds new strength. NOTABLE CHILDREN'S TRADE BOOK IN THE FIELD OF SOCIAL STUDIES

HBJ LIBRARY BOOK

PYRAMID
BY DAVID MACAULAY

Did you know that a pyramid is *solid*, not hollow? In this fascinating book you can follow the construction of an ancient Egyptian pyramid from start to finish. ALA NOTABLE BOOK, CHILDREN'S CHOICE

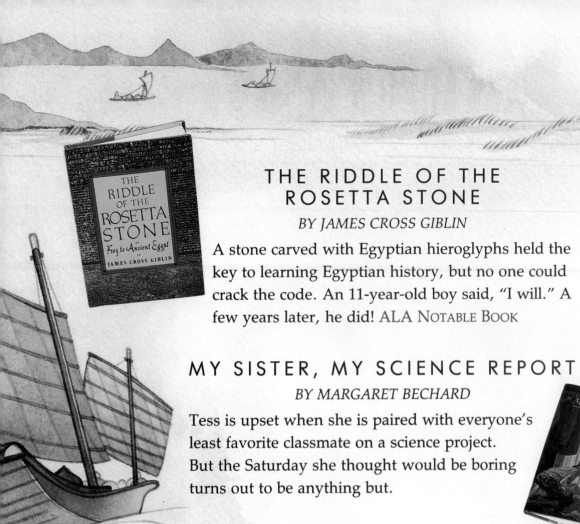

THE RIDDLE OF THE ROSETTA STONE

BY JAMES CROSS GIBLIN

A stone carved with Egyptian hieroglyphs held the key to learning Egyptian history, but no one could crack the code. An 11-year-old boy said, "I will." A few years later, he did! ALA NOTABLE BOOK

MY SISTER, MY SCIENCE REPORT

BY MARGARET BECHARD

Tess is upset when she is paired with everyone's least favorite classmate on a science project. But the Saturday she thought would be boring turns out to be anything but.

TWO SHORT AND ONE LONG

BY NINA RING AAMUNDSEN

Jonas and Einar are best friends who live in Norway. When Jonas makes friends with a new neighbor, a boy from Afghanistan, he finds out how little he knows about Einar.
ALA NOTABLE BOOK

199

CROSSING BORDERS

Language helps us communicate, but what happens when we meet a language we don't know? A language barrier is a challenge to the people in the following selections.

C O N T E N T S

Name / Nombres

by Julia Alvarez

When we arrived in New York City, our names changed almost immediately. At Immigration, the officer asked my father, *Mister Elbures,* if he had anything to declare. My father shook his head, "No," and we were waved through. I was too afraid we wouldn't be let in if I corrected the man's pronunciation, but I said our name to myself, opening my mouth wide for the organ blast of the *a,* trilling my tongue for the drumroll of the *r, All-vah-rrr-es!* How could anyone get *Elbures* out of that orchestra of sound?

At the hotel my mother was *Missus Alburest,* and I was *little girl,* as in, "Hey, little girl, stop riding the elevator up and down. It's *not* a toy."

When we moved into our new apartment building, the super called my father, *Mister Alberase,* and the neighbors who became mother's friends pronounced her name, *Jew-lee-ah* instead of *Hoo-lee-ah.* I, her namesake, was known as *Hoo-lee-tah* at home. But at school, I was *Judy* or *Judith,* and once an English teacher mistook me for *Juliet.*

It took awhile to get used to my new names. I wondered if I shouldn't correct my teachers and new friends. But my mother argued that it didn't matter. "You know what your friend Shakespeare said, *'A rose by any other name would smell as sweet.'*" My family had gotten into the habit of calling any famous author "my friend" because I had begun to write poems and stories in English class.

By the time I was in high school, I was a popular kid, and it showed in my name. Friends called me *Jules* or *Hey Jude,* and once a group of troublemaking friends my mother forbid me to hang out with called me *Alcatraz.* I was *Hoo-lee-tah* only to Mami and Papi and uncles and aunts who came over to eat *sancocho*[1] on Sunday afternoons—old world folk whom I would just as soon go back to where they came from and leave me to pursue whatever mischief I wanted to in America. *JUDY ALCATRAZ*: the name on the Wanted Poster would read. Who would ever trace her to me?

My older sister had the hardest time getting an American name for herself because *Mauricia* did not translate into English. Ironically, although she had the most foreign-sounding name, she and I were the Americans in the family. We had been born in New York City when our parents had first tried immigration and then gone back "home," too homesick to stay. My mother often told the story of how she had almost changed my sister's name in the hospital.

After the delivery, Mami and some other new mothers were cooing over their new baby sons and daughters and exchanging names and weights and delivery stories. My mother was embarrassed among the Sally's and Jane's and George's and John's to reveal the rich, noisy name of *Mauricia,* so when her turn came to brag, she gave her baby's name as *Maureen.*

"Why'd ya give her an Irish name with so many pretty Spanish names to choose from?" one of the women asked.

My mother blushed and admitted her baby's real name to the group. Her mother-in-law had recently died, she apologized, and her husband had insisted that the first daughter be named after his mother, *Mauran.* My mother thought it the ugliest name she had ever heard, and she talked my father into what she believed was an improvement, a combination of *Mauran* and her own mother's name, *Felicia.*

---

[1] sancocho: stew

"Her name is *Mao-ree-shee-ah*," my mother said to the group of women.

"Why that's a beautiful name," the new mothers cried. "*Moor-ee-sha, Moor-ee-sha*," they cooed into the pink blanket. *Moor-ee-sha* it was when we returned to the States eleven years later. Sometimes, American tongues found even that mispronunciation tough to say and called her *Maria* or *Marsha* or *Maudy* from her nickname *Maury*. I pitied her. What an awful name to have to transport across borders!

My little sister, Ana, had the easiest time of all. She was plain *Anne*—that is, only her name was plain, for she turned out to be the pale, blond "American beauty" in the family. The only Hispanic thing about her was the affectionate nicknames her boyfriends sometimes gave her. *Anita*, or as one goofy guy used to sing to her to the tune of the banana advertisement, *Anita Banana*.

Later, during her college years in the late 60s, there was a push to pronounce Third World names correctly. I remember calling her long distance at her group house and a roommate answering.

"Can I speak to Ana?" I asked, pronouncing her name the American way.

"Ana?" The man's voice hesitated. "Oh! you must mean *Ah-nah*!"

Our first few years in the States, though, ethnicity was not yet "in." Those were the blond, blue-eyed, bobby sock years of junior high and high school before the '60s ushered in peasant blouses, hoop earrings, sarapes.[2] My initial desire to be known by my correct Dominican name faded. I just wanted to be Judy and merge with the Sally's and Jane's in my class. But inevitably, my accent and coloring gave me away. "So where are you from, Judy?"

"New York," I told my classmates. After all, I had been born blocks away at Columbia Presbyterian Hospital.

"I mean, *originally*."

---

[2] sarapes: brightly colored shawls

"From the Caribbean," I answered vaguely, for if I specified, no one was quite sure on what continent our island was located.

"Really? I've been to Bermuda. We went last April for spring vacation. I got the worst sunburn! So, are you from Portoriko?"

"No," I sighed. "From the Dominican Republic."

"Where's that?"

"South of Bermuda."

They were just being curious, I knew, but I burned with shame whenever they singled me out as a "foreigner," a rare, exotic friend.

"Say your name in Spanish, oh please say it!" I had made mouths drop one day by rattling off my full name, which according to Dominican custom, included my middle names, Mother's and Father's surnames for four generations back.

"Julia Altagracia María Teresa Álvarez Tavares Perello Espaillat Julia Pérez Rochet González," I pronounced it slowly, a name as chaotic with sounds as a Middle Eastern bazaar or market day in a South American village.

My Dominican heritage was never more apparent than when my extended family attended school occasions. For my graduation, they all came, the whole lot of aunts and uncles and the many little cousins who snuck in without tickets. They sat in the first row in order to better understand the Americans' fast-spoken English. But how could they listen when they were constantly speaking among themselves in florid-sounding phrases, rococo consonants, rich, rhyming vowels.

Introducing them to my friends was a further trial to me. These relatives had such complicated names and there were so many of them, and their relationships to myself were so convoluted. There was my Tía[3] Josefina, who was not really an aunt but a much older cousin. And her daughter, Aida Margarita, who was adopted, *una hija de crianza*.[4] My uncle of

[3] Tía, Tío: Aunt, Uncle
[4] una hija de crianza: an adopted daughter

206

affection, Tío José brought my *madrina*[5] Tía Amelia and her *comadre*[6] Tía Pilar. My friends rarely had more than a "Mom and Dad" to introduce.

After the commencement ceremony my family waited outside in the parking lot while my friends and I signed yearbooks with nicknames which recalled our high school good times: "Beans" and "Pepperoni" and "Alcatraz." We hugged and cried and promised to keep in touch.

Our goodbyes went on too long. I heard my father's voice calling out across the parking lot, *"Hoo-lee-tah! Vamonos!*[7]"

Back home, my *tíos* and *tías* and *primas*, Mami and Papi, and *mis hermanas*[8] had a party for me with *sancocho* and a store-bought *pudín*,[9] inscribed with *Happy Graduation, Julie.* There were many gifts—that was a plus to a large family! I got several wallets and a suitcase with my initials and a graduation charm from my godmother and money from my uncles. The biggest gift was a portable typewriter from my parents for writing my stories and poems.

Someday, the family predicted, my name would be well-known throughout the United States. I laughed to myself, wondering which one I would go by.

THINK IT OVER

1. *Julia Alvarez did not like it when people mispronounced her name. Do you think she objected to all her nicknames? Explain your answers.*

2. *Do you agree with Julia's mother that it did not matter that Julia's friends and teachers could not pronounce her name? Explain your answer.*

WRITE

Julia Alvarez tells about different versions of her name used by her family, friends, and strangers. Write a few paragraphs telling about your name. Tell about any nicknames you may have and how they originated.

[5] madrina: godmother
[6] comadre: woman friend
[7] Vamonos!: Let's go!
[8] mis hermanas: my sisters
[9] pudín: dessert

from *The Vietnamese in America*

A NEW WAY OF
Life

by Paul Rutledge

Immigrants have been coming to the United States since early in its history. Among the most recent groups of immigrants are people from Vietnam, a country in Southeast Asia.

Almost every aspect of daily life changes for Vietnamese refugees who settle in the United States. Attitudes toward the family, methods of education, language, even as common a matter as shopping for food—all these can be sources of culture shock for the Vietnamese. Their backgrounds, habits, and ways of everyday life are sometimes the opposite of American customs, and trying to blend the old ways with the new may cause the refugees bewilderment, pain, and conflict.

FAMILY

The Vietnamese family is under a great deal of pressure in trying to adjust to the American way of life. In the United States, a family usually consists of father, mother, and children. In Vietnam, a family is an extended one that includes the parents and the younger children, grandparents, married children, aunts, uncles, and a variety of other relatives. In some cases, all the members of an extended family live in the same house.

The family is the center of Vietnamese society, and it is the responsibility of every member to help the family survive. But the size of an extended Vietnamese family can make it difficult to find housing in America. Families want to establish themselves as close units but often cannot find adjacent housing large enough to accommodate 20 or 30 relatives.

In the Vietnamese culture, the older a person is, the more he or she is respected. Young people are always expected to seek the advice of older persons within the family. Children are taught to listen to and accept the decisions of their elders. In the traditional American family, however, individual members are more independent. In the United States, children are taught and advised by their parents in a less structured way.

When young Vietnamese refugees become friends with young Americans and see the more informal relationships between them and their families, the Vietnamese are likely to want the same kind of independence—something their Vietnamese parents find difficult to accept.

EDUCATION

The Vietnamese culture places a high value on education. As persons of knowledge, teachers are considered some of the most important members of society.

Before the Europeans entered Vietnam, the Confucian system of education dominated the country. This system was based on memorization. People could memorize large amounts of material and then take exams in which they quoted the memorized material. If they passed, they could improve their employment and social standing. Anyone —farmer or aristocrat—could take the exams.

During the French colonial period[1] in Vietnam, public schools were built, and education was emphasized. Teachers in these schools were considered role models as well as instructors, and children were reluctant to question their statements. Discipline was an important part of the educational system.

When they attend American schools, refugee children may find a conflict between Vietnamese methods of education and those used in the United States. In Vietnam, children listen to, and learn from, the teacher, who is always correct. In America, students learn from the teacher but are also taught to think for themselves. Many Vietnamese children find this difficult to do. They will always agree with everything the teacher says because to do otherwise would show great disrespect.

Some other aspects of U.S. education are unfamiliar to Vietnamese students. Activities such as individual research, classroom debates, learning by doing, and group projects are new and strange to them. Despite these differences, many young Vietnamese have adapted well to American education and are making good grades.

---

[1] French colonial period: the period during which Vietnam was governed by France—from 1883 to 1945

LANGUAGE

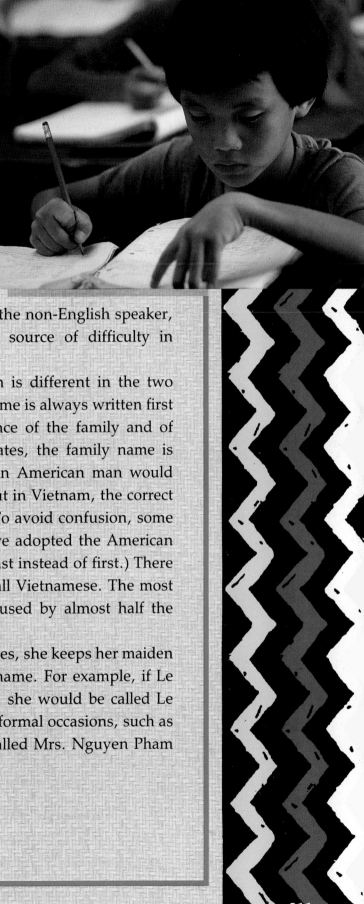

One of the most necessary, but also one of the hardest, tasks for a new refugee is learning the English language. The Vietnamese language contains six basic tones, and the sound of each word is part of the meaning of the word. English, which is not tonal, uses one word to mean many things. For the non-English speaker, this can be very confusing and a source of difficulty in attempting to learn English.

Even the way names are written is different in the two languages. In Vietnam, the family name is always written first in order to emphasize the importance of the family and of one's inheritance. In the United States, the family name is usually written last. For instance, an American man would write his name John Michael Doe, but in Vietnam, the correct form would be Doe John Michael. (To avoid confusion, some Vietnamese in the United States have adopted the American system and put their family names last instead of first.) There are only about 30 family names for all Vietnamese. The most common one is Nguyen, which is used by almost half the population.

When a Vietnamese woman marries, she keeps her maiden name and also uses her husband's name. For example, if Le Thi Ba married Nguyen Pham Binh, she would be called Le Thi Ba in informal situations, but on formal occasions, such as during a ceremony, she would be called Mrs. Nguyen Pham Binh.

CUSTOMS

The basic customs of Vietnamese life have been handed down from generation to generation just as American customs have been. There are many differences between the habits and attitudes of the two cultures.

Respect is very important to Vietnamese people. When greeting others, the Vietnamese bow their heads to show respect and honor. It takes some time for newly arrived refugees to get used to a casual "Hi" or "Hello" from people they pass on the street. In Vietnam, it is polite to look away when speaking to someone and rude to look directly at the person. This is exactly the opposite of behavior in the United States and often causes misunderstandings. Refugees are accused of being rude and unfriendly because they apparently ignore those speaking directly to them.

Even something as simple as color can be the source of conflict for the refugees. In Vietnam, the color white represents death. For the Vietnamese who enter an American hospital for the first time, seeing the white sheets and doctors and nurses dressed in white may convince them they are going to die.

Many of the practical aspects of life in the United States demand an adjustment by Vietnamese people. For example, the American transportation system presents a challenge, particularly for those used to living in farming areas. In Vietnam, walking and riding a bike were the most common forms of travel. Certainly not every family had a car. In the United States, the Vietnamese must cope with buses, subways, trains, airplanes, and especially cars.

Learning to drive is very difficult for older refugees, who are fearful of the heavy traffic and fast speeds in large U.S. cities. The younger generation, however, has fallen in love with American cars, and this causes some conflict in Vietnamese families. The parents feel that the car is breaking up the family, that the teenagers are always driving off by themselves or with friends when they should be spending time with relatives.

The ways in which food is prepared and even packaged can be confusing to recent arrivals. Fast-food hamburgers, pizza, and fried chicken are new to the refugees. In fact, the Vietnamese are not used to eating such greasily prepared items and usually do not like fried food at first.

Even the cans, boxes, and jars in American supermarkets can cause misunderstanding. One Vietnamese family in a large city spent several hours in a grocery looking at all the items. They were confused because they thought that the picture on each can and box showed what was inside the container. The family's young daughter was understandably frightened by a box of cereal with a monster pictured on it. These people would buy nothing but the fresh vegetables they could see and touch. Experience eventually made them more comfortable shopping for food American style.

Although Vietnamese immigrants want to learn as much as possible about American culture and to adapt to American life, most of them also want to keep the customs and language of their homeland alive. Like many earlier groups of immigrants, their goal is to become Americans without losing their ethnic identity.

THINK IT OVER

1. *What are some of the differences between the American and Vietnamese cultures?*

2. *How can the use of color be a source of conflict for Vietnamese refugees?*

3. *If you were Vietnamese, how would you write your name?*

4. *Compare the education a child in Vietnam receives with the education you are receiving. How do they differ and how are they similar?*

WRITE

Write an opinion paragraph convincing others of the importance of learning about different cultures.

Foreign Student

by Barbara B. Robinson

illustrated by Kevin Ghiglione

In September she appeared
    row three, seat seven,
    heavy pleated skirt,
    plastic purse, tidy notepad,
there she sat,
silent,
straight from Taipei,
and she bowed
when I entered the room.
A model student
I noticed,
    though she walked
    alone through the halls,
every assignment neat,
on time, complete,
and she'd listen
when I talked.

But now it's May
and Si Lan
is called Lani.
She strides in with Noriyo and
Lynne
and Natividad.
She wears slacks.
Her gear is crammed
into a macrame
shoulder sack.
And she chatters with Pete
during class
and
I'm glad.

TOM WIN, A·M·E·R·I·C·A·N

from *Hello, My Name Is Scrambled Eggs*
by Jamie Gilson

Harvey and Julia Trumble's family is hosting a family of Vietnamese refugees who have just arrived in America. Harvey knows it will be tough for the Nguyens to feel at home in their new country, so he takes on the responsibility of teaching young Tuan Nguyen everything he needs to know about American life. Harvey also wants to help Tuan make friends with the right people—and to keep him away from people like Quint Calkins, the class know-it-all. Right away, Harvey realizes that learning a new language is likely to be Tuan's biggest obstacle.

"Harvey, come look!" Julia called from the top of the third-floor steps. "They sleep funny."

"Quiet," I whispered and leaped the stairs two at a time to shush her. "Quiet, or they won't sleep at all." Still, it was the middle of Sunday afternoon, and they'd been up there almost twenty-four hours. The trip must really have zonked them out.

"Look at *that,*" she whispered back and pointed into Pete's room.

illustrated by Bernadette Lau

218

AWARD-WINNING
AUTHOR

The door was open and I could see inside. It wasn't true they slept funny. They were sleeping like people do, all curled up. It was *where* they were sleeping that was funny. They were all in Pete's bedroom, but they weren't in bed. They'd taken the bedspreads off and put them on the floor, and that's where they were sleeping. I'd only slept on the floor at sleepovers, but it never worked out too good. When I woke up in the morning, I always had a crick in my neck.

"Julia!" I pulled her away from the door. "Don't be nosy." And I headed her back down the steps. On the way, though, I coughed a little, hoping to wake the kid up. We had work to do.

When Tuan came downstairs about an hour later, he was a lot hungrier for food than for facts. He ate two apples from the bushel in the kitchen, some of the big bowl of rice Mom had made special, and a whole lot of beef stew. I would never have thought that using a fork could be so hard. Just watching him made me nervous. And I wondered how anybody could possibly eat all those slippery little grains of rice with sticks.

Right after he ate, I steered him down to the basement to meet Felix, trusty computer. I'd decided it was time for Felix to teach him some new words. The first one would be *marble.* My dad had dug out a wrinkled leather pouch of his old marbles and given them to me so I'd have something in common with the kid. I mean, it wasn't as though I could shoot marbles or anything like that. My dad said it was an old American sport, but since I wasn't an old American, I didn't play it. Anyway, I opened the bag and dug out a big yellow one with tiny bubbles in it and gave it to the kid. He looked it over but didn't remember what it was called.

"Marble," I said, and typed it out on Felix. "What is it called in Vietnamese?"

He typed DANH-BI. "Need mark through *d* and over *n*," he told me, but the computer couldn't handle that. "Say, *'đańh-bi.'*"

It was hard to say. It didn't fit my mouth, and so I only tried once. He started to hand the marble back. "Keep it," I said, holding my hands behind my back. "Keep it." He put it on the workbench.

Pete's bike was leaning up against the wall, in storage till he came home.

BICYCLE, I typed out on Felix and, giving the handlebars a pat, said it out loud.

So did the kid. "Bi-cyc-le."

"Close," I told him.

XE-DAP, he typed. "And mark through . . ." He pointed at the *d*. "*Bicycle* is *xe-dap.*"

"Shut up?" I asked. That's sure what it sounded like.

"Close," he said.

"Do you know what *shut up* means?"

"*Shut up*? No. What means *shut up*?"

"It means 'be quiet.'" I put my finger in front of my lips and said, "Shhhhhhhhhh." He nodded. "Shut up!" I yelled.

"You talk loud to ask be quiet?"

"Right. *Shut up!* That's the way to say it," I shouted.

"*Shut up!*" he yelled back, laughing.

"You boys all right down there?" Mom called down the steps.

"Fine," I told her. "We're OK."

"What means *OK*?" he asked.

"*OK* means 'good,' 'terrific.' *OK* is basic. *OK* is the best. We'll have Felix tell you 'OK' every time you get a word right, OK?"

"OK."

We sat there for a long time with me teaching him words like *follow*. First I marched around behind him. "I *follow* you." Then I got in front of him and made him say, "I *follow* you." I was the leader. He was my follower. We did verbs like *throw* and *hide* and *laugh* and *vomit*. After we'd both acted them out, I'd write them into the computer. And Tuan would write in the Vietnamese word so he'd remember what the English one meant. Input, output. Input, output. It was terrific. We were working on *hiccup* when Mom called down the steps again.

"Harvey, you've got company. It's almost ten o'clock, though, just about time for bed."

"Tuan just barely got up," I told her, "and he's got lots of work to do. Who's there?"

"Quint the Quintessential," he called down grandly.

Big deal, I thought. "Enter," I said, though, since nothing was likely to stop him. He took the steps slow and heavy, waving and grinning. I turned back to the computer.

"Hi, there, Zilch," he said. "Having a good time with your new toy?"

"The computer's not all that new," I told him, punching a few keys casually.

"I wasn't talking about the computer." He grinned, and leaning with his mouth close to my ear, he whispered, "Uncovering the mysteries of the Orient?"

"No!" I pushed him away with my shoulder. "I'm teaching Tuan English."

He gave the kid a big hello like he was his biggest admirer and then circled around behind him and rolled his eyes at me. "So, why bother?" he asked.

"He's got to learn it. He starts school Friday, the end of this week. With us."

"You're kidding. Our *class*?"

"Why not? He's twelve. Mom says it's fixed so he can be with me."

Quint laughed through his nose. "He doesn't know his elbow from an escalator and he's going to be in the same class with *me*? Gifted old me? He ought to be in Julia's room."

Tuan was working on the words we'd programmed. OK, Felix printed, turning on his computer charm. OK, TUAN. The kid glanced at Quint, who clapped his hands, yelled, "OK!" and nodded as if the kid had just won the Nobel Peace Prize.

Tuan turned back to the computer, smiling. Quint rolled his eyes again.

"You *are* good," he said to Tuan, as Felix went OK once again.

The kid beamed back.

"Will you teach me marbles?" Quint asked him.

"Teach?" He turned away from the computer. "*Teach* you?"

"Right." Quint picked up my yellow marble from the counter. "Will you teach me how?"

"Yes." Tuan grinned at him. "OK."

"Tomorrow?" Quint was trying to take my kid away from me. That's what he was trying to do. He handed Tuan the marble *I'd* given him just ten minutes before. "My uncle wants to ask the kid some questions," he whispered to me, like we were both in on some big joke. "Wayne knows a lot of words in Vietnamese. He wants to look him over."

"Sorry. Tuan's busy with important stuff tomorrow and Tuesday and Wednesday and Thursday, and he starts school Friday."

"After school Friday it is, then. You come to my house Friday," Quint told the kid. "OK?"

"I've got to work after school Friday," I told him.

"I didn't ask you," Quint explained like I was a little kid who'd begged to tag along to a party. "OK?" he said to Tuan again.

"OK! Marbles." You'd have thought the president had invited him to breakfast at the White House, he was so pleased.

"See you around." Quint took the stairs two at a time, slamming the basement door so we'd have something to remember him by.

When the place had stopped shaking, I said to the kid, patiently and slowly, "You don't want to go to Quint's."

"Yes," he said, smiling broadly, "I go to him house."

"*His* house."

"His house. He is . . . Quint?"

"Yes, he's Quint, all right."

"Quint is OK. Right way to use OK?"

"Right," I said. But I sure didn't mean it.

"Hello, my name is jelly," Julia said, staring at the name tag stuck to a jar on the kitchen table. She'd guessed wrong. It said, HELLO, MY NAME IS JAM. Tossing her stuffed owl Zachary onto her chair, Julia climbed on top of him, leaned back, and stared up.

"Hello, my name is Ceiling. Is that right?" I nodded. "I can read *ceiling*! Maybe they'll let me skip first grade." She craned her neck to look at the sign again. "Are you sure that says *ceiling*? Mrs. Broderick says the snake sound, *Sssssssssssssssssss*, is *S*. Silly Sally Ceiling. See, it's got to be wrong."

"Ceiling," Tuan said automatically, copying it into a small notebook I'd given him. NEW WORDS, I'd printed on the cover. He was eating breakfast and hadn't noticed that one yet.

"Remember 'I before E except after C,'" I told him as he wrote. He blinked at me.

I'd got the name tags from this huge stack left over from a party of Mom's where nobody wore them. The tags had little red wavy borders with HELLO, MY NAME IS printed on the front and sticky stuff on the back. I'd written about a hundred names of things on them. Then I'd matched them up, sticking them on the sugar bowl, the doors, floors, apples, toilet, computer, boot box. Every day after I came home from school, I'd take the kid around naming things for him. The house was beginning to look like a first-grade workbook.

"Hello, my name is Butter Dish," Julia said. "Harvey, make one for Zachary. He's jealous."

"That tag better not leave a mark on the ceiling," Dad told me, wiping his mouth with his napkin. "And the day you lay one on my scrambled eggs, you've had it."

Actually, I *had* made a Scrambled Eggs label, but I'd decided it would slide off, and so I'd just stuck it in my back pocket.

"Your father is absolutely right," Mom said. "If there's anything that flusters me, it's eggs that try to get too friendly. More toast, Tuan?"

He shook his head and leaned over his scrambled eggs with a fork, watching me closely as I ate. He waited a long time before picking up the bacon with his fingers as I did, making sure that's how Dad ate his, too. His grandmother sat by herself at the end of the table. He called her Ba Noi, which means, he said, "your father's mother." A white wool shawl Mom had found for her was tucked tightly around her like a cocoon. She was not having scrambled eggs for breakfast, but broth with noodles in it, first drinking the broth and then eating the noodles with chopsticks she'd brought with her.

"Get Tuan to school on time, now," Dad called, barreling out the back door. Then Ba Noi spoke. She said something to Tuan—low, fast, and kind of sharp. Tuan answered her quietly, glancing around at us and then down at his feet.

"Is something wrong?" Mom asked him. "May we help?"

The kid shook his head and took a deep breath. I wondered if he was trying to think what to say or how to say it. "Ba Noi say I not . . . look good for school," he whispered.

He looked good to me. I'd told him what to wear—faded jeans, a striped T-shirt, and the red, white, and blue tennis shoes Mom had bought him the day before. Perfect.

"Tell her I say it's *very* American."

"She want me *very* Vietnamese . . . blue pants. . . ." He sliced across his leg with his hand to show he meant the short ones he'd worn when he arrived.

I laughed. "You dress like that and everybody'll think you're weird. Besides, in this weather you'd die of terminal goose bumps." I knew he hadn't understood that. "Cold," I said, shaking myself with a shiver. "Short pants are for summer."

"Hello, my name is Clock," Julia announced. "We're going to be late."

Tuan spoke again to his grandmother. She still did not look pleased. But we waved good-bye to her and to Mom and hurried off. Tuan was smiling as if he liked looking very American.

On the way, we worked on tree names and street names. I named. He repeated. Once we got to school, I showed him the water fountain, the john, and the trophy case. People kept saying, "Hi," and so I taught him a few of the kids' names, too. It was an educational experience.

Finally, I got him to the principal's office. Mr. Saine was on the phone when I poked my head in. ". . . will deal with that matter immediately," he told the phone, motioning us to come on in.

Mr. Saine stood up, way up. I mean, he must be six-five. Tuan came about to his belt.

"Hi," Tuan said, holding out his hand when Mr. Saine came over to greet us.

"Why, hello, young man." Mr. Saine shook his hand, looking pleased by good manners and all that. "I've been expecting you. How's his English?" he asked me, his voice lowered.

"I'm teaching him," I said.

"Good, fine." He sat back in his chair and started looking through some papers. "First you take him to homeroom. And after that we'll line up some diagnostic tests to see where square one should be, since there aren't any transcripts. Understood?"

I nodded. The kid smiled, understanding nothing. I could read the look by now. Mr. Saine shuffled through a stack of papers on his desk. "Reverend Zito tells me your name is . . ." He clamped his hands together, took a deep breath, and pronounced it all wrong.

And that was when I got the idea. If the kid really did want to be an American and to be one fast, the name Tuan Nguyen wouldn't do. It wouldn't do any more than short pants on a cold day. You put that name in lights or across a headline and people would get it wrong almost every time.

"He's just decided to change it. The name you've got isn't right. It *used* to be Tuan Nguyen. But now he's going to be . . ."

I tossed the sounds around in my head a few times until his name turned, without any problem at all, into . . . "Tom. His first name is Tom." Mr. Saine glanced at Tuan/Tom, who smiled and nodded, but clearly understood not a word. Mr. Saine wrote down Thomas. I took a breath, and before I let it out, had the whole thing. From Nguyen to Gwen to Win, easy as that. "Win. His full American name is Tom Win. W-I-N." I felt like an artist painting a brand-new picture.

"And a fine name it is, too," Mr. Saine said loudly to the kid, who was still staring blankly into our fog of too-fast words. *"Welcome to Pittsfield and Pittsfield Junior High School, Tom Win!"* His voice made the trophies on the shelf vibrate.

"Thank you." Tuan smiled politely. "Shut up," he said, a little louder.

Mr. Saine's jaw dropped open. So did mine. The room turned suddenly still, as if somebody had vacuumed out all the sound. My knees felt like rubber bands. Mr. Saine's face was gray.

Tuan kept smiling, though he did look uneasy.

"I . . . I . . . I . . ." I stuttered, my voice turned high like I'd just swallowed a balloonful of helium. "I think . . . I think . . . See, I told him, I taught him, that 'shut up' means 'be quiet.' I think"—I swallowed hard because my throat had become a desert—"he means you don't have to shout. A lot of people have been shouting at him, thinking it will help him understand. And it *doesn't* help, really. I taught him 'shut up' because it sounds a lot like Vietnamese bicycles." Mr. Saine's frown deepened. "He means to be polite. He learns fast. I even *told* him to say it loud, I—"

"All right, Harvey," Mr. Saine interrupted me, still looking grim. His face was flushed. "I'll accept that." He said it, but I wasn't sure he meant it. "It's late," he said, using his normal voice. "Give these papers to your homeroom teacher, and, Harvey"—he took a deep breath—"*re*-explain 'shut up.'"

"Good night," the kid said, beaming.

We hurried out of the office toward homeroom, Tuan looking so cheerful I started to laugh out loud. He was positively the only kid in the whole school, in the whole world, maybe, who could get away with saying "shut up" to Mr. Saine. I was laughing, but my knees wobbled as I walked.

"Oh, by the way," I told Tuan as we reached the homeroom door, "your new American name is Tom." I stopped, opened my notebook, and wrote it down. "Tom," I repeated. "You."

"Tuan," he said. "Me."

"You have a new name, Tom Win. It's a terrific name. I made it up myself. I wish it was mine. I mean, like, it goes more with jeans and tennis shoes than the old one did. When you hit a homer at the bottom of the ninth with the bases loaded, they'll say, 'Win wins!' Tom Win," I repeated slowly. "The American you."

He stopped and thought about it. "Ba Noi say no. Father say no." The last bell rang.

"Do you want to be American or don't you?"

He nodded. "But Ba Noi say . . ."

"OK, then, just at school. Tom Win at school. Tuan Nguyen in the privacy of your own home. Ba Noi won't have to know. To her and your dad you'll stay Tuan. No kidding, could I be Vietnamese and have a name like Harvey Trumble?"

He laughed and shook his head. "OK," he said. "Tom Win is me."

I rushed him into homeroom, a new kid.

The class, most all of them in their seats by now, looked up from what they were doing and stared at us.

"Uh, Miss Schwalbach," I said, handing her the papers Mr. Saine had given me, "this is the new Vietnamese boy we've been talking about, only he's changed his name. It's . . . uh . . . Tom Win. Mr. Saine says after homeroom he's supposed to go to the office for tests."

"Of course." She beamed at him. "So it's to be Tom Win?"

He glanced at me. "Yes," he told her. He held his hand out, and she shook it.

"We're glad you're here, Tom. People," she told the class, "I want you to be sure to welcome Tom Win cordially."

"That's not what I heard him called." Quint tilted back in his chair.

"Goes to show you don't know everything," I said very casual, like of course *I* did. "He's called Tom Win," I announced to the class. My kid, named by me.

Miss Schwalbach motioned to an empty place in the front row. "Sit here, Tom."

He sat. Tom Win sat. He could host a game show with a name like that.

When the bell rang for first period, I delivered the kid to the office. Even though I said good-bye and wished him good luck, I was certain they'd be calling me out of science or language arts to help him with the tests. The morning went by without a messenger, though, and I guessed they'd given up on him or something. So I was really surprised when I got to the cafeteria at lunch and there he was, still smiling, sitting with Suzanna, eating a hamburger layered with pickles, mustard, and catsup.

"I just explained that hamburger isn't made out of ham." Suzanna popped a french fry in her mouth.

"It is cow," Tom told me. "It is good." He took another bite.

"Did the whole family change their names?" She drew a smiley face in a pool of catsup with her last fry.

"Not yet." That might take some doing. We'd break it to them slowly. It was going to be some trick keeping the Tom/Tuans straight. The kid had this double identity like a spy. If only I could change my name, too. Tom Win would have suited me fine. "How'd it go?" I asked him. "Were the tests hard?"

He took a gulp of chocolate milk and blinked at the taste, licking his upper lip. "Words hard, Harvey. Numbers . . . weird."

That was a word I'd taught him by making faces. *Weird*. He liked it, but I guess it was like *shut up*. He didn't know what it meant. Numbers are a lot of things—like impossible. Weird, though, they're not.

But Mr. Tandy, our math teacher, sounded like he thought so, too. "A little strange," he said when class started. He smiled at Tom, who had finished his tests in time to come to the last class of the day. "Yes, class, you'd think that math was math the whole world over, but there are differences. I talked to our remarkable new student, Tom Win, this morning as he was taking some tests, and he suggested that some of our ways with numbers were unusual. I thought I'd check it out with the rest of you."

The kid looked at the floor, embarrassed.

"Tom, go to the chalkboard. And Quint, you too, just to demonstrate the differences."

Quint, wearing his fabulous-me face, brought the kid with him to the board. They both took pieces of chalk and, when Mr. Tandy told them to, wrote down 675 divided by 15. Quint's problem looked normal: 15)675. When he finished doing the problem, he looked over at the kid, who already had the answer. "Bizarre," he said. Mr. Tandy grinned. The kid had written, very neatly:

$$
\begin{array}{c|c}
675 & 15 \\
075 & 45
\end{array}
$$

"Why'd he do it like that?" Quint asked, cocking his head. He shrugged. "I could have done it in my head."

"I expect he could have too, but that, of course, is not the point." Mr. Tandy was annoyed with him. "Now, both of you, write down twenty-five dollars."

Quint scribbled out $25.00 as fast as he could. Nobody was going to outrace him.

Carefully, the kid wrote: 25$00.

"More bizarre," Quint said, and everybody had to agree.

"You boys can sit down." I never saw Mr. Tandy quite so pleased. He grinned like everybody had gotten the extra-credit question right, or something equally miraculous. "And in Vietnam, when two thousand is written down it's . . ." Glancing first to the ceiling, where he always looks for approval, he wrote on the board 2.000. "There's a *point* after the thousand. On the other hand, they use a decimal *comma*. Thusly." He wrote 1,52. "Anybody think of a reason why one system is any better than the other, aside from the fact that you're used to it?"

Nobody raised a hand. He chuckled. "Neither can I. Isn't that fascinating!"

Quint rolled his eyes. "Knocks me out," he said sarcastically. A few kids giggled. Mr. Tandy laughed mildly, too. He knows not everybody is as crazy about math as he is. But he could afford to laugh. He was passing out a pop quiz. Aaarg.

"So, will this test count?" Caroline asked.

"Pieces of paper can't count. But I certainly hope you can. Any other questions?"

"Yes." Caroline sighed. "Do we have to take it?"

"You're wasting our time, Caroline."

All the time in the world wouldn't help. I knew I should have studied the night before instead of helping the kid learn English. We'd fooled around at Felix for a couple of hours, watched a little TV, sung with the commercials. I scratched on.

When Mr. Tandy said, "Exchange papers, please," a mass groan swelled out over the desks. I wasn't finished. A lot of kids weren't. The story problem was quicksand sucking me under.

Quint had already turned his paper over on his desk so no one could cheat from it. He was cleaning his fingernails with a toothpick.

Suzanna grabbed the kid's paper quick before I could. How she thought she was going to read it, I couldn't imagine. "What do I do about the commas and points?" she asked.

"If everything else is OK, grade them right. He'll get the knack of the mechanics soon enough."

"That's not fair," Quint complained.

Mr. Tandy started down the row, asking kids for answers and talking about problems.

"So, what do I do when Quint's decimal point's wrong?" Caroline asked. "Because one *is*."

"Mark it wrong. He knows better." Quint leaned over to look, not believing it.

When we got to the last problem, Suzanna raised her hand excitedly and said, "Tuan . . . or Tom, whatever, got them all right. He did most of the marks our way. But he skipped the story problem."

"Terrific! Tom? The story problem?" Mr. Tandy pointed to it.

"I cannot read it."

Mr. Tandy looked at the ceiling again with a smile. He'd found another math person. Big deal. "I think it's *remarkable* that he's adjusted so quickly. Suzanna, mark the paper one hundred percent. And a big A. It ought to give him a real boost. He'll be able to read the story problems as well as you can before long."

"That isn't fair," I said. "If it's wrong, it's wrong. He's got to learn that." *I'd* gotten it wrong. And half the other problems too. There's such a thing as being too nice. I didn't want my kid spoiled. Besides, he'd kept me from studying. And he'd had all day Wednesday and Thursday to look at the books I'd brought him from school. He couldn't read most of the stuff, and so he'd probably spent all his time on the math I'd told him we were doing. He'd been *studying.* Hours probably. He didn't have anything else to do with me gone. "No fair," I said again.

Quint, who'd been looking pretty mad himself, suddenly crossed his arms and tilted his chair back. "Oh, forget it. He's no real hotshot," he said to me. "But he's no Zilch either." Then he looked at me funny. "*You* didn't teach him that stuff, did you?"

I smiled, genius in disguise.

"Your problem," Mr. Tandy said to the class, "is that you're not reading carefully enough. You're not following directions. I want you all to read that story problem over tonight and then to work it correctly."

Caroline opened her assignment notebook. It was plastered with puffy and smelly stickers. "Tonight's Friday," she said. "That's T.G.I.F."

"As good a night as any. Do this as part of your weekend homework. You *must* learn to follow directions." He chopped the air with his hand to pound out every single syllable. "Fol-low the di-rec-tions!"

Tom Win stood up at once. All heads turned to him. He turned his to me. What did he think he was doing? "Harvey?" he asked me.

I shrugged and stared down at the field of initials scratched on my desk. I didn't know what he was getting at. He was embarrassing me, standing there all by himself saying, "Harvey?"

"Where," he asked Mr. Tandy, "where is . . . Directions . . . so I can follow him?"

The bell rang, but even though it was Friday, the kids stayed in their seats and laughed out loud. He was a big joke to them. A hundred percent in math, and he thought it was time for Follow the Leader. And they weren't just laughing at *him*. I could feel it in the hairs on the back of my neck. They knew he was mine. They were laughing at me, too.

But when I looked up again, Quint had already gathered the kid up and was heading him out the door.

"Marbles," Tom Win called, holding up his bag of them. "Good night."

Quint waved. "This foreign person may be more interesting than I thought. I'll find out if my uncle is right. Anyway, your clone," he said, "has flown."

I couldn't possibly have followed them, even though *follow* seemed to be the word of the day. I'd have been late for work. But, I decided, the kid seems to be pretty smart. He'll figure Quint out in a hurry. It'll be good for him. I headed off, whistling.

THINK IT OVER

1. After reading about the Trumble family's experience, do you think you would or would not enjoy hosting a family from another country? Explain your answer.

2. How does Harvey help Tuan learn the names of objects around the house?

3. Why does Mr. Saine, the principal, become upset with Tuan?

4. Is learning a new language Tuan's only obstacle? Explain your answer.

5. Do you think Harvey has a right to consider Tuan his *kid*?

WRITE

Write a brief set of instructions telling how to help someone feel at home in a new place and learn a new language.

CROSSING BORDERS

Compare Si Lan, the new student from the poem "Foreign Student," with Tuan Nguyen, from "Tom Win, American." Do you think Tom will change as the girl in the poem does?

How do the selections show that language can sometimes be a barrier between people from different countries?

WRITER'S WORKSHOP Imagine that you have recently moved to a country where you don't know the language. Write a funny and suspenseful scene in which you ask for directions to your new school. In your scene, you should misunderstand not just one word, but several words.

BIG BURGER FRENCH FRIES

THEME

EXPLORING EGYPT

Egypt . . . Mummy . . . Treasures . . . Yes, as these words tell you, you are going to read about ancient Egyptians—but perhaps not exactly in the way you think.

CONTENTS

TREASURES OF THE VALLEY

from *BEHIND THE SEALED DOOR*

by Irene and Laurence Swinburne

The great kings of Egypt built large tombs and piled them high with treasures. Jewels, precious oils, gold chairs and thrones, bracelets, rings, statues—all this and much more was stored in these final resting places. Why did the kings hoard so much wealth in their tombs? It was because of their religion. Someday, they firmly believed, the gods would raise them from the dead. Also, they believed that they themselves were gods and would be welcomed into the land of the dead by their fellow gods. When that happened, they would need the things they had used in this world.

Sarcophagus of King Tut

Wall painting in the tomb of Sen-Nefer

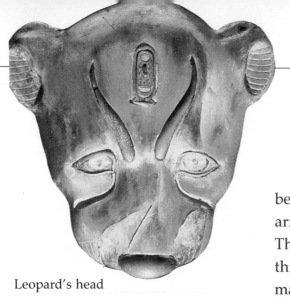

Leopard's head

But, in fact, the kings would be very poor indeed when they arrived in the other world. Through the centuries, grave thieves upset the royal plans and made off with the valuables buried in the tombs.

The thieves had no respect for the dead kings. They did not care if the rulers got to the land of the gods or not. They only cared about looting the riches in the tombs.

To get to the treasures, they had to dig through rock, break down huge doors, puzzle out mazes of passages that were found in the pyramids, and avoid traps that had been made to catch them. Often they bribed the guards to look the other way. The robbers did all this knowing that if they were caught, they would be horribly tortured and then put to death. Because of their greed, many priceless objects have been lost forever—golden statues melted down and sold, jewels removed from their settings, works of art destroyed.

Earring from King Tut's tomb

Between the years 2600 and 1529 B.C., the kings built enormous pyramids for their tombs. When a king died, his body would be

Statue of King Tut

244

Statue of
King Tut

carried into the tomb as high priests wailed funeral chants. But the dead king would not rest in peace for long. In a few years or even months, thieves would find their way to the heart of the pyramid where the king lay and carry off anything they could get their hands on. Even though probably many of the robbers were caught, just the sight of those massive tombs would remind others of the riches that lay within them, and a new gang would try its luck.

Finally, Tuthmosis I, who ruled from 1505 to 1493 B.C., realized a new way must be found to keep the royal graves from being looted. He decided to break with that long tradition and be buried in the valley that would be known as the Valley of the Kings. From this time on, the kings would be buried in tombs cut out of the rocky soil of the Valley.

Scarab bracelet
from King Tut's tomb

Queen Hatshepsot's Temple in the Valley of the Kings

You might think that the Valley would be a beautiful area, with shady trees, sparkling brooks, and flowers of every color. But you would be wrong. The Valley of the Kings is one of the most deserted and uninviting places in the world. Its landscape consists of brown rocks and brown sand. It has no trees, no streams, and no flowers. Few birds fly into this forbidding cemetery. However, it was much easier to protect than the pyramids.

Hundreds lived or worked in the Valley. There were men who did the heavy work of digging into the rock. There were craftsmen who performed such jobs as painting the walls of the tombs. There were the priests who were in charge of all activity in the Valley. And, of course, there were the soldiers, whose duty it was to keep out the thieves. The most important work was that of the mummifiers, people who made the kings' bodies into mummies. Mummifying is a process that can preserve bodies for hundreds, sometimes even thousands, of years.

The ancient Egyptian skill of mummifying has fascinated people up to our time. After the body had been specially treated, it was dried, a process that took seventy days. Then it was washed with special sweet-smelling oils. The body was carefully wrapped in linen. The linen had been soaked in gum, a sticky substance that came from a gum tree. Metal charms and special prayers on papyrus were enfolded in the wrappings. There was plenty of room for these items, for the linen was wound around the body many times.

The exact location of a king's tomb was usually kept a secret—though, of course, some people had to know about it. Tuthmosis I assigned a trusted official, Ineni, to prepare his tomb. Ineni carried out his duty faithfully. As he wrote later, "I alone supervised the construction of His Majesty's cliff tomb. No one saw it, no one heard it."

But nothing stopped the tomb robbers. In fact, the thieves became so successful that sometimes the priests, hoping to fool them, would have the royal mummies moved from cave to cave. Several mummies might be stored in one tomb for a time while other tombs were empty. This created puzzles for archaeologists much later, who might find the tomb of one king occupied by a different king's mummy.

The ancient Egyptian civilization lasted for over 3,000 years. Yet finally it too came to an end. At various times after that, other nations conquered the country, but the work of the tomb robbers continued as before. It was as if they had discovered an unending goldmine in the Valley of the Kings, and through the centuries they searched for undiscovered graves of kings.

By the late 1800s the Valley had been gone over carefully, and many archaeologists believed that nothing more would be found. However, in 1871 they were surprised to learn that objects of great value were being sold by people who lived on a hill near the Valley of the Kings. Experts agreed that these objects could only have come from the tombs of kings.

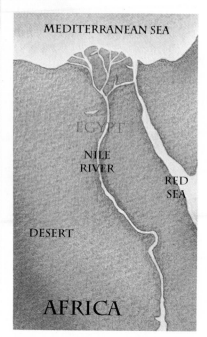

After some very clever detective work, it was found that most of the objects had been sold by a man named Abd-el-Rasul.

Abd-el-Rasul was arrested, and he confessed that he had been the seller of the valuable relics. Even more amazing was his statement that for years the entire income of the village of Qurna had been derived from selling such relics. What's more, his family had been in this business for six centuries!

Recently his people had found a tomb high on the face of a cliff. It could be entered only through a small hole, into which a thin man could squeeze. Hoping to please the officials and avoid a long jail sentence, he offered to lead the way to the grave.

Forty mummies were found in the small tomb! The mummies were taken to the Cairo Museum. As the boat carrying the remains of the kings passed down the Nile, hundreds of thousands of Egyptians lined the banks of the great river. They threw dust upon themselves, a sign of mourning. People fired rifles in the air in salute. All this was done to honor these dead kings who had ruled some 3,000 years before.

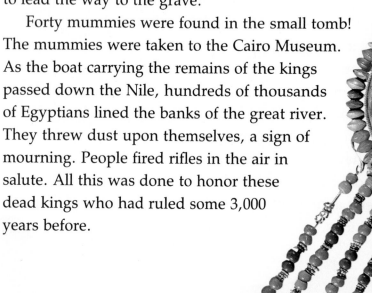

Earring from King Tut's tomb

Painting of King Sennedjem and his wife working in a field

THINK IT OVER

1. *Only in recent years have people begun to treat the tombs of the ancient Egyptian kings with respect. In your opinion, why did people's attitudes change from disrespect to respect?*

2. *What did Abd-el-Rasul do with the objects he stole?*

3. *King Tuthmosis I was buried in a tomb cut out of the rocky soil. Was he better protected than the kings who were buried in the pyramids? Explain your answer.*

WRITE

How do you feel about the thefts from the Egyptian kings' tombs? Write a few paragraphs explaining your answer.

The MUMMY PROJECT

from *Make Like a Tree and Leave*
by Paula Danziger

Matthew Martin and his friends
only wanted to make the best
Egyptian project for their sixth-
grade class. Instead they made
a big mistake.

"The suspense builds." Matthew, holding
up a baseball cap, looks at the three
classmates, who are sitting on his bedroom
floor. "Inside this very hat are four small
blank, folded pieces of paper. The fifth has
an X on it. One of us and only one will get
that X. Who, I ask you, who will get that
paper?"

illustrated by
Deborah Nourse Lattimore

"If you'd cut out the drama and let us pick, we could answer that question very quickly." Brian Bruno looks like he's ready to grab the cap out of Matthew's hands.

Holding the cap behind his back, Matthew says, "How can the suspense build if we pick right away?"

"I don't want suspense. I want to find out now," Billy Kellerman says. "Why do you always have to turn everything into a major production?"

"Because it's more fun that way." Matthew grins. "Anyway, Mrs. Stanton made me the chairman of the Mummy Committee, so I get to do it my way."

"Baloney," Billy says. "I overheard Mrs. Stanton tell Ms. Wagner that she only made you the chairman of the Mummy Committee because she's 'trying to get you to use your leadership qualities in a more positive way.'"

"Baloney to you. . . . I don't believe it." Matthew glares.

"It's true. I was in the bathroom in the nurse's office and the nurse had gone out for a minute, and the two of them came in and didn't know I was there. I also found out that Ms. Wagner is going out with Mr. King. You can learn a lot hanging out in the nurse's office." Billy grins. "And Ms. Wagner told her about the time she made you the chairman of the fourth-grade Volcano Committee."

"That explosion was NOT my fault!" Matthew protests.

"We only have two weeks to finish. . . . We better get started," Joshua Jackson reminds them. "Come on, Matthew. Let's not start fighting and instead of letting the suspense build, let's build the mummy."

"Oh, okay." Matthew relents, holding out the baseball cap. "Hurry up and pick, then. See if I care."

Joshua closes his eyes and selects a piece of paper.

Billy Kellerman keeps his open and stares at the papers, wishing that he had X-ray vision, and then he chooses.

Brian Bruno crosses his fingers and then picks a piece of paper.

The paper falls to the ground because Brian Bruno is not good at holding on to paper with crossed fingers.

Matthew takes the last one out of the cap, puts the cap back on his head with the visor facing backward, and says, "At the count of three, everyone open his paper. . . . One . . . two . . . three . . . go."

Matthew looks down at his paper. There is no *X*.

He's not sure whether he's sad or happy . . . or relieved.

There's no question that Joshua is happy. He's waving his paper and yelling, "No *X*. No *X*."

For a minute Matthew thinks that he should have put an *L* on the paper instead of an *X* so that Joshua could have yelled out "No *L*. No *L*," since he's acting like it's Christmas even though it's only October.

Then he looks around.

Billy's smiling.

Brian says, "How about if we make it the first person who gets two *X*'s? Isn't that a great idea?"

"Come on. It'll be fun. All we have to do is turn you into a mummy like the Egyptians used to do," Matthew reminds him. "It'll be easy. Billy got all the stuff to do it from his father's supply cabinet. It took the Egyptians seventy days to prepare a body. We'll be done today."

"The Egyptians only did it to dead people," Brian reminds him.

"Dead animals too." Joshua has been doing a lot of research.

"I'm still alive." Brian gets up and starts pacing around. "I'm not a dead person. I'm not a dead animal. I'm not sure that this is a good idea."

"You thought it was a great idea until you got the X." Matthew gets up too. "It'll be fun. We'll use the plaster gauze stuff that Dr. Kellerman uses all the time on his patients. Remember, we used that stuff in third grade to make face masks."

"That was just our faces. You're going to do it to my whole body. What if I get claustrophobia?" Brian looks less than overjoyed.

"Claustrophobia." Matthew grins. "Isn't that fear of a little old fat man in a red suit who shows up at Christmas?"

"That's so funny I forgot to laugh." Brian scowls. "You know that means fear of being closed in."

"Look." Billy starts taking out the boxes of plaster gauze that they've been storing at the bottom of Matthew's already messy closet. "I'm planning to be an orthopedist just like my dad and I've watched him work before. It'll be a breeze . . . and the plaster dries very quickly and then we'll cut it off of you. Nothing to it. Nothing at all."

"And I'll teach you how to win at Super Gonzorga, that new computer game. You'll be able to beat everyone but me," Matthew says.

"Everyone but you and Chloe Fulton," Billy reminds him. "You know she's almost as good as you are . . . sometimes she even beats you."

Matthew chooses to ignore Billy. "And Brian, I'll do the hieroglyphics poster with you. We'll do a poster about a guy named Hy Roglifics, who invents the Egyptian alphabet."

"Let's not and say we did." Brian shakes his head.

Joshua puts his hand on Brian's shoulder to stop him from pacing. "I'll ask my father to make you the peanut butter cookies that you like so much."

"It's a deal." Brian smiles for the first time since he's picked the X.

The boys hear a door slam downstairs as Amanda Martin enters the house.

"Matthew? Are you home, you little creepling?"

Matthew helps Billy take out more boxes of plaster.

"Aren't you going to answer her?" Billy asks.

"Not when she calls me names. I bet that one of her dumb friends is with her. She always acts like a big shot when that happens." Matthew makes a face. "Maybe we should tie her up and put this stuff around her, but not leave the mouth, eye, and nose openings for her, and put her in the bottom of my closet for seventy days and use her for our school project."

"Sisters." Joshua says, knowing what it feels like to have an older sister, since he has one who is Amanda's best friend.

There's a pounding on Matthew's door, and Amanda flings the door open.

She's wearing a sweatshirt and a pair of old blue jeans. Blonde-haired, with blue eyes, Amanda squints as she glares at the boys, since she has given up wearing her glasses, except for when she absolutely needs to see. She is wearing at least one ring on each of her fingers, dozens of silver bangle bracelets on her right arm, and earrings. The one on the right side has stars and moons on it. The earring in her left earlobe is a heart that is engraved "Amanda and Danny Forever."

"Privacy." Matthew yells, thinking that every time he looks at his sister, she seems to be getting much older . . . and much meaner.

"You didn't answer. I needed to know if you were here, since Mom and Dad said that I have to check on you. It's not my fault that they both work and I have to check." She looks around the room at all the boxes. "What are you guys planning to do . . . make face masks like they do in third grade? You better do it downstairs, on the back porch, so it doesn't make a mess. You know that our parents will kill you if you ruin the new wall-to-wall carpeting."

Matthew realizes she's right but still doesn't answer.

Amanda stares at him. "Cindy's with me and we're going to be upstairs in my room discussing private stuff. So don't bother me."

Matthew is getting sick of the way that she acts toward him in front of his friends but knows that if he says something, it will get worse.

It's not fair that one kid gets to be older and the boss all the time.

Amanda leaves.

Matthew looks at his friends and says, "Let's go downstairs and get as far away from the dweeb as possible."

"And as close to the refrigerator as possible." Joshua is getting hungry until he remembers how Mrs. Martin believes in health food. "Is there anything good in there . . . anything edible?"

Matthew grins widely, showing his dimples. "My dad and I made a deal with her. We can have one box of stuff in the freezer and one thing in the refrigerator that she isn't allowed to complain about."

"Great. Let's get these boxes downstairs and then do some serious snacking before we get to work," Joshua suggests.

As the boys head down the steps carrying the plaster gauze, Matthew thinks about how this is going to be the best sixth-grade project ever. Mrs. Stanton is NOT going to be sorry that she picked him to be chairman.

*　　*　　*　　*　　*

Brian Bruno stands on the porch wondering why he didn't join the Pyramid Committee instead.

A giant garbage bag with a hole in the middle for his head has been placed over his body so that only his feet, neck, and head show.

A bathing cap covers his ears and red hair.

"We're going to have to stop feeding you soon," Matthew informs him. "We're almost up to your chest area and what if you start to choke? We won't be able to do the Heimlich maneuver on you because you'll be all covered up with plaster."

Matthew is trying to be the most responsible chairman of a Mummy Committee that ever was. The other guys look at each other and think that it's time to change the subject.

Billy looks at the mummy/Brian and says, "We should use the three-inch tape for his face, not the four-, five-, or six-."

"Let's do another layer or two first on the rest of the body," Matthew says. "We have to make sure that it'll be strong enough not to break after we cut it off Brian, put the two sides back together, and plaster it together."

"Fair deal." Billy is really enjoying pretending to be a doctor.

As they work, Joshua holds up a glass of soda and a straw so that Brian can sip.

He keeps talking to Brian to help him keep his mind off what's happening. "It's a shame that Amanda and Cindy are so rotten that they'd never give us any old jewelry even if we asked them. Did you know that there should be magic amulets tucked between the wrappings? That would make it more accurate."

Brian doesn't want a history lesson. "Would you guys please hurry up? I'm beginning to have trouble standing here. This is getting heavy . . . and I think I'm going to have to go to the bathroom soon."

Joshua immediately puts the soda away.

"We're almost done." Matthew starts putting the gauze on Brian's face, careful to leave large holes for his eyes, nose, and mouth. "Billy, stop working on the body. Help me with Brian's face."

As Billy starts working on the face, Joshua helps to prop up Brian.

Matthew goes for his mother's biggest pair of scissors.

He returns just as Billy is finishing up.

It looks great.

"Get me out of here, you guys." Brian's voice sounds a little muffled.

Checking, Matthew sees that Brian is getting enough air.

Looking, he can see how Brian just might be getting a little tired.

"No sweat," Matthew says, to reassure him.

"Easy for you to say. You're not covered by a plastic garbage bag and a ton of cement." Brian does not sound happy.

Matthew sits down on the floor, ready to cut Brian out of the mummy cast.

It doesn't take him very long to realize that the scissors are not going to cut through the cast.

"Why don't *you* try this, Billy?" He hands the scissors over, trying to look and feel calm.

It takes Billy an equally short period to discover the limitations of the scissors. "This always worked in third grade."

"I don't think we had as many layers," Matthew says softly, knowing that he is in deep trouble, deep deep deep trouble.

"What's going on out there?" Brian begins to sound panicky.

Matthew goes up to his mummy/friend and says, "I don't know how to tell you this, but we've run into a minor problem."

"My father's going to kill me if he finds out," Billy says. "I asked if I could take just a few rolls. He thought that we were making masks again."

Joshua says, "Someone give me a hand supporting this. He's getting heavy."

Matthew makes a decision, one that he doesn't like but knows is necessary. "I'll be right back. I'm going to get Amanda."

"Hurry," everyone else says at once.

Rushing out of the room and racing up the steps, Matthew realizes that while Brian Bruno is in heavy-duty plaster, he, Matthew Martin, is in heavy-duty trouble.

And it's not going to be easy to get either of them out.

*   *   *   *   *

Matthew knocks at the bedroom door, yelling, "Amanda. Amanda. Open up."

"What do you want? I told you not to bother me." Her voice comes out loud and clear through the closed door.

Matthew opens it anyway.

Amanda and Cindy are sitting on the bed, using the machine that Amanda got for her birthday . . . a crimper.

Their hair looks like it's been caught in a waffle iron. Cindy's is totally wrinkly. Amanda's is half-finished.

"I told you—" Amanda starts to scream.

"Emergency. It's an emergency. You've got to come immediately." Matthew is almost out of breath. "And you can't tell on me, promise."

Amanda and Cindy jump off the bed.

As they run downstairs, Cindy remembers that the crimper is still on and runs back up the stairs.

Matthew explains to Amanda as they rush into the kitchen.

Amanda looks at Joshua and Billy, who are holding up the mummy and looking very scared.

The mummy doesn't look like it has much emotion, but it's obvious that Brian does.

He's yelling, "Get me out of here. I want to go home."

Amanda tries the scissors.

Cindy walks in and says, "We've got an electric carving knife at home, but that would be too dangerous, right?"

"Right." Amanda nods, knowing that she is going to have to be in charge of this situation and wishing this time that she were not the oldest.

"I'm calling Mom." She picks up the phone and dials.

Asking for her mother, she listens for a minute and then says, "Please have her call the second she gets back. Tell her it's an emergency. . . . No . . . Everything is all right . . . sort of . . . but please have her call."

Amanda informs everyone. "One of the gorillas called in sick. Mom had to put on the costume and go deliver the message."

Picking up the phone again and mumbling, "I've begged her . . . absolutely begged her to get a normal job . . . but did she listen? . . . no . . . and she's even bought the company and has to spend more time there."

"Hurry," Matthew pleads. "Do something."

"I'm thirsty," Brian says softly.

Rushing over to get the glass, Matthew realizes that the problem could get even worse . . . if that was possible to imagine.

Going back to Brian, he says, "Which is worse? Thirst . . . or having to go to the bathroom? Because if I give this to you . . . you know what's going to have to happen sooner or later. You're going to have to go."

Amanda is on the phone explaining the situation to her father. "And hurry, Dad, hurry."

Amanda hangs up and looks at Cindy as if to say, "Do you believe this?"

Then she looks at Matthew.

"Don't say 'I told you so,' because you didn't," he says. "When's Dad coming home?"

"He's on his way immediately . . . and he's going to call Dr. Kellerman from the car phone to find out what we should do," Amanda explains.

The boys look terrified.

All they wanted to do was make the best project.

"I can't stand up anymore." Brian sounds like he's going to cry. "And I want to talk to my parents and I can't because they went away on a vacation and my grandmother's watching us and she's going to have a heart attack if she finds out about this."

Amanda walks over and pats the cast. "Brian. It'll be all right. I promise you. . . . Just hang in there."

"Where else am I going to go?" Brian asks and for some reason finds what she's said very funny and starts to laugh . . . and laugh . . . and laugh.

"Hysteria." Amanda, who has been reading psychology magazines, thinks, What should I do? . . . Should I do what they always do in the pictures? . . . slap him and say, "Get a hold of yourself"? But how can that help? . . . I'd only be hitting the cast . . . and breaking one of my nails . . . and how can he get a hold of himself? . . . He's in a full-length body cast.

Amanda is beginning to feel a little hysterical herself.

Mr. Martin rushes into the house and looks at the situation. "Okay. Everyone stay calm. I've talked with Dr. Kellerman and here are the possibilities."

"I want to go home." Brian has stopped laughing and is very upset. "I want to get out of here."

"Okay. I promise that we will get you out of there as quickly as possible, in the best way possible." Mr. Martin looks over at the scissors and quickly realizes they are not going to work. "Dr. Kellerman says that we can put you in a warm tub of water and the cast will become soft enough to take off in about half an hour."

"He won't fit into the bathtub. He's too tall and standing too straight." Amanda is calming down, now that she is not the oldest person in the room.

"Then we're going to have to get you over to Dr. Kellerman's right away," Mr. Martin decides. "But he won't fit into my car. . . . We just may have to call an ambulance."

Brian starts to cry.

Actually no one in the room is feeling very good either.

There's a moment of silence, and then as Mr. Martin picks up the phone to call the emergency number, Mrs. Martin rushes in, wearing a gorilla costume.

"I just stopped by on my way back to work to see if you needed anything and . . . ." She looks at everyone. "What's going on?"

Quickly Mr. Martin explains.

Mrs. Martin says, "Amanda. Cindy. Come with me. I want you to help me empty out the station wagon, Amanda. First, though, I want you to put your glasses back on. You know that you must wear them."

As the females rush out, Mr. Martin says, "Brian. Everything's going to be all right. I'll be back in a minute. I'm going to get something out of the garage."

"Don't leave us alone." Billy is afraid that he's getting too tired to help keep Brian from falling.

"Just for a minute." Mr. Martin rushes out, returning in a few minutes with a piece of equipment that is used to move heavy things. "I just remembered this dolly. We haven't used it in years."

Mrs. Martin and the girls return.

Mr. Martin continues. "Honey, I want you to help the boys support Brian while he hops onto this dolly."

It takes a few minutes but finally Brian is on the dolly, and Mrs. Martin and the kids make sure that he stays on while Mr. Martin wheels the dolly over to the car.

Mrs. Martin works her way into the front of the back section of the station wagon. It is not an easy task for a person wearing a gorilla suit, but there is no time to change.

Everyone helps lift and slide Brian into the back section of the car.

"I want someone to hold my hand," he cries out.

"I'll get in and pat on the cast." Amanda crawls into the back, her hated glasses back on her face. "Cindy, could you wait here until we get back? If Danny calls, don't tell him about this. I want to . . . later."

"Okay." Cindy nods.

"I'll drive this car," Mrs. Martin says. "Honey, you take your car."

265

"I want to go. Please," Matthew pleads. "I want to help."

Mrs. Martin quickly says, "Billy. Matthew. You come with me. Joshua and Cindy, would you please put this stuff in the garage?"

She points to some of the things that are used by her message-delivery company . . . a chicken suit, boxes of balloons, mouse outfits, confetti, and heart-shaped boxes.

"Sure." The Jacksons immediately get to work.

Mrs. Martin talks quickly. "Just let your mother know what's going on. And we'll call Brian's family as soon as we get to the doctor's."

While they're driving along, Matthew looks at his mother, who has taken the gorilla head off but is still wearing the gorilla body. "Mom, I'm sorry. We didn't mean to do anything wrong. I promise. Is Brian going to be all right?"

Mrs. Martin nods. "I think so. Just stay calm. We'll discuss this later. The important thing right now is to get him out of there and never do anything like this again."

"I promise." Matthew sits quietly for the rest of the drive.

Amanda also sits quietly, hoping that no one she knows sees them. A mother in a gorilla suit and her own half-crimped hair are just too embarrassing for words.

Billy Kellerman sits in the backseat wondering what his father is going to do. He knows what he's going to do to Brian . . . help him. . . . He's not so sure what his father is going to do to him, his son.

Everyone gets to the office at the same time. Dr. Kellerman is waiting at the door with a stretcher. He and his nurses and the Martins, as well as some of the relatives of waiting patients, lift Brian onto the stretcher and get him into the office.

Once Brian is on the examining table, everyone except the medical staff and Mr. and Mrs. Martin go back into the waiting room.

266

Matthew and Billy explain to everyone how it was all a mistake, how they were just trying to do the best sixth-grade project, that they had no idea that it would all end like this, that they hope that Brian is going to be okay.

"He'll be fine, boys. Don't worry." An older woman tries to comfort them. "Dr. Kellerman is a wonderful doctor."

Her husband looks at Amanda and says, "Is she also part of your Egypt unit, or did she just stick her hand in an electric socket?"

Amanda puts one hand up to her half-crimped hair, puts her other hand over her face, and tries to think of the best way to get back at Matthew.

"Don't listen to him," the old woman says. "My husband is quite a kidder. He just likes to joke around."

Amanda is all ready to say, "Yeah. He's about as funny as a rubber crutch," until she remembers where she is, in an orthopedic doctor's office. She says nothing.

The old man continues. "I guess your little mummy friend is all wrapped up in his problems. . . . But don't worry . . . there's really no gauze for concern. . . . Get it? No *gauze* for concern."

"Melvin, that's enough." His wife pats him on the hand. "Remember, there is a little boy in the office who needs help. This is not the time for your corny jokes."

Everyone in the office quiets down and thinks about Brian, who is at that moment being talked to by Dr. Kellerman.

"Brian, there is nothing to worry about. In a little while we will have you out of there." Dr. Kellerman speaks softly, calming down not only Brian but also Mrs. and Mr. Martin, who are standing nearby.

In a very muffled voice, Brian says something.

Leaning over, Dr. Kellerman asks him to repeat it and then tells the Martins, "Brian says that as long as it's gone this far, I should try to save the cast so that they can still use it for the mummy project."

"What a guy." Mr. Martin pats the cast. "Brian. Don't worry. We'll do whatever is best for YOU."

"What is best?" he asks the doctor.

Dr. Kellerman smiles. "We can do both. Get him out quickly and save the cast."

Leaning over, he explains. "Okay, Brian. I'm going to use the cast cutter. Don't worry. I know that it looks like a pizza cutter and sounds like a buzz saw . . . but it's not. It'll be a little noisy because attached to the saw is a vacuum cleaner, which sucks up the dust from the cut cast. Brian, don't worry. The saw doesn't even turn around and around. It vibrates quickly. First I'm going to take the face mask off to give you more breathing room and then I'll take off the rest."

The Martins stand there and watch the doctor work.

Dr. Kellerman cuts through the plaster around Brian's face, uses a cast spreader, and then lifts off the face mask.

Everyone looks down at Brian's face, which is all scrunched up and covered with dust.

As Dr. Kellerman brushes off the dust, he says, "See, I told you it would get better. How are you feeling?"

Brian nods. "Better."

Dr. Kellerman continues working.

Mrs. Martin strokes Brian's face and talks to him.

Dr. Kellerman and his nurse lift the front of the cast off.

Taking it, Mr. Martin leans it against the wall.

The doctor asks the nurse for a pair of scissors.

"No." Brian yells. "Don't cut me. You promised."

"I'm only going to cut off the garbage bag," Dr. Kellerman explains. "It's not good for you to be in it, and it's covered with plaster."

"But I only have underpants on under this." Brian looks up at everyone.

"I'll loan you one of my doctor jackets," Dr. Kellerman says.

"Now, let's get you up and out of there."

Mr. Martin and Dr. Kellerman help Brian sit up.

Brian looks at Mrs. Martin. "You're dressed like a gorilla." And then he starts laughing.

Everyone begins to laugh.

Dr. Kellerman and Mr. Martin help Brian get out of the plastic bag.

The nurse and Mrs. Martin look the other way, since that was the only way that Brian would agree to get out of the garbage bag.

Then Mr. Martin helps Brian to rush to the bathroom.

When they come back, Dr. Kellerman gives Brian an examination to make sure that everything is okay.

It is and Brian stands up to get a hug from Mrs. Martin.

Brian, dressed in a doctor's coat that is about five times too large for him, gets a hug from Mrs. Martin, dressed in her gorilla suit.

Dr. Kellerman takes a Polaroid picture and then looks at Mr. Martin. "I believe that there are several young men in my waiting room, one related to you, one related to me. Something tells me that these young men should have a talking to."

"I agree." Mr. Martin nods.

"I'll take Brian to his house and meet you at home soon," Mrs. Martin says and leads Brian out into the waiting room, where all the waiting patients, their families, their friends, and Amanda applaud the release of Brian from his plaster prison.

The two people cheering the most are extremely happy, even though they know that they are due for the lecture of their young lifetimes.

Nurse Payne sticks her head out the door. "William. Matthew. Please come in. The doctor and Mr. Martin will see you now."

THINK IT OVER

1. *In what ways is this story both humorous and serious?*

2. *How does Matthew get along with Amanda, his sister?*

3. *Why can't the boys get Brian out of the mummy cast?*

4. *Is Matthew's decision to get Amanda to help a good one? Explain your answer.*

5. *What steps does Matthew's dad take to get Brian out of the cast?*

WRITE

If you had to do an Egyptian project, how would you do it differently from the way Matthew and his friends do theirs? Write a description of your project.

WORDS
ABOUT THE
AUTHOR
PAULA DANZIGER

AWARD-WINNING
AUTHOR

Like many other authors, Paula Danziger knew even as a child that she wanted to be a writer. "When I was a senior in high school and was supposed to be studying for a final exam, I spent the night setting goals for myself," she writes. One of her goals was to be a published writer by the time she was twenty-one years old. She knew it would not be easy, especially since she had always had her own way of doing things.

Born in Washington, D.C., in 1944, Danziger grew up in Virginia and New Jersey. After studying English in college, she became a teacher. Later she went back to college to specialize in teaching reading. Afterward, she counseled, ran a tutoring program, and taught reading.

271

When
she went
back to college,
she missed her students,
so she decided to write a book
to tell students about survival and
"learning to like oneself, dealing with
school systems, and being able to celebrate one's

own
unique-
ness." The result
was *The Cat Ate My
Gymsuit*, her first novel.
Paula Danziger had finally met her
goal of becoming a published writer.

After the success of her first book, Danziger continued to write about the problems of growing up. She thinks it is important to write young people's books that tell about living everyday lives. "It is important for all of us to know that there are people that care," she believes.

Characters are very important to Paula Danziger. "As a writer, I create worlds for my characters and show how they react in certain situations. I really care about the people and want them to survive the worst and celebrate the best," she says.

After publishing many award-winning books, Paula Danziger still thinks of writing as the center of her life. She likes writing because it lets her use her sense of humor. "Writing is an exciting, often frustrating process," she says. "It's filled with change, pain, joy, revision, and refinement. It's life."

EXPLORING EGYPT

What information from the first selection helped you to better understand the mummy project in the second selection?

. . . .

Compare the way the real mummies were wrapped with the job the boys do in "The Mummy Project."

. . . .

WRITER'S WORKSHOP   The boys in "The Mummy Project" could have been chosen for the Pyramid Committee instead of the Mummy Committee. Research the history of the Egyptian pyramids and prepare a two- or three-paragraph report.

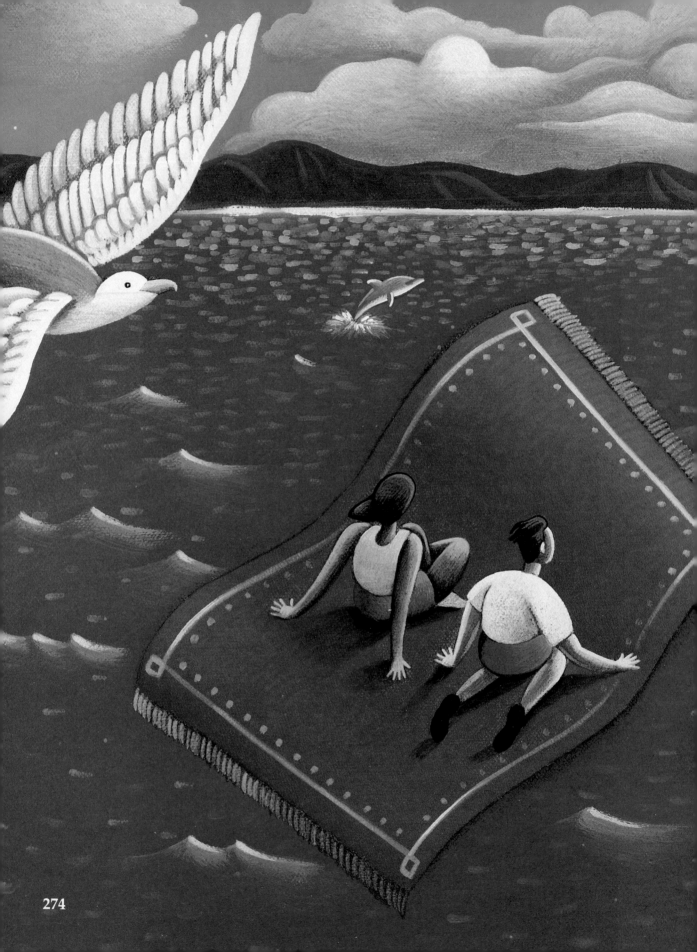

ACROSS THE SEA

Folktales often contain lessons hidden in amusing stories. Listen to The Hodja and another storyteller. You may discover some excellent advice.

C O N T E N T S

Listen to The Hodja

A Turkish Folktale

by Barbara Winther
illustrated by Jody Hewgill

Characters

TOURIST	WIFE	DONKEY
STORYTELLER	JAMAL	TAMERLANE
THE HODJA	TWO GUESTS	GUARD
	TWO SERVANT GIRLS	

Scene One

BEFORE RISE: *Spotlight shines on STORYTELLER, who sits on a pillow on the floor. Beside her, there are a cushion and two cups, and a coffeepot is heating on an open pan of coals (a "mongal"). TOURIST enters, center, wrapped in an enormous towel, gasps upon seeing STORYTELLER and starts to back away.*

TOURIST: Excuse me! I'm looking for the Turkish bath. Where am I?

STORYTELLER: Come in. This is the house of the old storyteller.

TOURIST (*Laughing nervously*): I'm really not dressed properly.

STORYTELLER: The Hodja would not agree.

TOURIST: The Hodja?

STORYTELLER (*Smiling*): You have not heard of him? (*TOURIST shakes head.*) Would you care for a cup of coffee? (*Pours coffee into cup*)

TOURIST (*Still nervous*): Well, perhaps a little. (*Sits down on pillow, and takes cup*) Thank you.

STORYTELLER: You appear tired.

TOURIST: I am! I flew to Switzerland this morning—the Alps, the yodelers, the cuckoo clocks—everything. Then, to Greece this afternoon to see the Parthenon and the Coliseum. Oh, no! That's wrong. The Coliseum was in Rome yester-

day. (*Sighs*) Now I am in Turkey this evening. Whew! It's a lot to keep straight. (*Sips coffee*)

STORYTELLER: You are an American? (*Sipping from cup*)

TOURIST: Yes.

STORYTELLER: I thought so. Americans are always dashing about doing many things at once. Although you accomplish much, The Hodja might tell you that if you run too fast, you might lose part of yourself and stumble over it trying to find out where you are.

TOURIST: I am not certain that I understand. Who is The Hodja?

STORYTELLER: There are many hodjas in Turkey, for hodjas are teachers. Only one is called *The* Hodja. We think he may have lived hundreds of years ago. Nobody knows when or if he ever existed. However, we have many stories about him. Some people call The Hodja simple-minded. Others consider him wise.

TOURIST: Which is he?

STORYTELLER: Listen to The Hodja, and you be the judge. (*Puts cup down on floor*) One evening The Hodja came riding home on his little gray donkey. He had spent the day working in his vineyard, and his clothes were dirty and ragged. (*Spotlight goes out.*)

277

SETTING: *A Turkish village. There are two houses open to the street which runs across stage, so that action within houses is visible to audience. In Jamal's house, left, there is a low table set with four bowls and spoons and four pillows on floor around it. In The Hodja's house, right, there is a large pillow on the floor with a tall water jar beside it. The jar is empty.*

AT RISE: *JAMAL is sitting on pillow in his house. THE HODJA enters left, riding his gray DONKEY or walking beside it. TWO GUESTS are standing on street, in front of houses.* NOTE: *During the play, spotlights shine on each house as action shifts.*

1ST GUEST (*Calling to* THE HODJA): Are you going to Jamal's house for dinner?

THE HODJA: Yes! I am looking forward to it.

2ND GUEST: You had best hurry, or you will be late.

THE HODJA: I cannot insult my little gray donkey by calling him slow. (*DONKEY turns head and looks at* THE HODJA.) I realize that it is *I* who am moving slowly, and my little gray donkey cannot make *me* go any faster. (*DONKEY lifts head and brays.*) I do not have time to change my old clothes. I shall have to go to the dinner just as I am. (*Turns* DONKEY *around and rides up to* JAMAL's *house, then climbs off, pats* DONKEY's *head*

and ties him to a post*) Stay there and guard the house.

(*DONKEY brays, lies down and goes to sleep. TWO GUESTS approach doorway of* JAMAL's *house.* THE HODJA *gives one last look at* DONKEY, *shrugs, then goes to stand behind* GUESTS, *as* JAMAL *rises from pillow, and comes to doorway.*)

JAMAL (*To* GUESTS, *ignoring* THE HODJA): My dear friends, I am honored that you came to my house this evening.

1ST GUEST: Your dinners are always excellent, Jamal.

2ND GUEST: And your company is exceedingly entertaining.

THE HODJA: Good evening, everyone. (*The three men turn, look appraisingly at* THE HODJA, *then turn away and continue talking, ignoring him.*)

JAMAL: Although I do not like to brag, I do believe that the pilaf which my wife prepares is the finest in all of Turkey. Come in.

1ST GUEST: She is a fine cook, Jamal.

2ND GUEST: My mouth waters at the mention of good food. I have not eaten since morning. (*JAMAL walks to table, and* GUESTS *and* THE HODJA *follow.*)

THE HODJA (*Clearing throat*): Jamal, I have been out tending my grapes today. I noticed that your grapes were twice as large as mine.

JAMAL (*Ignoring him, to GUESTS*): Let us sit down at the table. (*JAMAL points to pillows for GUESTS.*) You sit here on this side of me, and you sit here on the other side. (*JAMAL and GUESTS sit.*)

THE HODJA (*Clearing throat louder*): Jamal. Where do you wish me to sit?

JAMAL (*Ignoring him, clapping hands and calling off*): Servants! Bring the food and place it before us. (*Veiled SERVANT GIRLS enter left, carrying platter of meat and bowls of pilaf and pistachio nuts, which they pass to JAMAL and GUESTS. THE HODJA stands back,*

coughs, then nervously strokes his beard. *SERVANTS exit. THE HODJA, as if making decision, clears throat again very loudly, then steps over to table.*)

THE HODJA: Jamal, was I not invited to dinner at your house this evening?

JAMAL (*Ignoring him*): When our meal is over, honored guests, I have an excellent dancer from Constantinople to entertain us.

GUESTS: Ah! (*THE HODJA looks down at his clothes, shrugs, quietly turns away and goes into street. He unties DONKEY.*)

THE HODJA: Up, up, little gray donkey. We are going home. (*DONKEY rises with much effort, braying. THE HODJA climbs on.*) Forward! (*DONKEY walks slowly around stage to THE HODJA's doorway.*) Whoa! (*He climbs off, pats DONKEY's head, and ties him to a post in front of his house.*) Now you have *my* house to guard. (*DONKEY brays, lies down and goes to sleep. THE HODJA shrugs, scratches his beard, thinking. Suddenly he gets idea, leaps over DONKEY, and enters doorway of his house, shouting excitedly.*) Wife! My wife, where are you? (*WIFE enters right.*)

WIFE: Husband, it is late. Are you not going to the dinner at Jamal's house?

THE HODJA (*Shouting*): Soap and water, wife! At once!

WIFE (*Picking up jar*): Yes, husband. At once! (*Exits*)

THE HODJA (*Sitting on pillow*): All of the gentlemen were clean and finely dressed, and I was a disgrace to behold.

WIFE (*Re-entering with soap, towel, and water jar, which she gives to THE HODJA*): Do you wish your best turban?

THE HODJA (*Washing*): Yes! And bring my handsome new coat immediately.

WIFE: Immediately! (*Exits*)

THE HODJA (*Removing shoes and calling to WIFE*): I have no other shoes, and these are covered with dust.

WIFE (*Re-entering with turban and coat, and handing them to THE HODJA*): The dust will come right off. (*Bangs shoes together so that dust flies*) See? Now they are clean. (*Helps him slip on shoes and coat*) Oh, your beard is tangled, husband. (*Hands him brush*)

THE HODJA (*Brushing beard*): How do I look now, wife?

WIFE (*Standing back and admiring him*): Ah! I have not seen you look so fine in years. Surely you will impress your friends.

THE HODJA (*Swaggering out doorway and untying DONKEY*): Up, up, little gray donkey. Stand like the noble beast you are. (*DONKEY looks up at THE HODJA with surprise, brays, and jumps up. THE HODJA climbs on with great dignity.*) Forward! (*WIFE runs to window to wave as THE HODJA, nodding stiffly to her, rides down the street and crosses to JAMAL's doorway. Meanwhile WIFE gathers up everything but pillow and exits right.*) Whoa! (*Climbs off and ties DONKEY to post*) Guard my friend's house. Since you are the donkey of a gentleman, I suggest, indeed, I *insist* that you do not go to sleep. (*DONKEY brays loudly, sits down on rear haunches and peers down street. THE HODJA swaggers through*

the door.) Good evening! (*JAMAL and GUESTS look up, smile, and rise. JAMAL rushes over to grasp THE HODJA's arm.*)

JAMAL: My friend, you are late. I was worried that some terrible disaster had happened to keep you away. Welcome! Welcome, my Hodja!

1ST GUEST: It is good to see you again, O great Hodja.

2ND GUEST: You will find the dinner a most delightful one, divine Hodja.

JAMAL: Sit beside me. (*To* 1ST GUEST) Would you mind moving over so that my dear friend can sit beside me?

1ST GUEST: Of course not, seeing that it is The Hodja who will sit next to *me*. (*All sit.*)

JAMAL (*Clapping hands, calling*): Servants! Bring food for The Hodja! (*SERVANT GIRLS enter left with food, bowing to THE HODJA. One offers pilaf.*)

THE HODJA: This is some of your wife's excellent pilaf. (*Takes a spoonful and drops it into a fold of his turban.*) Eat, turban, eat! (*Others gasp.*)

2ND GUEST (*Aside, to JAMAL*): Look! The Hodja is putting pilaf into his turban!

JAMAL (*To THE HODJA*): Effendi,[1] are you feeling well?

---

[1] Effendi: a former Turkish title of respect

THE HODJA: Quite well! Do I smell some wonderful roast mutton? (*SERVANT brings platter of meat. THE HODJA takes pieces of meat and stuffs them into pockets of his coat.*) Eat, coat, eat! (*Others gasp.*)

2ND GUEST (*Rising to knees and whispering to JAMAL*): Look! The Hodja is putting the meat into his coat pockets!

JAMAL: Yes, yes, I see, but I find it hard to believe.

THE HODJA (*Loudly, startling* 1ST GUEST): And now, the pistachio nuts! Jamal, you set a tremendous table for your friends. (*SERVANT offers him bowl of nuts. THE HODJA takes a handful of nuts and stuffs them into his shoes.*) Eat, shoes, eat! (*GUESTS gasp.*)

JAMAL (*Rising*): This is too much. Why are you taking my good food and wasting it that way?

THE HODJA: You do not wish my turban to eat?

JAMAL: No, of course not!

THE HODJA (*Rising to knees*): You do not wish my coat to eat?

JAMAL (*Striding away from table*): No, of course not!

THE HODJA (*Standing*): You do not wish my shoes to eat?

GUESTS: No, of course not!

THE HODJA (*Shrugging, looking around innocently*): When I came to this house a short time ago in my old, dirty clothes, I was ignored, and there was no place at the table for me. When I come to this house in my fine, new clothes, everyone notices me, and nothing is too good for me. Therefore, I thought it was my *clothes* you had invited to dinner. Certainly, it could not have been *me*. (*All look at each other in amazement. Quick blackout and curtain.*)

Scene Two

BEFORE RISE: *Spotlight comes up on TOURIST and STORYTELLER sitting in front of curtain.*

TOURIST (*Laughing*): The Hodja is quite a character!

STORYTELLER: He is a favorite with my people. Do you have time for another tale? (*Sips coffee*)

TOURIST: Probably not, but I can't resist.

STORYTELLER: I am glad to see you more relaxed. So, once again we will listen to The Hodja. (*Sets cup down*) When Tamerlane the Great, the fearful Mongol conqueror, was ruling his vast empire, he took a liking to The Hodja because he found the little man amusing. One morning he sent word that he was coming to visit The Hodja in his home. (*Curtain opens.*)

SETTING: *Jamal's and The Hodja's houses, the same as in Scene 1. There is a bowl of figs on Jamal's table. Six large beets with tops are on the floor at center, as if growing in the ground.*

AT RISE: *DONKEY grazes near beets. WIFE is sweeping THE HODJA's house and beating the pillows.*

THE HODJA (*Entering right*): Wife, Tamerlane will not notice if the floor is swept or the pillows beaten. He is coming here to be amused.

WIFE: A clean house may not be amusing, but it is more pleasant. Have you considered what we shall give to him as a present?

THE HODJA: We'll give him nothing! We are not visiting him. He is visiting us.

WIFE: But, he is important—famous! It is a gift to us for him to enter our humble house. We must show our appreciation.

THE HODJA (*Scratching beard, thoughtfully*): Once again you are right. I shall pull some firm, red beets out of our garden and give them to Tamerlane.

WIFE: Good. (*Exits right*)

THE HODJA (*Humming happily, crossing to center*): Good morning, little gray donkey. (*DONKEY brays loudly.*) Will you kindly move so that I may pull up my beets? (*DONKEY shakes head and sits down on haunches.*) You are still in the way. (*Pushes DONKEY from behind*) There! (*DONKEY peers around as THE HODJA pulls on his beet tops. All six beets come out at once. THE HODJA falls over backwards. DONKEY brays in amusement, and THE HODJA rises with dignity. JAMAL, hearing the noise, enters and runs to his door.*)

283

JAMAL: What is the matter? Are you hurt?

THE HODJA (*Waving beets*): No, effendi. I have six beautiful, firm red beets to give to Tamerlane when he visits my house.

JAMAL: Hm-m! They appear to be of good quality. Let me examine them. (*THE HODJA follows JAMAL into his house. JAMAL takes beets, thumps and sniffs them, and hands them back.*) Indeed, they will make a fine gift.

THE HODJA: Thank you, my friend. (*He turns to leave. JAMAL looks at bowl of figs on table, picks it up and sniffs it, and wrinkles his nose at the smell. Then he calls THE HODJA.*)

JAMAL: Wait, my friend. (*THE HODJA turns. JAMAL holds out bowl of figs, hiding his distaste.*) I think you should give this bowl of figs to Tamerlane instead of those beets.

THE HODJA (*Looking at figs*): But your figs appear to be rotten.

JAMAL: Not so. They are at the peak of their ripeness. I have heard that Tamerlane has a fondness for very ripe figs.

THE HODJA: I did not know that.

JAMAL: I will show you what a good friend I am. We will make an even trade—the beets for the figs.

THE HODJA: It is done. (*Hands beets to JAMAL and takes figs, then crosses to his house, humming happily. DONKEY sniffs figs and brays loudly. JAMAL dances about gleefully with beets.*)

284

GUARD (*Entering*): Make way for Tamerlane the Great, lord of the land, military genius, expert horseman, fearless warrior, and winner of the local chess tournament. (*Drum roll is heard from offstage. SERVANT GIRLS enter, dancing and shaking bells, followed by GUARD, beating drum, and TAMERLANE, marching with arms folded and a fierce frown. JAMAL peers out window, suppresses mirth, and withdraws. SERVANTS stop at right, bowing, as TAMERLANE and GUARDS pass; then they sit down to wait. THE HODJA rushes into his house, shouting excitedly.*)

THE HODJA: Wife! Wife! Tamerlane is here. (*He holds basket behind him and stands at left. WIFE, veiled, enters, and stands next to THE HODJA. Both bow low as TAMERLANE and GUARD stride into house. GUARD takes his place and stands at attention at right of door.*) Good morning, noble Tamerlane. Please sit down.

TAMERLANE: It is a *bad* morning! (*TAMERLANE sits on cushion on floor.*)

THE HODJA: I suppose it is. I have never seen such a bad morning. I do believe the world will end by this afternoon.

TAMERLANE (*With a sneer*): My soldiers are shooting poorly with their bows. Their arrows do not seem to know where the target is.

THE HODJA: What a shame! If you like, I shall speak to the arrows at once.

TAMERLANE (*Smiling a little*): That will not be necessary. What do you have hidden behind you?

THE HODJA: A gift for you.

TAMERLANE: I notice a funny smell. I trust it is not the gift that has such an odor.

THE HODJA: It might, but a gift which smells has more meaning than one with no odor at all. (*Gives bowl of figs to TAMERLANE*) Figs for Tamerlane! Figs for you!

TAMERLANE (*Leaping up, holding nose*): What a smell! Guard, take these rotten figs away. (*GUARD takes bowl and rushes down street; SERVANT GIRLS squeal, hold noses, run off left. GUARD stops center, as if undecided what to do with figs. TAMERLANE rushes to window and shouts.*) Throw them at The Hodja. I have never been so insulted. He deserves to have the rotten figs on his head.

THE HODJA (*Dismayed*): Throw the figs at me? (*Bewildered, he runs through doorway into street, stops, peers around at GUARD, then rushes off right. GUARD follows, and, standing right, throws figs at departing HODJA. TAMERLANE laughs heartily, slaps his knees in amusement, then hurries out of house onto street.*)

GUARD (*Shouting excitedly*): I hit him. Right on target, noble Tamerlane. (*Continues to throw figs off*) Another hit. We should give figs to our soldiers. They might scare the enemy off. (*As he continues throwing figs after THE HODJA*) There's another. These are the squishiest figs I've ever seen—and the worst smelling! No one could stand up under these. There's the last one. (*GUARD turns, hands empty bowl to WIFE, who has been watching from doorway.*)

TAMERLANE (*Gesturing imperiously to GUARD*): Come, we must go back to our armies and make plans for using figs in our next battle. (*He laughs, then exits, followed by GUARD. THE HODJA re-enters, his turban askew, his clothes disheveled, his face dirty.*)

THE HODJA (*Shouting angrily*): Jamal, you villain, Jamal!

WIFE (*Going to him*): Oh, my poor husband! Are you all right?

THE HODJA: Quite well, wife! (*Shouts*) Jamal! (*Crosses left and enters JAMAL's house*) Jamal, my friend!

JAMAL (*Entering his house, left; nervously*): I can explain everything. I know you must be upset. Before you do anything—

THE HODJA (*Falling to his knees*): I am extremely lucky to have a friend like you, Jamal.

JAMAL: What is this?

THE HODJA (*Rising*): I wish to thank you seven times above and seven times below the earth for the good you have done.

JAMAL: What good?

THE HODJA: You took my *hard* beets and gave me the *soft* figs.

JAMAL: I know!

THE HODJA: If it had been the hard beets which had been thrown at me, I might not be here at all. How wise it is to take the advice of a good friend. (*Quick blackout and curtain. Spotlight comes up on TOURIST and STORYTELLER, who sit on pillows in front of curtain.*)

STORYTELLER (*Laughing*): Come now, tell me whether The Hodja is simple-minded or wise.

TOURIST: It is hard to tell. I would say he is a little of both.

STORYTELLER: So it is with most of us, I believe. More coffee?

TOURIST (*Rising*): No, thank you. I still must find the Turkish bath.

STORYTELLER: It is next door.

TOURIST: You have been very kind. I wish I weren't leaving in the morning. I'd like to hear another story.

STORYTELLER: Next time you come to Turkey, stay a bit longer.

TOURIST: I shall. The Hodja could teach me many things. Goodbye.

STORYTELLER: Goodbye, my friend. (*TOURIST exits right.*)

THE HODJA (*Entering left, waving arms excitedly*): Wife! Come quickly!

STORYTELLER (*Rising*): What is it? What is wrong?

THE HODJA: I just looked into my well and saw the moon and seven stars in there. Surely they will drown if we do not pull them out.

STORYTELLER: What you see is only a reflection.

THE HODJA: Are you sure? How can we understand what is a reflection and what is real, if we do not have both? (*Exits right, calling*) Wife! My wife, where are you? (*STORYTELLER shrugs. Quick blackout.*)

THE END

THINK IT OVER

1. *The storyteller asks if The Hodja is simple-minded or wise. How would you answer her question?*

2. *How is The Hodja greeted the first time he goes to Jamal's house for dinner? How is he greeted the second time?*

3. *At the end of the story, why does The Hodja say he is lucky to have Jamal as a friend? Is he?*

4. *The tourist tells the storyteller he isn't dressed properly. What do you think The Hodja would tell the tourist?*

WRITE

By the end of the play, the tourist thinks The Hodja is a good teacher. Write what lessons you think The Hodja teaches in the play.

287

The STUB-BOOK

by Pedro Antonio de Alarcón

illustrated by Laura Fernandez

The action begins in Rota. Rota is the
smallest of those pretty towns that form
the great semi-circle of the bay of Cádiz.[1]
But despite its being the smallest, the
grand duke of Osuna[2] preferred it,
building there his famous castle,
which I could describe stone by
stone. But now we are dealing with
neither castles nor dukes, but with
the fields surrounding Rota, and with
a most humble gardener, whom we
shall call Tío Buscabeatas, though
this was not his true name.

[1]Cádiz (kə•diz′): a major seaport on
the southwestern coast of Spain
[2]Osuna (ō•sōō′nə): a Spanish town
located 100 miles northeast of Rota

From the fertile fields of Rota, particularly its gardens, come the fruits and vegetables that fill the markets of Huelva and Seville. The quality of its tomatoes and pumpkins is such that in Andalusia the Roteños are always referred to as pumpkin- and tomato-growers, titles which they accept with pride.

And, indeed, they have reason to be proud; for the fact is that the soil of Rota, which produces so much, that is to say, the soil of the gardens, that soil which yields three or four crops a year, is not soil, but sand, pure and clean, cast up by the ocean, blown by the furious west winds and thus scattered over the entire region of Rota.

But the ingratitude of nature is here more than compensated for by the constant diligence of man. I have never seen, nor do I believe there is in all the world, any farmer who works as hard as the Roteño. Not even a tiny stream runs through those melancholy fields. No matter! The pumpkin-grower has made many wells from which he draws the precious liquid that is the lifeblood of his vegetables. The tomato-grower spends half his life seeking substances which may be used as fertilizer. And when he has both elements, water and fertilizer, the gardener of Rota begins to fertilize his tiny plots of ground, and in each of them sows a tomato-seed, or a pumpkin pip which he then waters by hand, like a person who gives a child a drink.

From then until harvest time, he attends daily, one by one, to the plants which grow there, treating them with a love only comparable to that of parents for children. One day he applies to such a plant a bit of fertilizer; on another he pours a pitcherful of water; today he kills the insects which are eating up the leaves; tomorrow he covers with reeds and dry leaves those which cannot bear the rays of the sun, or those which are too exposed to the sea winds. One day, he counts the stalks, the flowers, and even the fruits of the earliest ripeners; another day, he talks to them, pets them, kisses them, blesses them, and even gives them expressive names in order to tell them apart and individualize them in his imagination.

Without exaggerating, it is now a proverb (and I have often heard it repeated in Rota) that the gardener of that region touches with his own hands at least forty times a day every tomato plant growing in his garden. And this explains why the gardeners of that locality get to be so bent over that their knees almost touch their chins.

Well, now, Tío Buscabeatas was one of those gardeners. He had begun to stoop at the time of the event which I am about to relate. He was already sixty years old . . . and had spent forty of them tilling a garden near the shore.

That year he had grown some enormous pumpkins that were already beginning to turn yellow, which meant it was the month of June. Tío Buscabeatas knew them perfectly by color, shape, and even by name, especially the forty fattest and yellowest, which were already saying "cook me."

"Soon we shall have to part," he said tenderly, with a melancholy look.

Finally, one afternoon he made up his mind to the sacrifice and pronounced the dreadful sentence.

"Tomorrow," he said, "I shall cut these forty and take them to the market at Cádiz. Happy the man who eats them!" Then he returned home at a leisurely pace, and spent the night as anxiously as a father whose daughter is to be married the following day.

"My poor pumpkins!" he would occasionally sigh, unable to sleep. But then he reflected and concluded by saying, "What can I do but sell them? For that I raised them! They will be worth at least fifteen *duros!*"[1]

---

[1] duros (dōō′rōs): a unit of Spanish currency no longer in use; *syn. pesos*

Imagine, then, how great was his astonishment, his fury and despair when, as he went to the garden the next morning, he found that, during the night, he had been robbed of his forty pumpkins. He began calculating coldly, and knew that his pumpkins could not be in Rota, where it would be impossible to sell them without the risk of his recognizing them.

"They must be in Cádiz, I can almost see them!" he suddenly said to himself. "The thief who stole them from me last night at nine or ten o'clock, escaped on the freight boat. . . . I'll leave for Cádiz this morning on the hour boat, and there I'll catch the thief and recover the daughters of my toil!"

So saying, he lingered for some twenty minutes more at the scene of the catastrophe, counting the pumpkins that were missing, until, at about eight o'clock, he left for the wharf.

Now the hour boat was ready to leave. It was a small craft which carries passengers to Cádiz every morning at nine o'clock, just as the freight boat leaves every night at twelve, laden with fruit and vegetables.

The former is called the hour boat because in an hour, and occasionally in less time, it cruises the three leagues separating Rota from Cádiz.

It was, then, ten-thirty in the morning when Tío Buscabeatas stopped before a vegetable stand in the Cádiz market, and said to a policeman who accompanied him:

"These are my pumpkins! Arrest that man!" and pointed to the vendor.

"Arrest *me?* " cried the latter, astonished and enraged. "These pumpkins are mine; I bought them."

"You can tell that to the judge," answered Tío Buscabeatas.

"No, I won't!"

"Yes, you will!"

"You old thief!"

"You old scoundrel!"

"Keep a civil tongue. Men shouldn't insult each other like that," said the policeman very calmly, giving them each a punch in the chest.

By this time several people had gathered, among them the inspector of public markets. When the policeman had informed the inspector of all that was going on, the latter asked the vendor in accents majestic:

"From whom did you buy these pumpkins?"

"From Tío Fulano, near Rota," answered the vendor.

"He *would* be the one," cried Tío Buscabeatas. "When his own garden, which is very poor, yields next to nothing, he robs from his neighbors'."

"But, supposing your forty pumpkins were stolen last night," said the inspector, addressing the gardener, "how do you know that these, and not some others, are yours?"

"Well," replied Tío Buscabeatas, "because I know them as well as you know your daughters, if you have any. Don't you see that I raised them? Look here, this one's name is Fatty, this one, Plumpy Cheeks, this one, Pot Belly, this one, Little Blush Bottom, and this one Manuela, because it reminds me so much of my youngest daughter."

And the poor old man started weeping like a child.

"That is all very well," said the inspector, "but it is not enough for the law that you recognize your pumpkins. You must identify them with incontrovertible proof. Gentlemen, this is no laughing matter. I am a lawyer!"

"Then you'll soon see me prove to everyone's satisfaction, without stirring from this spot, that these pumpkins were raised in my garden," said Tío Buscabeatas.

And throwing on the ground a sack he was holding in his hand, he kneeled, and quietly began to untie it. The curiosity of those around him was overwhelming.

"What's he going to pull out of there?" they all wondered.

At the same time another person came to see what was going on in that group and when the vendor saw him, he exclaimed:

"I'm glad you have come, Tío Fulano. This man says that the pumpkins you sold me last night were stolen. Answer . . ."

The newcomer turned yellower than wax, and tried to escape, but the others prevented him, and the inspector himself ordered him to stay.

As for Tío Buscabeatas, he had already faced the supposed thief, saying:

"Now you will see something good!"

Tío Fulano, recovering his presence of mind, replied:

"You are the one who should be careful about what you say, because if you don't prove your accusation, and I know you can't, you will go to jail. Those pumpkins were mine; I raised them in my garden, like all the others I brought to Cádiz this year, and no one could prove I didn't."

"Now you shall see!" repeated Tío Buscabeatas, as he finished untying the sack.

A multitude of green stems rolled on the ground, while the old gardener, seated on his heels, addressed the gathering as follows:

"Gentlemen, have you never paid taxes? And haven't you seen that green book the tax-collector has, from which he cuts receipts, always leaving a stub in the book so he can prove afterwards whether the receipt is counterfeit or not?"

"What you are talking about is called the stub-book," said the inspector gravely.

"Well, that's what I have here: the stub-book of my garden; that is, the stems to which these pumpkins were attached before this thief stole them from me. Look here: this stem belongs to this pumpkin. No one can deny it . . . this other one . . . now you're getting the idea . . . belongs to this one . . . this thicker one . . . belongs to that one . . . exactly! And this one to that one . . . that one, to that one over there . . ."

And as he spoke, he fitted the stem to the pumpkins, one by one. The spectators were amazed to see that the stems really fitted the pumpkins exactly, and delighted by such strange proof, they all began to help Tío Buscabeatas, exclaiming:

"He's right! He's right! No doubt about it. Look: this one belongs here . . . That one goes there . . . That one there belongs to this one . . . This one goes there . . ."

The laughter of the men mingled with the catcalls of the boys, the insults of the women, the joyous and triumphant tears of the old gardener and the shoves the policemen were giving the convicted thief.

Needless to say, besides going to jail, the thief was compelled to return to the vendor the fifteen *duros* he had received, and the latter handed the money to Tío Buscabeatas, who left for Rota very pleased with himself, saying, on his way home:

"How beautiful they looked in the market! I should have brought back Manuela to eat tonight and kept the seeds."

THINK IT OVER

1. *How does Tío Buscabeatas prove that the stolen pumpkins are his?*

2. *How does Tío Buscabeatas first show that he knows his pumpkins as well as a father knows his own children?*

3. *What does Tío Fulano say when Tío Buscabeatas accuses him of stealing his pumpkins?*

4. *Why does Tío Buscabeatas compare the pumpkin stems to a tax collector's stub-book?*

WRITE

The thief receives a jail sentence and is required to pay back the money he received. In your opinion, is this punishment too harsh, fair, or too light? Write a few paragraphs explaining why you think the way you do.

ACROSS THE SEA

What lessons can be learned from these stories?

· ·

"Listen to The Hodja" and "The Stub-Book" are both folktales. In what other ways are they similar? In what ways are they different?

· ·

WRITER'S WORKSHOP Imagine that a tourist from another country is visiting your town. The tourist does not know your customs and manners. Write a how-to paragraph explaining how to prepare and eat breakfast.

HOW TO MAKE
BREAKFAST

295

AFRICAN STORYTELLERS

People around the world tell many kinds of stories in many different ways. In West Africa, storyteller-musicians known as *griots* tell the myths and legends of their people through song.

The *griots* have a long and fascinating history. In ancient times, before there were written languages in West Africa, the *griots* were counselors to great African kings. They memorized stories of important events and people and put those stories to music.

The *griots* of today maintain their link with the past. Although they no longer advise kings, they still entertain people with their story-songs rooted in African history and customs. Throughout West Africa, they can be found singing their proverbs and tales, accompanied by traditional African instruments.

■ *Have a "World Storytelling Festival" in your class. Find a folktale from another land or a song that tells a story. Then share your story with a group of classmates.*

ART/LANGUAGE ARTS CONNECTION

PUBLISH A BOOK

Create your own book using a favorite folktale from another land. Write the story on sheets of art paper and add illustrations. Then make a cover for your book and fasten the pages together. Display your book at a class book fair.

SOCIAL STUDIES CONNECTION

CUSTOMS IN OTHER LANDS

With a partner, find out about ways of life and customs in another country. Then organize your findings in a chart like the following. Use headings such as *Geography, Housing, Food, Clothing, Work,* and *Family Life.* Add photos, drawings, and maps to your chart if you like.

(NAME OF COUNTRY): LIFE AND CUSTOMS	
Geography	
Housing	
Food	

Nairobi, Kenya

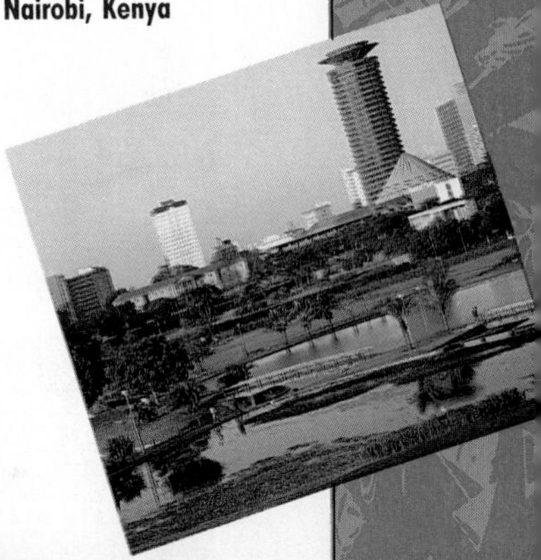

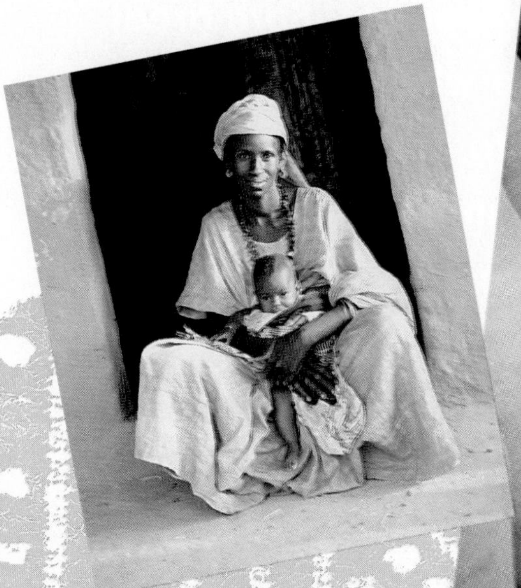

Father teaching daughter to read, Luxor, Egypt

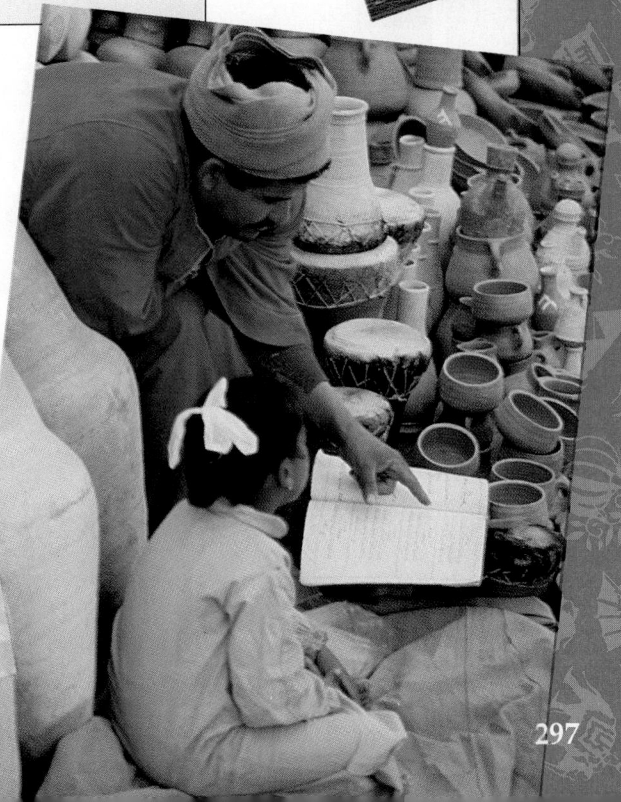

UNIT FOUR
LIGHT·MOMENTS

Kitty started laughing . . . she kept on laughing until the tears ran down her face.

Walter Dean Myers

Humorous stories and exciting sports events are enjoyed throughout the world. From time to time, we all need to laugh at a funny story or to root for a superb athlete, such as Jim Thorpe or Lynette Woodard. Both great athletes and people who provide laughs have to work hard to entertain us. As you read the selections in this unit, remember to appreciate the people who created these light moments.

DOG TALES
· ·

HUMOR FROM THE HEART
· ·

GOOD SPORTS
· ·

BOOKSHELF

SUMMER OF THE DODO
BY PATRICIA BAEHR

Dorothy Penny—Dodo to her friends—
hates her nickname. Then she and her
brother, who live in Australia, find a real
dodo bird. Their attempts to save the dodo
will keep you laughing.

HBJ LIBRARY BOOK

BUNNICULA
BY DEBORAH AND JAMES HOWE

Bunnicula seems like an ordinary rabbit,
but his housemates begin to worry when
they find vegetables drained white
with two little toothmarks in
them. ALA NOTABLE BOOK,
CHILDREN'S CHOICE

DOG POEMS
SELECTED BY MYRA COHN LIVINGSTON

Here is a celebration of dogs! In poems old and new, puppies frolic, grown dogs are friends, and old dogs lie by the fire.

BINGO BROWN, GYPSY LOVER
BY BETSY BYARS

Bingo's reputation as an authority on romance is developing nicely when life throws him a curve—he's about to become a big brother! ALA NOTABLE BOOK

TAKING SIDES
BY GARY SOTO

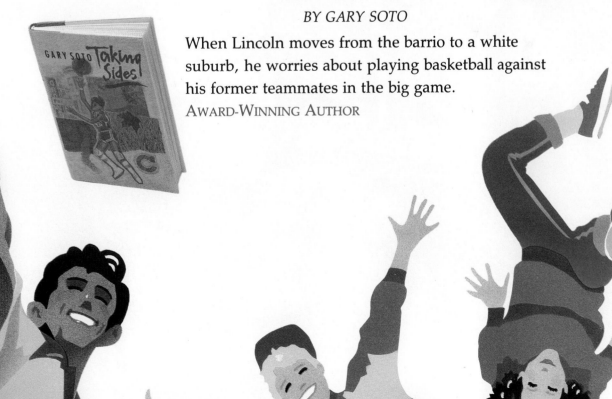

When Lincoln moves from the barrio to a white suburb, he worries about playing basketball against his former teammates in the big game. AWARD-WINNING AUTHOR

DOG TALES

Dogs can be cute. Dogs can be smart. But can dogs be funny? Meet Vergil, Major, and some other dogs, and decide for yourself.

C O N T E N T S

Vergil, THE LAID-BACK DOG

from *My Brother Louis Measures Worms*

by **Barbara Robinson**

illustrated by **Oleana Kassian**

Mary Elizabeth Lawson comes from a most unusual family. Her brother Louis and other members of her family are always getting themselves into wacky and unpredictable situations. In this story, you'll read about the Lawsons' adventures with Vergil, a very laid-back dog.

Most of Mother's relatives had animals of one kind or another, and most of the animals, according to my father, were as strange as the people they belonged to.

"I don't know," he often said, "whether they actively seek out screwy dogs and cats, or whether the dogs and cats just turn screwy after a while." He included our cat Leroy in this overall opinion, although by then Leroy was gone. He/she had produced four kittens and immediately took off for greener pastures, abandoning both us and the kittens, which my father said was completely unnatural behavior, and proved his point.

Actually there were any number of perfectly ordinary pets in the family—faithful nondescript dogs, companionable cats—but, just as good news is less dramatic than bad news and therefore less publicized, these humdrum animals were never the ones my father heard about, and the ones he *did* hear about left him forever cool to the idea of having one of his own.

Mother knew this; but, as she later said, having a dog was one thing, and having a dog come to visit for a few days was something else. So when her cousin Lloyd Otway deposited his dog Vergil on our doorstep, Mother didn't think twice about offering to keep Vergil while Lloyd went off to Milwaukee, Wisconsin, to acquire a wife.

My father said he could understand that Lloyd might find the pickings slim and overfamiliar right here at home, "—but why take off for Milwaukee?"

"Because that's where Pauline lives," Mother said. "Pauline Swavel. That's where she went back to after she and Lloyd met and fell in love. Oh, Fred, you remember Pauline!"

Obviously he didn't; but in view of the romantic circumstances involving Lloyd and Pauline Swavel, I did; and I remembered, too, that my father had been out of town that day.

"That's right, he was," Mother said. "He was in Columbus.

You were in Columbus that day, at your state convention. I know I told you about it, but you probably didn't hear me, or else you didn't listen."

"That *day*?!?" My father stared at her. "Lloyd and this Pauline met and fell in love in one day?"

"Yes," Mother said—and this was, indeed, the case: a one-day, whirlwind, love-at-first-sight affair, attended by the usual monkey puzzle of mistakes and coincidences.

Pauline Swavel, while driving through town on her way from West Virginia, was run into by Aunt Mildred, who had been distracted by the unexpected appearance in her car of Lloyd's dog Vergil.

"All of a sudden, there he was," she said. "Don't know where he came from. Just sat up in the backseat and yawned and stretched and groaned—scared me to death, and I hit the gas instead of the brake."

Vergil, equally alarmed, began to leap up and down in the car and to scramble from back to front, howling and barking. This behavior was so unnatural in Vergil—who had, at various times, slept through a fire, a burglary, and an explosion at the fertilizer plant—that Aunt Mildred lost all control, careened through a traffic light and bounced off a milk truck and into Pauline, who had pulled over to study her road map.

Pauline had taken a wrong turn somewhere north of Parkersburg and was not only completely lost but, now, involved in a traffic accident as well—with a car that seemed to her, at first glance, to be driven by a dog.

At this point Lloyd appeared. He had been delivering lawn fertilizer to Aunt Mildred, missed Vergil, and knew immediately what had happened, since it was Vergil's habit to climb into whatever car was handy and open and go to sleep.

Lloyd set out at once to find and follow Aunt Mildred— never an easy task, but a little easier this time because of all the commotion at the scene of the accident.

He arrived; retrieved Vergil; assessed the damage, which was minor; ignored Aunt Mildred (or so she said); and, on the spot, fell in love with Pauline. That Pauline should, at the very same moment, fall in love with Lloyd seemed insane to Aunt Mildred and my mother; unlikely to Louis—"Unless it was a movie," he said—and gloriously romantic to me.

"But, Lloyd," Mother said when he arrived at our house later that day, arm in arm with Pauline, to tell us the news, "isn't this awfully sudden?"

"Like a lightning bolt," Lloyd said.

"And, Pauline," Mother went on, "of course we think the world and all of Lloyd . . . but you don't even know him!"

"I feel I do," Pauline said, "after just these few hours. I've never felt so comfortable with a person, nor found anyone so easy to talk to. I figure that whatever I don't know about Lloyd, or what he doesn't know about me, will give us conversation for years. Do you believe in fate, Mrs. Lawson?"

"No, I don't," Mother said, "not when it's mixed up with Mildred and a bird dog."

"Neither do I," Pauline said, "or never did till now. But just think about it. . . . Why did I get lost and end up here? Why did Lloyd's dog get into someone else's car? Why did your sister run into me instead of someone else?"

Now, explaining it all to my father, Mother agreed that these were not mysterious events: Vergil was famous for getting into anybody's car, Aunt Mildred was famous for colliding with anybody's car, and . . . "I know all about getting lost," Mother said, "but even I know there are only two main roads north from Parkersburg, and if you miss the other one you'll end up here. But after all, they're both grown-up people—Lloyd's thirty-three years old, it's time he got married—and it wasn't as if they were going to get married that very minute. Besides, I thought it would all fizzle out. Of course, it didn't"—she smiled happily—"and now Lloyd's gone off to Milwaukee to marry Pauline."

My father eyed Vergil. "I think if I were Lloyd," he said, "I'd take that dog along with me for good luck, since he was in on the beginning of this romance."

"Well, so was Mildred," Mother said, "but she can't just go off to Milwaukee either—and you don't fool me a bit. You just don't want Vergil underfoot."

Unfortunately, because of his large and rangy size, Vergil was automatically underfoot, and he usually chose to sprawl,

full-length, in awkward places: at the top of the stairs or at the bottom of the stairs, under the dining-room table, under my father's car and, from time to time, on very warm days, in the bathtub.

The first time this happened Louis tried to make Vergil more comfortable by turning on the water; but Vergil scrambled out of the bathtub (moving faster than we had ever seen him move before) and tore all around the upstairs, barking and howling and shaking himself and spraying water everywhere.

"I think he was asleep," Louis said, "and it surprised him."

I thought so too, because Vergil was asleep most of the time . . . but when Louis tried it again, Vergil was awake and the same thing happened.

"He doesn't like the water," Mother said. "He just likes to feel the cool porcelain tub."

"So do I," my father said, "but I don't want to take turns with a big hairy dog. Isn't Lloyd back yet? He must be married by now."

"Yes," Mother said, "but they're on their honeymoon. Surely you don't begrudge them a honeymoon?"

"That depends on where they went," my father said. "They could have a very nice honeymoon between Milwaukee and here—two or three days in Chicago, maybe."

"Yes," Mother said, "they could. Listen, is that the telephone?"

"Well, hurry up and answer it. Maybe it's Lloyd."

It wasn't Lloyd. Actually, it wasn't even the telephone— Mother just made that up because she didn't want to explain that Lloyd and Pauline had gone in the opposite direction—to San Francisco—and were going to stop along the way wherever Pauline had relatives who wanted to welcome Lloyd into the family. We found out later that all these relatives lived in places like Middle Mine, Wyoming, and Clash, Nebraska, and were probably overjoyed to see anybody at all.

Of course, after two or three weeks, Mother had to admit that they weren't in Chicago and, as far as she knew, never had been. "They probably aren't even to San Francisco yet," she said. "You know how southerners are—sometimes newlywed couples visit around for months."

"But Pauline isn't a southerner, she's from Milwaukee!"

"I was giving you an example," Mother said. "It wouldn't have to be southerners. Amish people do the same thing."

"Is Pauline Amish?"

"She didn't say."

My father thought that over briefly and then shook his head. "You don't have any idea where they are, do you."

"No . . . but I do know that Lloyd is lucky, to marry into such a close and loving family."

"Lloyd is lucky," my father said, "because he was able to unload this dog on us while he tours the entire western half of the country. Oh, well," he sighed. "I'm going to take a bath—he isn't in the bathtub, is he?"

"No," Mother said, "but be careful when you come downstairs. He's asleep on the top step."

Three or four minutes later Louis and I heard the unmistakable *thump, thump, bang, thump, bang* of something or somebody falling downstairs, and went to see who or what it was.

My father heard the noise too, assumed that Mother had tripped over Vergil and came stumbling out of the bathroom with his pants half off, calling for us to get help. Mother, in the back bedroom, heard both the thumps and the cries for help, came running from that end of the house and fell over my father, who was trapped by his pants.

Meanwhile, Vergil lay at the foot of the stairs in his customary position: full-length and flat on his back—and ominously still. We thought he might be dead, and Louis got down on the floor to listen to his heart . . . which led Mother to conclude that it was Louis who had fallen *over* Vergil and then down the stairs along *with* Vergil.

"What else would I think?" she said. "Everybody on the floor in a heap." She felt responsible, though, and made my father pull on his pants and take Vergil to the animal hospital, where, as it turned out, he was well known.

"He isn't moving," Mother said. "He fell down the stairs."

"Does it all the time," the doctor told us. "This is the laziest dog in the world. He'd *rather* fall down stairs than stand up. Fell off a shed roof once. Fell out of Lloyd's truck that was loaded with fertilizer bags."

"But he isn't moving," Mother said.

"That's because he's asleep."

My father said this was the last straw—that he hadn't wanted a dog at all, and he especially didn't want a dog who was too lazy to stand up—but Mother was relieved.

"I'd hate to have Lloyd come back," she said, "and have to tell him that his dog died of injuries."

"At this rate," my father said, "his dog will die of old age before he shows up."

Vergil didn't die, but Lloyd and Pauline never did show up, either. Their car broke down in a place called Faltrey, Arkansas . . . *and we couldn't find anyone to fix it,* Lloyd wrote. *They had a garage, had a gas station, had parts and equipment, had no mechanic. The mechanic couldn't stand Arkansas, they said, and he got on his motorcycle and left. So I fixed our car and two or three other people's cars . . . and to make a long story short, they just wouldn't let us leave. And now you couldn't pay us to leave, because we love it here in Faltrey, especially Pauline. But don't worry, because we'll be back to get Vergil, the first chance we get.*

"'Yours truly, Lloyd,'" Mother finished reading. "Well, what do you know about that!"

"I know it's a long way to Arkansas," my father said, looking at Vergil.

After that we got a few postcards from Lloyd and a few letters from Pauline, who sent us a picture of the garage and a picture of their house and, eventually, a picture of their baby. All the cards and letters said they would be back for Vergil . . . *as soon as Lloyd's work lets up a little* or *as soon as we get the tomatoes in the garden* or *as soon as the baby's old enough to travel.*

My mother believed all these assurances (or said she did), and she would never admit that Vergil was anything but a temporary house guest. If anyone mentioned "your dog," she would always say, "Oh, this is Lloyd's dog. We're just keeping him for Lloyd."

In a way, my father wouldn't admit it either, because he never referred to Vergil as "our dog" or "my dog" or anything except "that dog"; but when Lloyd and Pauline finally did come back they had a sizeable family—Lloyd, Jr., was in the second grade, and the twin girls were two and a half years old—and their car was full of infant seats and baby beds and toys. My mother said the last thing they needed was Vergil. "Where would you put him?" she said.

Lloyd agreed. "I guess I just forgot how big he is. We'd better bring the truck next time."

Mother didn't mention this to my father, and in fact, Lloyd and Pauline had been gone for three days before he realized that Vergil didn't go with them, although Vergil was in plain sight, asleep, the whole time.

"You're just used to him," Mother said, "and you would miss him a lot."

"How could I possibly miss him if I haven't even noticed him for three days?"

"There!" she said. "How could any dog be less trouble!"

She was right, of course. Vergil didn't bark, or bite people, or dig up gardens, or upset trash cans, and by then we were all used to stepping over him or around him. By then, too, he was too old to climb into the bathtub; but sometimes, on very hot days, my father would lift him in—to get him out of the way, he said—and then get mad because Vergil wouldn't climb back out.

Despite Vergil's lack of interest in us, Louis and I were very fond of him. We thought of him as our dog, played with him during those brief and very occasional moments when he was awake, and whenever we had to write a paper for school about *My Best Friend*, or *My Favorite Pet*, we wrote about Vergil.

We never got very good grades on these papers because there was so little to tell, but we did share the glory when Vergil won a blue ribbon in the YMCA Pet Show. He won it for "Unusual Obedience to Command"—we commanded him to "play dead," and no dog did it better or for so long.

THINK IT OVER

1. *Which of Vergil's habits seem the most unusual to you?*

2. *How do Lloyd and Pauline first meet?*

3. *Does the family think of Vergil as their dog? Explain your answer.*

4. *Why is Mother hesitant to tell her husband about Lloyd and Pauline's whereabouts after their wedding?*

5. *Why do you think Lloyd never retrieves Vergil?*

WRITE

Write your own paper on the topic "My Favorite Pet." In your paper, write a vivid description of a pet you have owned or an animal you would like to own.

Sleeping Simon

by Deborah Chandra • illustrated by Kevin Ghiglione

Old Simon swims
A moonlit river
On the kitchen floor—
His chin quivers.
Cold water ripples
Round his whiskers.
Closed eyes roll.

Stiff, kicking legs
Keep him from
Sinking out of sight.
A splash, a sputter,
Deep growls down under—
Dark waters foam.
Simon fights.

The river swallows Simon:
Paws, claws, tail, nose,
Gulping air, he
Wakens with a yelp—
Thumping his tail to see
Stove, chairs and door,
And sighing, slumps upon the
Friendly floor.

The Dollar Dog

by John Ciardi
illustrated by Bernadette Lau

AWARD-WINNING
POET

A dollar dog is all mixed up.

A bit of this, a bit of that.

We got ours when he was a pup

So small he slept in an old hat.

So small we borrowed a doll's beads

To make him his first collar.

Too small to see how many breeds

We got for just one dollar.

But not at all too small to see

He had an appetite.

An appetite? It seems to me

He ate up everything in sight!

The more he ate, the more we saw.

He got to be as big as two.

The more we saw, the more we knew

We had a genuine drooly-jaw,

Mishmash mongrel, all-around,

Flop-eared, bull-faced, bumble-paw,

Stub-tailed, short-haired, Biscuit Hound.

Mother Doesn't Want a Dog

by Judith Viorst

AWARD-WINNING POET

Mother doesn't want a dog.
Mother says they smell,
And never sit when you say sit,
Or even when you yell.
And when you come home late at night
And there is ice and snow,
You have to go back out because
The dumb dog has to go.

Mother doesn't want a dog.
Mother says they shed,
And always let the strangers in
And bark at friends instead,
And do disgraceful things on rugs,
And track mud on the floor,
And flop upon your bed at night
And snore their doggy snore.

Mother doesn't want a dog.
She's making a mistake.
Because, more than a dog, I think
She will not want this snake.

KWAMI GREEN, TEACHER SUPREME

FROM *MOJO AND THE RUSSIANS* ▪ BY WALTER DEAN MYERS

ILLUSTRATED BY CHARLES LILLY

The project at hand was teaching Major to talk. It was mainly my idea, but Kwami tried to take credit for it. We had got into this big argument about communicating with other people. Kwami said that you could communicate with anything if you knew how to. He had read this article in an old magazine where some people were teaching a monkey to talk. Now Kwami figured that a dog must be smarter than a monkey. I told him that I had learned in biology that monkeys were the next smartest things to people. He said that if monkeys were so smart how come they didn't live in apartments like dogs did. He said that he saw a program about dogs once and that some dogs got a lot of money left to them when their owners died.

"Some of those dogs are millionaires," Kwami said. "I ain't no millionaire, and I ain't never read about no monkey millionaire, either. Which is why I say that dogs is smarter than monkeys."

It didn't make a lot of book sense, but it made a lot of seeing-is-believing sense. So when I thought about trying to teach Major to talk, I knew Kwami would go for the idea. As I said, he even tried to take credit for it.

We decided to take Major up to Leslie's house to teach him how to talk. The reason we decided to take him to Leslie's house was Leslie's grandmother stayed with them, and anytime you went to her house her grandmother would always come up with sandwiches or something.

Leslie had to go up first and make sure it was okay, and Kwami had to go home and tell his mother where he would be, and Judy took Major for a short walk while she was waiting for everyone to get ready. Anthony and Wayne were playing handball, and that left me and Kitty on the stoop. Me and Kitty and the beginning of the worst day in my life. Or, if not the worst day, at least the most embarrassing moment.

Kitty had this book of word games she was doing. What you had to do was unscramble a word. Like LOTEH is HOTEL scrambled. So she was doing these and I was thinking about how she had held my hand that time in the park and how I really liked her, and it all seemed pretty nice. So I asked Kitty if she wanted a picture of me.

"A picture of you?" She turned toward me real slow.

"Yeah." I was still feeling pretty good.

"What would I want a picture of you for?" she asked.

"Well, you could put it up on your wall or something," I said.

"Oh, I see," Kitty said. She was smiling a little and so I smiled a little, too. "And we could kind of be boyfriend and girlfriend."

"Yeah, kind of."

I was just about ready to figure out what picture I was going to give her when Kitty started laughing. She dropped her book and her pencil and really started to crack up. Then she rolled off the stoop and lay on the sidewalk. I never saw anybody laugh so hard. Wayne and Anthony came over and asked me what happened, and I said I didn't know. They tried to ask Kitty but she kept on laughing until the tears ran down her face. Finally she stopped enough to get back on the stoop and then she looked over at me and started laughing again until she was really crying.

Judy got back the same time that Leslie did. They asked Kitty what she was laughing about.

"This character wants me to . . ." She slapped her leg and started laughing again.

By this time I was really feeling bad because everyone was asking me why Kitty was laughing and naturally I didn't want to tell them.

"This character . . ." Kitty started telling what had happened again and was pointing at me.

"This character wants me to be his girlfriend and hang his picture on my wall." Kitty finished just in time for more laughter to come out.

Wayne started laughing, and Anthony started laughing, and Leslie just kind of held her hand over her mouth and started giggling. I also knew that when Kwami got back I'd have to go through the whole thing all over again.

I was right. After they told him why Kitty was laughing, Kwami said, "When you people getting married, man?" Kwami and his big mouth.

Kwami put his hand on my shoulder and I pushed it off.

"Oh, I see, only Kitty can put her hand on your shoulder," he said. "I can understand that."

Then everybody started to crack up again. We started up the stairs to Leslie's house and they were still on my case. I would have liked to punch out Kwami and Kitty right then and there. I really didn't think I was good enough to beat Kwami, though—in fact, I was pretty sure that I wasn't. I had had a fight with Kitty about a year ago and it came out even, but she had gotten taller so I just tried to forget about the whole thing. At least when we started teaching Major to talk they got off me.

"The first thing we got to do," said Kwami, "is to decide what he's going to say."

"Seems to me that if he says anything he'll be just about the coolest dog in the world," Kitty said.

"'Cause he's not a puppy, see?" Kwami lifted Major's chin slightly and looked at the dog as he spoke. "If he was a puppy you could teach him to say anything because he couldn't know any better. But he knows a lot of things now, so you got to be careful. Say you try to teach him to ask for a piece of fried chicken and he don't like fried chicken. He might not say anything just because he don't like what you're trying to teach him to say, dig?"

"Suppose he don't speak English?" Wayne asked.

"Don't be dumb, Wayne. American dogs all understand American and that's what we're going to teach Major to speak." Kwami gave Wayne a mean look. "And if you come up with one more dumb statement I'm going to wait till the next time it rains and then turn your nose upside down and drown you."

"So what are we going to teach Major to say?" I asked.

"Something patriotic," Kwami said. "So he'll feel good saying it."

"How about 'Give me liberty or give me death'?"

"He might think we're trying to bump him off."

"How about 'I regret that I have only one life—'"

"There you go with that dying stuff again," said Kwami.

"All that good patriotic stuff is about being dead or how you gonna die if something don't happen." Wayne was beginning to whine. Wayne always whined when somebody got on him.

"How about 'Tip-a-canoe and Tyler too'?"

"What's that mean?"

"I don't know. But it's got to be famous 'cause we learned it in history."

"The only thing you got to be to be famous in history is dead a bunch of years."

"I have it. How about 'Don't tread on me'?"

That was the famous American saying that we decided we would teach Major. The first thing that we did was to write the words on four large pieces of paper. Then Kwami and Kitty took turns reading the words to Major as Judy held him in her arms.

"Don't," Kwami said. He looked at Major and the dog seemed to understand him.

"Tread." Major still looked at Kwami.

"On." Major's tail began to wag.

"Me." Major squirmed.

"Now comes the hard part," Kitty said.

"You meaning getting my main dog here to talk?"

"No, just getting him to try," Kitty answered. "Dogs have been treated so badly over the years that they don't even try to talk. People usually just tell them to do things like sit down, and heel, and play dead, or get off the sidewalk, and that's what they think they're supposed to be doing. We got to convince Major that he's really supposed to talk."

"Leave that to the big K," Kwami said. "Kwami Green, teacher of frogs and dogs. Kwami Green, teacher supreme. Not only will I have your frog hopping, I'll get his foot to pattin' and not only will your dog talk, he'll speak Pig Latin."

"Don't be telling us that jive, tell Major," Judy said.

Kwami knelt down in front of Major and looked him right in the eye.

"Not only can you talk if you want to, Major, but you can converse on any level on which you choose. Now, dig, watch Kwami's lips as he speaks and then you repeat after me. Don't feel self-conscious if you don't get it right the first time 'cause I got until nearly three o'clock to get you together. Now, repeat after me: Don't . . . tread . . . on . . . me."

Major just looked at Kwami and wagged his tail.

Kwami got a little closer to Major until their noses were almost touching. "Look into my eyes and believe you can talk, dog," Kwami said. "I'm not teaching you anything jive to say. I'm teaching you some good stuff. This is a famous American saying. Now, I'm going to lift my head a little so you can watch my lips. See?" Kwami lifted his head so that Major could see his lips. "Now repeat after me." Kwami moved his lips in slow, exaggerated movements as he repeated the phrase. "Don't . . . tread . . . on . . . me!"

Major barked once.

"I think he got it!" Kwami said.

"All he said was woof!"

"He's warming up," Kwami said. "Give him a little time. What's the first thing you said when you started talking, turkey? You probably couldn't even say woof.

"Don't . . . tread . . . on . . . me!"

Major got closer to Kwami and licked him on the mouth. Kwami didn't move.

"Oh, sweat!" Wayne said. "Major kissed Kwami right on the lips and Kwami didn't even move."

"I can't reject him at this crucial point, man," Kwami said, but he looked a bit uncomfortable. "That would be like leaving a kid back in kindergarten.

"Don't . . . tread . . . on . . . me!"

Major licked Kwami's face again.

"I think Major's in love with Kwami." Judy grinned.

"That's what's wrong with you people." Kwami jumped up. "Anytime you try to do something serious you people start clowning around. You don't know nothing about no psychology or nothing. I give up."

Kwami sat down on a hassock and ate one of the grilled cheese sandwiches Leslie's grandmother had made. It was obvious that he was mad.

"Don't get upset, Kwami," Kitty said. "Maybe it just takes a while. We'll try again some other time."

"He might be ready to talk now," Judy said, "and just waiting for the right time. I know a woman who had a little boy who didn't talk until he was almost seven years old and then he just started talking one day like he had been talking all along."

"That's right," Leslie added. "I've heard of that kind of thing happening myself. He may get up in the middle of the night and start talking."

"You know, I was thinking," I said. "Maybe you made more progress than you think you did."

"What do you mean?" asked Kwami.

"Well, what's the saying you were trying to teach him?"

"Don't tread on me," answered Kwami.

"Well, he didn't tread on you, did he?"

Kwami just sighed.

That night I got home and my father was all set to have one of his "meaningful" conversations with me. We had one about twice a month. He usually gets on this real calm attitude and asks me something like what I thought of the crises in South Africa, or some other good doing thing like that. Only, halfway through my answer, he would interrupt to tell me what he thought, and that would be the end of the conversation. I'd sit there and listen until he was satisfied, then it would be over. Sometimes, just to be different, he would start the conversation off by asking me what I did that day. Then he would tell me what I should have been doing to better myself and what he would have been doing if he had been me. Then he'd watch television until he fell asleep in his chair.

This was one of those days when he was asking about what I did during the day, so I told him about trying to teach Major to talk.

"Trying to do what?" he asked.

"Trying to teach Major to talk," I repeated.

"Okay." He nodded his head up and down, but I knew he didn't believe a word I was saying. "Major is that little blond girl's dog, isn't he?"

"Yep," I said, really enjoying the fact that he didn't know what was going on.

"Well, okay," he said, switching on the television. "I guess you know what you're doing. By the way, there's something on your dresser for you. It was pushed under the door."

On the dresser was a white envelope with my name on it. Inside the envelope was a picture of Kitty. On the back it said 'to my friend, Dean.' Things were looking up.

THINK IT OVER

1. *Why does Dean, the narrator, say the day begins as "the worst day in [his] life"? How do you think he feels at the end of the day?*

2. *Why does Kwami think it will be easy to teach a dog to talk?*

3. *Why does Kwami want to teach Major to say something patriotic?*

4. *Why do you think Kitty acts the way she does when Dean asks if she wants his picture?*

WRITE

Write a set of instructions that explain how to teach an animal to do something. Your instructions may be serious or humorous.

THEME WRAP-UP

DOG TALES

Compare Vergil and Major to the dogs described in the poems. What are the similarities and differences?

. . . .

Do you think Kwami and his friends would have been successful in teaching Vergil new tricks? Explain your answer.

. . . .

WRITER'S WORKSHOP Imagine that you are a newspaper columnist who writes columns about pet care. List all the reasons people should keep their dogs on a leash. Use the most persuasive reasons from your list to write a newspaper column in which you try to convince people that dogs should always be on a leash when they are outside.

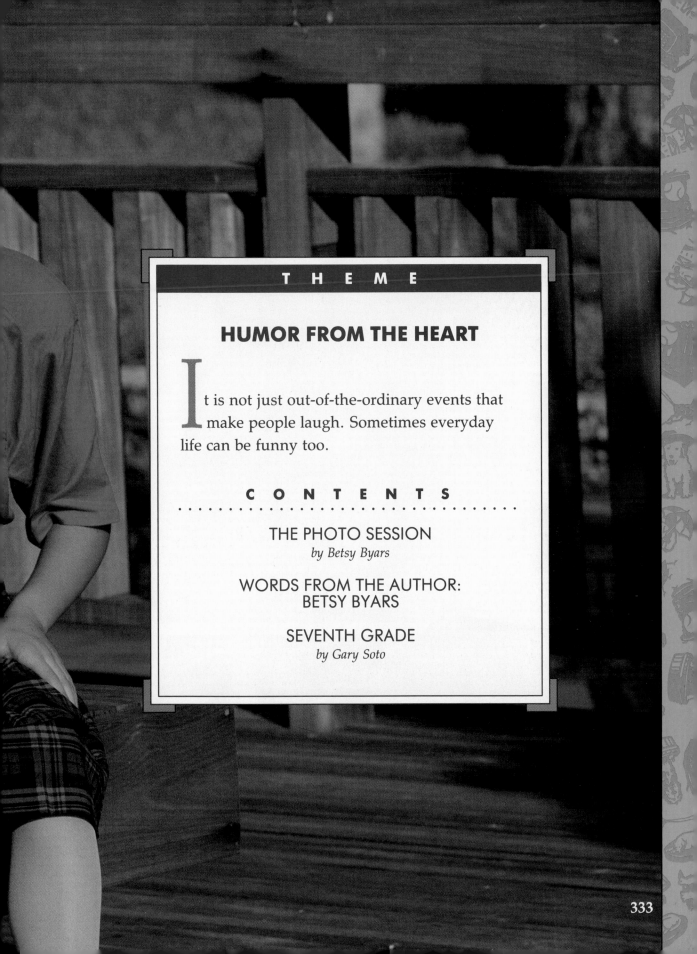

T H E M E

HUMOR FROM THE HEART

I t is not just out-of-the-ordinary events that make people laugh. Sometimes everyday life can be funny too.

C O N T E N T S

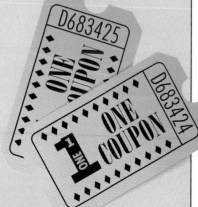

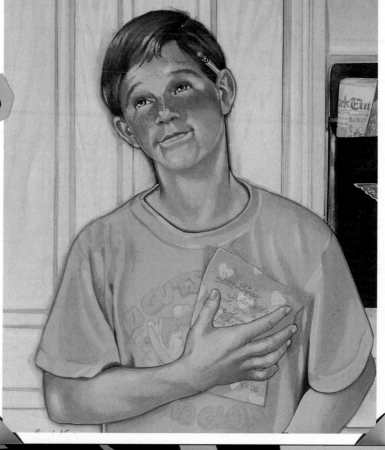

BETSY BYARS
Bingo Brown and the
Language of Love

You're Invited

THE PHOTO SESSION

from *Bingo Brown and the Language of Love*

by Betsy Byars ▼ illustrated by Susan Melrath

Every time Bingo Brown smelled gingersnaps, he wanted to call Melissa long distance.

Actually, it was more of a burning desire than a want, Bingo decided. One minute ago he had been standing here, smiling at himself in the bathroom mirror, when without any warning he had caught a whiff of ginger. Now he had to call Melissa. Had to!

"Are you still admiring yourself?" his mom asked as she passed the door.

"Mom, come here a minute."

His mom leaned in the doorway.

"Is that a mustache on my face or what?"

"Dirt."

"Mom, you didn't even look."

"Do your lip like that."

Obediently Bingo stretched his upper lip down over his teeth.

His mom said, "Ah, yes, I was right the first time—dirt."

"Mom, it's not dirt. It's hair. There may be dirt on the hair but . . ." He leaned closer to the mirror. "I would be the first student in Roosevelt Middle School to have a mustache."

"Supper!" his dad called from the kitchen. His dad was stir-frying tonight.

"A lot of women would be thrilled to have a son with a mustache," Bingo said, "though I'll have to shave before I go to high school. You aren't allowed to have mustaches in high school."

Bingo moved away from the mirror, still watching himself. "You can't see it from here, but"—he stepped closer—"from right here, it's definitely a premature mustache."

"Bingo, supper's ready." His mother picked up a bill as she went through the living room.

Bingo followed quickly. "Hey, Dad," he said. "Notice anything different about me?"

His father turned—he was holding the wok in both hands—but before he could spy the mustache, Bingo's mom interrupted. "You will not believe the trouble I'm having with the telephone company."

Bingo's father said, "Oh?" He put down the wok and wiped his hands on his apron before taking the bill.

"Can you believe that? They're trying to tell me that somebody in this family made fifty-four dollars and twenty-nine cents worth of calls to a place called Bixby, Oklahoma."

Bingo gasped. He caught the door to keep from falling to his knees.

"Fifty-four dollars and twenty-nine cents! I told the phone company, 'Nobody in this family knows anybody in the whole state of Oklahoma, much less Bixby.' Bixby!"

Bingo said, "Mom—"

"The woman obviously did not believe me. Where does the telephone company get these idiots? I said to her, 'Are you calling me a liar?' She said, 'Now, Madame—'"

Bingo said, "Mom—"

"Wait till I'm through talking to your father, Bingo."

"This can't wait," Bingo said.

"Bingo, if it's about your invisible mustache—"

"It's n-not. I wish it were," he said, stuttering a little.

Bingo's mom sighed with impatience. Bingo knew that she got a lot of pleasure from a righteous battle with a big company and must hate his interruption. He hated it himself.

"So?" she said. "Be quick."

Bingo cleared his throat. He walked into the room in the heavy-footed way he walked in his dreams. He clutched the back of his chair for support.

"Remember Melissa—that girl that used to be in my room at school?"

"Yes, Bingo, get on with it."

"M-member I said she moved?" he was reverting back to the way he talked when he was a child.

"No, I don't, but go on."

"You have to remember! You and Dad drove me over to say good-bye! It was Grammy's birthday!"

"Yes, I remember that she moved. What about it, Bingo? Get on with it."

"Well, she m-moved to Oklahoma."

"Bixby, Oklahoma?"

Bingo nodded.

There was a long silence while his parents looked at him. The moment stretched like a rubber band. Before it snapped, Bingo cleared his throat to speak.

His mom beat him to it. "Are you telling me," she said in a voice that chilled his bones, "that you made"—she whipped the bill from his father's fingers and consulted it—"seven calls"—now she looked at him again—"for a total of"—eyes back to the bill—"fifty-four dollars and twenty-nine cents"—eyes back to him—"to this person in Bixby, Oklahoma?"

"She's not a person! She's Melissa! Anyway, Mom, you knew she had moved. I showed you the picture postcard she sent me."

"I thought she'd moved across town."

"She drew the postcard herself. I'll get it and show it to you if you don't believe me. It said, 'Greetings from Bixby, OK.' Her address was there, and her phone number.

"As soon as I got the postcard, I went into the living room. You were sitting on the sofa, studying for your real estate license. I showed you the postcard and asked you if I could call Melissa."

He was now clutching the back of the chair the way old people clutch walkers.

"My exact words were, 'Would it be all right if I called Melissa?' Your exact words were, 'Yes, but don't make a pest of yourself.' That's why the calls were so short, Mom. I didn't want to make a pest of myself!"

His mother was still looking at the bill. "I cannot believe this. Fifty-four dollars and twenty-nine cents worth of calls to Bixby, Oklahoma."

"I'm sorry, Mom. It was just a misunderstanding."

"I'll say."

"I should have explained it was long distance."

"I'll say."

Bingo's father said, "Well, it's done. Can we eat?" He glanced at the wok with a sigh. "Dinner's probably ruined."

"I don't see how you can eat when we owe the phone company fifty-four dollars and twenty-nine cents," Bingo's mother said.

"I can always eat."

"May I remind you that I have not actually gotten one single commission yet?"

"You may remind me. Now can we eat?"

In a sideways slip Bingo moved around the back of his chair and sat. He began to breathe again.

"Mom, can I ask one question?" Bingo asked, encouraged by the fact that his mother was sitting down, too.

"What?"

"Promise you won't get mad."

"I'm already furious. Just being mad would be a wonderful relief."

"Well, promise you won't get any madder."

"What is the question, Bingo?"

"Can I make one more call to Melissa? Just one? You can take it out of my allowance."

"What do you think?" she asked.

"Mom, it's important. I need to tell her why I won't be calling anymore."

"Bingo, when you put fifty-four dollars and twenty-nine cents into my hand, then we'll talk about telephone calls. Until then you are not to make any calls whatsoever. You are not to touch the telephone. Understood?"

"Understood."

"Now eat."

"I'm really not terribly hungry."

"Eat anyway."

Bingo helped himself to the stir-fry. The smell of ginger was overpowering now. It was coming from the wok! No wonder he was being driven mad. And if the mere scent of ginger had this

effect on him—it was at the moment twining around his head, pulling him like a noose toward the phone—what would the taste do to him? Would he run helplessly to the phone? Would he dial? Would he cry hoarsely to Melissa of his passion while his parents looked on in disgust?

Bingo broke off. He had promised to give up burning questions for the summer, cold turkey, but how could he do that when questions blazed like meteors across the sky of his mind? When they—

"Eat!"

Bingo put a small piece of chicken into his mouth. The taste of ginger, fortunately, did not live up to its smell.

As he swallowed, he rubbed his fingers over his upper lip. The mustache—as he had known it would be—was gone. It had come out like the groundhog, seen its shadow in the glare of his mom's anger, and done the sensible thing—made a U-turn and gone back underground.

After supper Bingo went to his room and pulled out his summer notebook. There were two headings in the notebook. One was "Trials of Today." Under that, Bingo now listed:

1. Parental misunderstanding of a mere phone bill and, more importantly, their total disregard and concern for the depth of my feeling for Melissa.

2. Disappearance of a beloved mustache and the accompanying new sensation of manliness.

3. Breaking my vow to give up burning questions for the summer.

4. Tasting ginger, which, while it did not drive me as mad as I had feared, has left me with a bad case of indigestion.

The second heading was "Triumphs of Today." Under that Bingo wrote only one word: none.

"Dear Melissa,"

Bingo lay on his Smurf sheets. He had always been able to count on a peaceful night's sleep on his Smurf sheets. But last Tuesday Billy Wentworth had come over, looked at his unmade bed, and smiled condescendingly at the Smurfs. After that, Bingo had not been easy on them.

Right now he was as uncomfortable as if he were lying on real Smurfs. However, he knew tonight was not a good time to ask his mother for more manly sheets.

He glanced at his letter and read what he had written.

"Dear Melissa,"

He retraced the comma and stared up at the ceiling.

Writing Melissa was not the same as calling her, because as soon as she heard his voice, she always said something like, "Oh, Bingo, it's you! That's exactly who I was hoping it would be."

Her voice would actually change, get warmer somehow, deeper with pleasure. Girls were fortunate to have high voices so they could deepen them so effectively. His own voice got higher when he was pleased, which wasn't a good effect at all.

If his mom only knew how it made a man feel to hear a girl's voice deepen with pleasure. He knew there was no point in trying to explain that to his mom. His mom was in no mood to understand.

After supper, he had asked her for a stamp, one measly stamp, and she had said, "I'll sell you one."

"Sell?"

"Yes, sell." She walked to the desk, tore one stamp off the roll, and held it out. Her other hand was out, too, palm up. "That'll be twenty-five cents."

"Mom!"

"One quarter, please."

Then he had to go through the indignity of borrowing a quarter from his father.

And after all that humiliation, he couldn't seem to get the letter started.

"Dear Melissa,"

He changed the comma to a semicolon.

"Dear Melissa;"

As he lay there, he thought of that terrible, heart-stopping moment when he had learned Melissa was moving.

It had been a spring day. Mr. Mark, their teacher, was back after his motorcycle accident. He walked with a cane, but there was the general feeling in the classroom that everything was back to normal at last and things would go well for the rest of the year.

Bingo was at the pencil sharpener, grinding down a pencil, admiring the April day, when Melissa stood up behind him.

Bingo had not heard the snap of pencil lead, but his pulse quickened because he thought Melissa was going to join him. He and Melissa had had pleasant, even thrilling, pencil sharpener encounters before.

He turned toward her with an encouraging smile. Melissa was standing stiffly by her desk, arms at her sides. She said, "Mr. Mark?"

"Yes, Melissa."

"May I make an announcement?"

"Can't it wait a bit? Some people are still working on their journals."

Melissa's eyes filled with tears. She started to sit down, and Mr. Mark reconsidered. "Gang, is anyone working so hard on his or her journal that their train of thought would be shattered forever by an announcement from Melissa?" His bright eyes looked them over. "Melissa, it's all yours."

"This is a personal announcement. Is that all right?"

He nodded.

Bingo's heart had moved up into his throat. As soon as he had seen the tears, he had started closing the distance between them. He and Melissa were now two feet apart, close enough so that Bingo could see her tears were getting ready to spill.

Bingo could stand tears if they stayed where they were supposed to, but if they spilled . . .

"My dad," Melissa said. She looked down at her desk and blinked her eyes. Two tears plopped onto her open journal.

Bingo gasped with concern.

"My father," she began again with brave determination, "is being transferred to Bixby, Oklahoma, and we'll be moving next month. I hope some of you will write to me. That's the end of my announcement."

Melissa sat down, but Bingo stood there. He vowed with silent fervor to write daily, and to write such letters as the post office had never seen, letters so thick postal workers would marvel at their weight. His letters would go down in postal history. Years later, an unusually thick letter would be referred to as a "Bingo letter." His letters—

"Bingo?"

"What? Oh, yes, Mr. Mark?"

"Melissa said that was the end of her announcement. I believe you might begin to think in terms of returning to your seat."

"I'm on my way."

That memory caused Bingo to pick up his pen with renewed determination.

"Well," he wrote firmly, "I guess you're surprised to be getting a letter from me instead of a call, but our telephone bill came today."

There was a knock on his window. Bingo leaped in alarm. No one had ever knocked on his window before. He was as shocked as if someone had knocked on his forehead.

He got to his feet. Whoever was doing the knocking was either incredibly stupid or incredibly impolite!

Bingo strode to the window and bent down. The reflection of his own face, frowning, was all he could see.

"Who's out there?" Bingo asked. "Didn't your mother ever teach you not to knock on—"

"It's me, Worm Brain."

Bingo swallowed the rest of his words.

"Open up."

"Oh, all right." Bingo opened the window and looked at Billy Wentworth. Billy was wearing his camouflage T-shirt. "What can I do for you?" Bingo asked.

"Why can't you talk on the phone?"

"Who says I can't?"

"Your mom. I called and asked to speak to you, and she said, 'Bingo is no longer allowed to receive calls.' Bam! She could have busted my eardrum. You being punished?"

"Unjustly," Bingo said.

"Is there any other way? What'd you do?"

"I ran up a fifty-four-dollar phone bill," Bingo said. "So, why did you knock on my window?"

"I wanted to ask you something. Well, my mom wanted me to ask you something."

"What?"

"We're going on vacation and we can't take our dog."

"Misty the poodle?" Bingo asked.

A feeling of dread began deep within Bingo's soul. Before Misty had moved next door, Bingo had not known it was possible to actually dread being stared at by a dog.

"Mom, she stares at me all the time, right into my eyes."

"That's known as eye contact," his mom had said, in her usual unconcerned way.

"And I don't know what she wants me to do. Mom, she can stare for hours. Sometimes I have to go in the house!"

"You better get used to eye contact," his mom had said. "Later on you'll be having eye contact with girls, and if you run in the house then, you've blown it."

"Yes," Billy Wentworth went on, "Misty the poodle. How many dogs you think we got, Worm Brain?"

"That's the only one I know about."

"You want to keep her?" Billy asked.

"Well, I don't know. We're probably going on vacation, too."

"Go ask your mom."

"Er, I think she's in the bathroom just—"

"No, she's in the living room. I saw her through the window."

Bingo went into the living room. "We can't keep Misty, can we?"

His mother glanced up. "The Wentworth dog? Sure, why not?"

Bingo lowered his voice. "Mom, you know I can't stand to be stared at by that dog. She—"

"You ought to be ashamed of yourself, Bingo Brown, to mind being looked at by a ten-year-old half-blind miniature poodle with kidney trouble!"

Bingo stood in silence. Up until the business of the phone bill, Bingo and his mother had been getting along unusually well. His mother had a new job selling real estate, and even though she hadn't gotten a commission yet, she was very happy.

"Tell Billy yes!" she went on forcefully. "Tell Billy we will be glad to keep the poodle. Certainly it will make up, in part, for their having to keep you last fall."

This last humiliation, being put in the category of a dog, made Bingo turn—he hoped with dignity—and start back to his room.

He went directly to Billy, at the open window. "Yes," he said. He closed the window and went back to his bed.

Well, at least he now had something to write to Melissa. "Billy Wentworth's poodle, Misty, will be spending next week with me, so this will probably be my last letter for a while. I'll have to keep an eye on her. Sincerely, but somewhat despondently, Bingo Brown"

He fumbled under the bed for his summer notebook and flipped to "Trials of Today." He wrote:

1. Continued animosity from my mother and the cruel implication that I am, socially, on the same level with a poodle.

2. Having the privacy of my bedroom invaded by an enemy agent.

3. Inability to create postal history by writing Bingo letters to Melissa.

4. Continued failure in reaching the mainstream of life.

It made Bingo feel somewhat better to have survived four trials of this magnitude, but he still had only one word to list under "Triumphs": none.

Bingo tied on his apron and looked down at the cookbook on the counter. It was open to page forty-four: chicken breasts in tarragon sauce.

Bingo cracked his knuckles, cheflike.

"Let's see," he said. Beneath his breath, he began to read the ingredients. "Chicken breasts—I have those. Onions—I have those. . . ."

In order to make up for his phone debt, Bingo had agreed to cook supper for his mom and dad for thirty-six nights. His mom had originally wanted fifty-four. "That's fair, Bingo," she had argued, "a dollar a night." But he had bargained her up to a dollar and a half.

"All right, thirty-six," she'd said finally.

This was Bingo's third supper, and he was ready for something from the spice rack. As he rummaged through the little scented tins, he caught the aroma of ginger, but with a quick glance of regret at the telephone, he continued to rummage.

"Tarragon . . . tarragon. I wonder if that's anything like oregano? Garlic . . . dill . . .

"What else do I need to do? Oven"—Bingo turned on the oven with a flourish—"three-fifty." Bingo had already learned that 350 degrees was the perfect cooking temperature. He never planned to use anything else. For example, this tarragon chicken thing called for—he checked the recipe—275, but—

The phone rang and Bingo moved sideways toward it. Bingo was now allowed to answer the phone, but he couldn't place any calls. With his eyes on the cookbook, he picked up the phone.

"Hello."

A voice said, "Could I speak to Bingo, please?"

It was a girl's voice!

Bingo was so shocked he almost dropped the phone. He had not spoken to a girl on the phone since his last call to Melissa. He did not think he would ever speak to a girl again.

Now not only was he going to speak to a girl, but it was a strange girl.

A rash of questions burned out of control in his brain. Why

was a strange girl calling him? What did she want? He was too young for magazine subscriptions, wasn't he? Could she be conducting a survey? Could it be a woman with a little girl voice wanting him to contribute to a good cause? Could it be—

"Is this Bingo?"

"Well, this is Bingo Brown," he said, emphasizing his last name.

That was quick thinking. After all, there might be other Bingos. He didn't want to proceed with the conversation only to have it end with something like, "Well, boo, I thought I was talking to Bingo Schwartznecker."

"Oh, Bingo. Hi!"

There was a faint tinge of that long-remembered deepening of pleasure. How did girls do that? Did they have two sets of vocal cords, one for everyday use and one for special occasions? Did they shift gears like a car and their motor actually—

"Bingo," she went on in a more businesslike voice, "you don't know me, but my name's Cici, with two *i*'s."

"Oh?"

Bingo's free hand had begun to twitch nervously, as if it wanted to make some sort of gesture but was unsure what the gesture should be.

Bingo put his hand firmly into his apron pocket.

"Cici Boles."

"Oh."

"I'm a good friend of Melissa's, you know? I lived next door to her. But you probably don't recognize my name because I'm not in your grade."

"Oh."

"I'm the same age as Melissa, but I started school in Georgia, and you have to already be, like, five to start kindergarten in Georgia. . . . Are you still there?"

"Yes." At least, Bingo thought, he had broken his string of *oh*s.

"Because I, like, panic when people don't answer me. I think they've gone. I think I'm talking to, you know, empty air!"

"I'm still here."

"Then answer me."

"I will."

"You're probably wondering why I called."

This time Bingo answered as quickly as a bride. "I do."

"You're going to think this is silly, Bingo, but promise you won't hang up on me."

"I promise."

Bingo switched hands, putting his telephone hand—it had started twitching now—into his pocket.

"Well, here goes. Melissa wants me to take a picture of you with my camera and send it to her. See, I knew you'd think it was silly."

Bingo breathed deeply. This was the last thing he had expected, that a girl would want to take his picture. Even his own parents never particularly wanted to take his picture, and now this! A mixed-sex photography session!

"Are you still there?" Cici asked.

"Yes."

"See, you have to answer or I panic. Like, he's gone! I am talking to empty air!"

"Actually, I was thinking."

"Oh, I never stop to do that. I just, you know, go for it. What were you thinking?"

"Er, when do you want to take this picture?"

"Would right now be too soon?"

"Right now?" Bingo bent down to check his reflection in the toaster oven.

"Yes."

Bingo reached for his apron strings. He untied them in a flourish.

"I'll need a few minutes."

"Sure."

Bingo wondered if there was any mousse in the house. He hadn't used mousse since Melissa moved. He had given it up in a sort of religious way, like for Lent.

But if he didn't use it now, Melissa might not recognize him. Worse, she might think he had gotten ugly!

"Better make that fifteen minutes," Bingo told Cici Boles.

He turned off the oven and ran for the bathroom.

As he ran, heart pumping in a way it had not pumped in months, Bingo had burning questions.

Could this mixed-sex photography session turn out to be my first Triumph of Today? Or, more likely, will it be just another Trial?

Will there be mousse?

Is a Triumph possible without mousse?

With hands that trembled, Bingo opened the medicine cabinet. "Ah," he sighed, "mousse." And he reached for the can.

Bingo was at the window, watching for Cici Boles. He was getting unhappier by the minute.

Bingo was not ready for another mixed-sex conversation. He had realized this when he was moussing his hair. He hadn't had one in such a long time that he wasn't sure he even remembered how.

Plus the fact that the only good mixed-sex conversations were those with Melissa. When you had a mixed-sex conversation with Melissa, it was like the Olympics of mixed-sex conversations.

This mixed-sex conversation might be mercifully brief.

"Smile."

"Like this?"

"Yes."

Click.

"Thank you."

"Anytime."

But still, with girls you could never tell. This Cici Boles might come up with something like, "By the way, are you doing anything Friday night?"

This thought made his heart throw itself against the wall of his chest, as if to escape.

"By the way, are you doing anything Friday night?" was exactly the kind of mixed-sex conversation he wasn't up to. Probably never would be.

He glanced at his watch. Was it too late to cancel? "Hello, Cici, this is Bingo Brown." No. No! "This is Bingo Brown's brother, and Bingo has been called out of town unexpectedly and—"

Bingo gasped. He leaned forward. A bicycle was coming down the street. There was a girl on the bike!

No, Bingo decided, putting one hand over his racing heart, this girl was much too big and too blond to be Cici. This girl was more like a high school girl—no, make that a college girl.

Bingo gasped again. There was a camera around the big blond's neck.

Bingo ran back to the kitchen so she wouldn't see him peering out the glass. When the bell rang, he walked in a brisk, businesslike manner to the door.

She said, "Well, here I am. I'm Cici."

Bingo said, "So you are."

He attempted to put his hands in his apron pockets, but his apron was back in the kitchen. He slid his hands sideways into his jeans pockets.

"I'll have to take the picture outside," Cici said, "because, you know, I don't have a flash. Is that all right?"

"Yes."

"Front or back?"

Bingo smiled slightly. "Perhaps you should take it from the front so Melissa can see my face. Otherwise, she might not recognize me."

"Oh, Bingo." Cici blinked rapidly. "I meant front yard or backyard."

"Just a little humor," Bingo mumbled.

"Oh, I get it. . . . front . . . back." With one finger—this was awkward because she had long, long nails—she pointed to her front and then her back. "Melissa told me how funny you are."

She might be as big and blond as a college girl, but that was where the similarity ended, Bingo thought. "Backyard," he said firmly.

In silence, Bingo led the way through the living room, the kitchen, past his apron and the half-skinned chicken breasts, out the back door.

"Oh, let's do it over here by the fence," Cici said. "The roses make a nice background. Melissa's the kind that couldn't care less about the background. She just wants a picture of you. I'm the kind that always likes to do my best."

Bingo stood stiffly against the rosebush, with his hands in his pockets. He said quickly, "How's this?"

"It's fine, but I'm not in focus yet."

"Go ahead and take it," he said through tight lips. He'd only been smiling for a short time, but the day was so hot his teeth were dry.

"There! I've almost got it."

Why had he let this happen? Bingo wondered. Here he was with the sun in his eyes, smelling of mousse, while important chicken breasts waited to be skinned in the kitchen.

Well, he understood now man's weakness for having his picture made. He was living proof of it. The trouble with living proofs was that you actually had to become the living proof before you—

A voice from the other side of the hedge said, "Hey, Worm Brain, is that you over there?"

It was Billy Wentworth!

Bingo pulled back into the rosebush. Thorns raked his arms, but he did not feel the sting. He wanted to pull the branches around him like a blanket and disappear.

"Take it! Quick!"

"All right! Oops! Now see what you made me do! My thumb was on the lens. I got a picture of my thumb. Now we've got to start all over again."

"Hurry!"

But it was too late. Billy Wentworth, in his camouflage T-shirt, peered over the hedge. His monkey eyes landed on Bingo.

He gave a small smile, as if he had come across an enemy without any means of defense. "Here's Misty and her stuff," he said.

"In a minute," Bingo said stiffly. The main reason he had chosen the back of the house was because there was less likelihood of being spotted. Now this!

Wentworth's smile continued. "What are you taking the Worm Brain's picture for?"

"I'm doing it for a friend of mine, you know, Melissa? She wants a picture of him."

"What for?"

"I don't know. What does anybody want a picture for? To look at. Smile, Bingo."

Bingo pulled his lips back into a smile.

"Not like that. Smile like you mean it."

Bingo suddenly remembered how natural it had been to smile at Melissa. Sometimes, at night in the darkness, he had smiled just thinking of smiling at her.

"Perfect!" Cici said. "She'll love it!"

The camera clicked and Bingo started gratefully for the hedge. Without meeting Wentworth's eyes, he took Misty and her suitcase.

Cici followed. She said, "Oh, let me get one of you with the dog. This will be so precious. Hold the dog up! Oh, its face is so sweet. Could I pat it?"

Wentworth said, "Be my guest."

Cici rushed forward and scratched Misty's head with what Bingo now realized were press-on nails, some of which needed repressing.

"Oh, and it has a little suitcase for its things. Can I look in it?"

Bingo surrendered the handle of the suitcase and stood stiffly, looking over the roof of his garage.

Cici knelt and unzipped the bag—another awkward move with the press-ons. She reached inside and pulled out a squeaky rubber newspaper.

"Oh, isn't that precious? It has its own newspaper. And I can tell that it really plays with it." Cici browsed through the rest of the suitcase. "Oh, vitamins and a chew stick, and what's this in the bottom?"

"Her blanket," Billy Wentworth said.

Bingo turned in astonishment. He stared at Billy Wentworth. Billy's voice had actually deepened on those two words, "her blanket."

What was happening here?

"It's like a real baby blanket."

"It is a real baby blanket," Wentworth said. His voice was almost purring with pleasure now, like a well-tuned engine. "It was mine."

Bingo's mouth dropped open as he gaped at the faded blue square. Billy Wentworth had once been a baby!

"She doesn't have, like, you know, a basket or bed or something?"

"No, she just drags her blanket around and sleeps where she wants to."

"That's what a little neighbor of mine does! I baby-sit her. Bingo, is this darling little dog yours or"—she nodded to the face above the hedge—"his?"

"His."

"And I," the deep voice from the hedge said, "am Willy Bentworth."

THINK IT OVER

1. *Do you think it is reasonable of Mrs. Brown to make Bingo prepare dinner as repayment for the phone bill? State an argument either for or against Mrs. Brown's decision.*

2. *When does Bingo come up with the idea of the "Bingo letter"?*

3. *What is the purpose of the photo session?*

4. *Why does the phone call from Cici bother Bingo?*

WRITE

Write a list of your own trials and triumphs of the day. Choose a day you found particularly eventful.

WORDS *from the* AUTHOR

AWARD-WINNING
AUTHOR

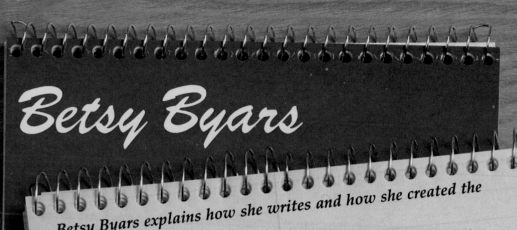

Betsy Byars

Betsy Byars explains how she writes and how she created the character of Bingo Brown.

When I write, I do it in longhand first. Then I put it into the word processor. I used to write eight hours a day when I was first starting out, because I needed that discipline. Sometimes when I'm writing a book, it doesn't seem like I'm writing. In the beginning, before I put down the words, I just stare into space. People may think I'm doing nothing, but I'm actually writing the book in my head. Writing is easier for me at this stage of my career, and more pleasurable. I used to resist the idea of writing sequels. But now I find I enjoy following the same characters. You know your characters, you know what they're thinking. It's a romp, really.

As far as Bingo Brown goes, the name Bingo came to me first. I was writing another book, and I was trying to think of a name for one of the characters. When Bingo popped into my mind, I thought, I don't want to waste that name on a minor character. Bingo just stuck with me. I thought of how he came to have that name—when he was being born, the doctor yelled out, "Bingo!" Finally I put aside the book I was writing. Bingo had just taken over.

I've received more mail about Bingo than any other character I've ever written about. I think kids like him because they identify with him. He's so open and vulnerable. He's really out there. Boys write and tell me they *are* Bingo. Girls enjoy Bingo, too. It gives them insight into the ways boys think. I really do enjoy writing the Bingo books because I like writing humor best.

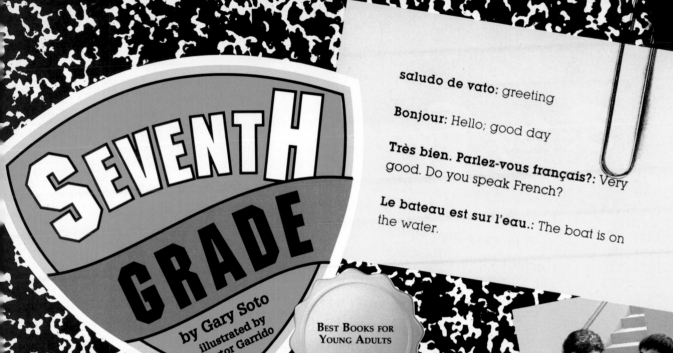

SEVENTH GRADE

by Gary Soto

illustrated by Hector Garrido

BEST BOOKS FOR YOUNG ADULTS

saludo de vato: greeting

Bonjour: Hello; good day

Très bien. Parlez-vous français?: Very good. Do you speak French?

Le bateau est sur l'eau.: The boat is on the water.

from *Baseball in April and Other Stories*

On the first day of school, Victor stood in line half an hour before he came to a wobbly card table. He was handed a packet of papers and a computer card on which he listed his one elective, French. He already spoke Spanish and English, but he thought some day he might travel to France, where it was cool; not like Fresno, where summer days reached 110 degrees in the shade. There were rivers in France, and huge churches, and fair-skinned people everywhere, the way there were brown people all around Victor.

Besides, Teresa, a girl he had liked since they were in catechism classes at Saint Theresa's, was taking French, too. With any luck they would be in the same class. Teresa is going to be my girl this year, he promised himself as he left the gym full of students in their new fall clothes. She was cute. And good at math, too, Victor thought as he walked down the hall to his homeroom. He ran into his friend, Michael Torres, by the water fountain that never turned off.

They shook hands, *raza*-style, and jerked their heads at one another in a *saludo de vato*. "How come you're making a face?" asked Victor.

"I ain't making a face, *ese*. This *is* my face." Michael said his face had changed during the summer. He had read a *GQ* magazine that his older brother borrowed from the Book Mobile and noticed that the male models all had the same look on their faces. They would stand, one arm around a beautiful woman, and *scowl*. They would sit at a pool, their rippled stomachs dark with shadow, and *scowl*. They would sit at dinner tables, cool drinks in their hands, and *scowl*.

"I think it works," Michael said. He scowled and let his upper lip quiver. His teeth showed along with the ferocity of his soul. "Belinda Reyes walked by a while ago and looked at me," he said.

Victor didn't say anything, though he thought his friend looked pretty strange. They talked about recent movies, baseball, their parents, and the horrors of picking grapes in order to buy their fall clothes. Picking grapes was like living in Siberia, except hot and more boring.

"What classes are you taking?" Michael said, scowling.

"French. How 'bout you?"

"Spanish. I ain't so good at it, even if I'm Mexican."

"I'm not either, but I'm better at it than math, that's for sure."

A tinny, three-beat bell propelled students to their homerooms. The two friends socked each other in the arm and went their ways, Victor thinking, man, that's weird. Michael thinks making a face makes him handsome.

On the way to his homeroom, Victor tried a scowl. He felt foolish, until out of the corner of his eye he saw a girl looking at him. Umm, he thought, maybe it does work. He scowled with greater conviction.

In homeroom, roll was taken, emergency cards were passed out, and they were given a bulletin to take home to their parents. The principal, Mr. Belton, spoke over the crackling loudspeaker, welcoming the students to a new year, new experiences, and new friendships. The students squirmed in their chairs and ignored him. They were anxious to go to first period. Victor sat calmly, thinking of Teresa, who sat two rows away, reading a paperback novel. This would be his lucky year. She was in his homeroom, and would probably be in his English and math classes. And, of course, French.

The bell rang for first period, and the students herded noisily through the door. Only Teresa lingered, talking with the homeroom teacher.

"So you think I should talk to Mrs. Gaines?" she asked the teacher. "She would know about ballet?"

"She would be a good bet," the teacher said. Then added, "Or the gym teacher, Mrs. Garza."

Victor lingered, keeping his head down and staring at his desk. He wanted to leave when she did so he could bump into her and say something clever.

He watched her on the sly. As she turned to leave, he stood up and hurried to the door, where he managed to catch her eye. She smiled and said, "Hi, Victor."

He smiled back and said, "Yeah, that's me." His brown face blushed. Why hadn't he said, "Hi, Teresa," or "How was your summer?" or something nice?

As Teresa walked down the hall, Victor walked the other way, looking back, admiring how gracefully she walked, one foot in front of the other. So much for being in the same class, he thought. As he trudged to English, he practiced scowling.

In English they reviewed the parts of speech. Mr. Lucas, a portly man, waddled down the aisle, asking, "What is a noun?"

"A person, place, or thing," said the class in unison.

"Yes, now somebody give me an example of a person— you, Victor Rodriguez."

"Teresa," Victor said automatically. Some of the girls giggled. They knew he had a crush on Teresa. He felt himself blushing again.

"Correct," Mr. Lucas said. "Now provide me with a place."

Mr. Lucas called on a freckled kid who answered, "Teresa's house with a kitchen full of big brothers."

After English, Victor had math, his weakest subject. He sat in the back by the window, hoping that he would not be called on. Victor understood most of the problems, but some of the stuff looked like the teacher made it up as she went along. It was confusing, like the inside of a watch.

After math he had a fifteen-minute break, then social studies, and, finally, lunch. He bought a tuna casserole with buttered rolls, some fruit cocktail, and milk. He sat with Michael, who practiced scowling between bites.

Girls walked by and looked at him.

"See what I mean, Vic?" Michael scowled. "They love it."

"Yeah, I guess so."

They ate slowly, Victor scanning the horizon for a glimpse of Teresa. He didn't see her. She must have brought lunch, he thought, and is eating outside. Victor scraped his plate and left Michael, who was busy scowling at a girl two tables away.

The small, triangle-shaped campus bustled with students talking about their new classes. Everyone was in a sunny mood. Victor hurried to the bag lunch area, where he sat down and opened his math book. He moved his lips as if he were reading, but his mind was somewhere else. He raised his eyes slowly and looked around. No Teresa.

He lowered his eyes, pretending to study, then looked slowly to the left. No Teresa. He turned a page in the book and stared at some math problems that scared him because he knew he would have to do them eventually. He looked to the right. Still no sign of her. He stretched out lazily in an attempt to disguise his snooping.

Then he saw her. She was sitting with a girlfriend under a plum tree. Victor moved to a table near her and daydreamed about taking her to a movie. When the bell sounded, Teresa looked up, and their eyes met. She smiled sweetly and gathered her books. Her next class was French, same as Victor's.

They were among the last students to arrive in class, so all the good desks in the back had already been taken. Victor was forced to sit near the front, a few desks away from Teresa, while Mr. Bueller wrote French words on the chalkboard. The bell rang, and Mr. Bueller wiped his hands, turned to the class, and said, *"Bonjour."*

"Bonjour," braved a few students.

"Bonjour," Victor whispered. He wondered if Teresa heard him.

Mr. Bueller said that if the students studied hard, at the end of the year they could go to France and be understood by the populace.

One kid raised his hand and asked, "What's 'populace'?"

"The people, the people of France."

Mr. Bueller asked if anyone knew French. Victor raised his hand, wanting to impress Teresa. The teacher beamed and said, *"Très bien. Parlez-vous français?"*

Victor didn't know what to say. The teacher wet his lips and asked something else in French. The room grew silent. Victor felt all eyes staring at him. He tried to bluff his way out by making noises that sounded French.

"La me vava me con le grandma," he said uncertainly.

Mr. Bueller, wrinkling his face in curiosity, asked him to speak up.

Great rosebushes of red bloomed on Victor's cheeks. A river of nervous sweat ran down his palms. He felt awful. Teresa sat a few desks away, no doubt thinking he was a fool. Without looking at Mr. Bueller, Victor mumbled, "Frenchie oh wewe gee in September."

Mr. Bueller asked Victor to repeat what he had said.

"Frenchie oh wewe gee in September," Victor repeated.

Mr. Bueller understood that the boy didn't know French and turned away. He walked to the blackboard and pointed to the words on the board with his steel-edged ruler.

"*Le bateau*," he sang.

"*Le bateau*," the students repeated.

"*Le bateau est sur l'eau*," he sang.

"*Le bateau est sur l'eau*."

Victor was too weak from failure to join the class. He stared at the board and wished he had taken Spanish, not French. Better yet, he wished he could start his life over. He had never been so embarrassed. He bit his thumb until he tore off a sliver of skin.

The bell sounded for fifth period, and Victor shot out of the room, avoiding the stares of the other kids, but had to return for his math book. He looked sheepishly at the teacher, who was erasing the board, then widened his eyes in terror at Teresa who stood in front of him. "I didn't know you knew French," she said. "That was good."

Mr. Bueller looked at Victor, and Victor looked back. Oh please, don't say anything, Victor pleaded with his eyes. I'll wash your car, mow your lawn, walk your dog—anything! I'll be your best student, and I'll clean your erasers after school.

Mr. Bueller shuffled through the papers on his desk. He smiled and hummed as he sat down to work. He remembered his college years when he dated a girlfriend in borrowed cars. She thought he was rich because each time

365

he picked her up he had a different car. It was fun until he had spent all his money on her and had to write home to his parents because he was broke.

Victor couldn't stand to look at Teresa. He was sweaty with shame. "Yeah, well, I picked up a few things from movies and books and stuff like that." They left the class together. Teresa asked him if he would help her with her French.

"Sure, anytime," Victor said.

"I won't be bothering you, will I?"

"Oh no, I like being bothered."

"Bonjour," Teresa said, leaving him outside her next class. She smiled and pushed wisps of hair from her face.

"Yeah, right, *bonjour,"* Victor said. He turned and headed to his class. The rosebushes of shame on his face became bouquets of love. Teresa is a great girl, he thought. And Mr. Bueller is a good guy.

He raced to metal shop. After metal shop there was biology, and after biology a long sprint to the public library, where he checked out three French textbooks.

He was going to like seventh grade.

THINK IT OVER

1. *Do you think Victor should have pretended to know French? Explain your answer.*

2. *What does Victor think of Michael's scowling?*

3. *What does Mr. Bueller do when he realizes that Victor doesn't know French?*

4. *Why do you think Victor will like seventh grade?*

WRITE

Imagine that Teresa finds out that Victor doesn't really know French. Write a short letter from Teresa's point of view telling what she thinks and feels about Victor after discovering that he doesn't know French.

HUMOR FROM THE HEART

Both Bingo and Victor become embarrassed in the classroom. How are these scenes similar? How are they different?

∙∙∙∙∙∙∙∙∙∙∙∙∙∙∙∙∙∙∙∙∙∙∙∙∙∙∙∙∙∙∙∙∙∙∙∙∙∙∙

Which of these selections did you enjoy reading more? Tell why you liked that selection better than the other.

∙∙∙∙∙∙∙∙∙∙∙∙∙∙∙∙∙∙∙∙∙∙∙∙∙∙∙∙∙∙∙∙∙∙∙∙∙∙∙

WRITER'S WORKSHOP Make a list of some of the advantages of having a long-distance friendship like the one Bingo has with Melissa. Then list some of the disadvantages. Imagine that you have a friend who has recently moved far away. Write a letter to this friend, explaining some of the advantages and disadvantages of long-distance friendships.

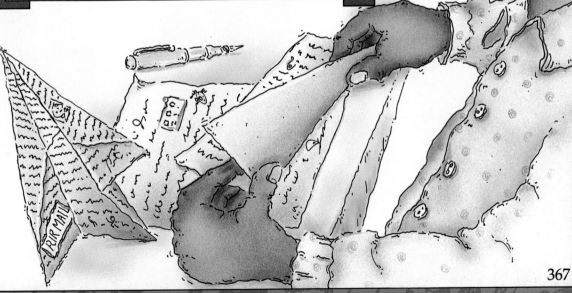

367

GOOD SPORTS

QUESTION: What's funny about a baseball game?

ANSWER: A horse in the outfield.

QUESTION: What are two good reasons for canceling a baseball game?

ANSWER: Rain—and grasshoppers!

QUESTION: What's so funny about sports stories?

ANSWER: Read the following selections and find out.

CONTENTS

369

The Horse That Played the Outfield

by William Heuman   illustrated by Mike Lester

f anybody has told you this story before, don't believe him because it's very likely that the facts have been exaggerated to the point where they are unbelievable. For instance, some people will tell you that this horse—whose name, by the way, was Edgar—could hit up in the neighborhood of .350 and that he was a terror on the bases.

This is patently ridiculous. A horse could never hit a baseball and, as for running the bases, you can just imagine a second baseman waiting to tag out a horse coming from first.

This horse could play the outfield, though. Maybe not as good as Mickey Mantle, or somebody like that, but he did play his position quite a lot better than Boone McCloud, for instance, who played left field for the Smokey Bellows Anvils.

It's a long story, and a lot of it you probably won't believe. But these are the facts, and I know them because I was there. I was manager of the Smokey Bellows Anvils, even though I wasn't quite eighteen years old at the time.

That was the year we moved out into the country because of my father's health. This country we moved to was so far out that there were people nearby who still thought Chester A. Arthur was President of the United States.[1] There were some hollows out there where as many as three generations of residents had never climbed the ridge to see what was on the other side.

When my father bought this farm and we moved out, I said to my brother Joe, who was a year younger than I, "This is it. By the time we get back to civilization, they'll be playing baseball on the moon."

My father said to us, "What you kids ought to do is start a baseball team around here."

"Baseball team?" I said. "I'd have as much chance getting nine players together out here as I'd have of finding Eskimos on the equator."

---

[1] Chester A. Arthur (1829–1886): U.S. President from 1881 to 1885.

"I don't know," Dad told me. "There are good ballplayers coming out of small towns. Go into Smokey Bellows. Look around."

At what? I should have asked him, because Smokey Bellows is not a particularly big town. It did have a post office, a constable, a general store, an ice-cream parlor, a poolroom and barbershop, which makes it sound as if it could be fairly good-sized, except that all of it was in one building. A Mr. Wilbur Sneed operated most of it with his son Ab, who was only a year or so older than I. Ab cut the hair.

It was through Ab Sneed that we heard about the horse.

"If you can't get enough players," Ab said, "you can use Tarp Mudweller's horse."

I didn't think I'd heard him right. I said, "For raking the field or something, Ab?"

Ab shook his head. He was a tall, skinny guy who said that he'd play first base for us because he had a first-baseman's mitt. "He plays the outfield," Ab said.

"Tarp?" I asked.

"No," Ab told me patiently. "This Edgar." All of a sudden Ab had sprung in this Edgar chap. We were talking about a ballplayer by the name of Tarp Mudweller.

Joe said, "What's Edgar's last name, Ab?"

Ab just shook his head. "Don't have a last name," he said. "Edgar's the horse I'm tellin' you about."

So we had to start from the beginning again, but I finally managed to get it clear in my mind that a young fellow by the name of Tarp Mudweller, an apple-grower over in High Valley, had a horse by the name of Edgar who played the outfield.

"I don't mean that Edgar's a real ballplayer," Ab explained. "Of course he can't hit or anything like that."

"Of course not," I agreed, and I looked at Joe.

Joe said solemnly, "What hoof does he put the glove on, Ab?"

I looked up at the ceiling, and then I walked over to sample some of the elder Sneed's free crackers in the barrel. I heard Ab say, "He don't use no glove. Edgar catches the ball with his teeth."

I nearly choked on the cracker, and Joe had to come and pound my back for a spell. I tried to be quite casual about it.

"I might stop in and see this Tarp Mudweller," I said, "and, of course, the horse."

"We won't forget the horse," Joe added.

When we got outside and climbed into the jalopy, I said, "Wow!"

"They didn't claim the horse talked," Joe said, "only that he played baseball."

I just looked at Joe. We did drive up to High Valley, however, and saw Tarp Mudweller, who was quite a nice young fellow, towheaded, freckle-faced, with very square shoulders and a nice smile.

"Sure would like to play some baseball this summer," Tarp said.

"What position do you play?" I asked.

"In the outfield," Tarp said. "Right or left field."

Joe said solemnly, "What position does Edgar play, Tarp?"

"Center," Tarp told us, without even cracking a smile. Then he turned to look at a white horse grazing in a little patch of grass beyond his house.

"That Edgar?" I asked.

"That's him," Tarp said.

Edgar looked like a very ordinary horse to me, not particularly a horse that could play baseball. He was all white—not the racehorse type and not the plowhorse type, just a horse. What I mean is, he wasn't heavy or anything like that, and he probably could run after those fly balls.

"He catches the ball with his teeth," I said.

"That's right," Tarp said.

Joe walked over to the jalopy. "I got a baseball in the car," he said. "Maybe we can try him out, Bud."

"Won't do any good," Tarp told us, "unless you hit the ball."

"It has to be hit?" I asked.

"It's the crack of the wood," Tarp explained. "When old Edgar hears that, he starts to go."

"I see," I said, but I didn't see anything, of course. "How did he get this way?" I asked next, almost as if I were believing this pretty tall tale.

"When he was a colt," Tarp told us, "I used to keep him tied up near where we kids played baseball. He was always trying to run after the balls. One day I untied him just for fun." He paused and he said apologetically, "Edgar didn't start catchin' the fly balls right away, of course. It took a little time."

"Of course," I nodded. "Anyway, you come out Saturday afternoon if you can, in the field back of Sneed's place. As soon as we get enough players, I'll line up a few ball games."

Joe said, "Bring Edgar."

I just looked at Joe. When we got into the car, I said to him, "What's the matter, you crazy or something? Whadda you mean, bring Edgar?"

"We can always use outfielders," Joe said.

"Oh shut up," I told him.

I had twelve players lined up for the following Saturday afternoon, our first practice session. I should amend that statement to make it eleven ballplayers and a horse. Tarp Mudweller brought Edgar down in an old battered truck, and he was now tied behind the backstop, munching away at the grass. He didn't seem to be interested in baseball.

I tried to forget about Edgar as I got a line on our players. Like Pop had said, they weren't too bad, either. Some were almost impossible, like Boone McCloud, who was big and fat and had flat feet. They weren't such hot fielders, but almost every one of them could hit a baseball pretty well.

After a while Joe came up to me and said, "When are you gonna try out Edgar, Bud?"

I took a deep breath. "OK," I said, "tell Tarp to put him in the outfield, and we'll see what he can do."

I'm not trying to say that this horse just loped out to center field when he was told to go. Like I said before, he didn't speak English. Tarp rode him out bareback and then slid down and walked away, leaving Edgar untied.

Joe handed me a fungo stick,[2] and he said, "I'll bet he can't throw the ball back to the infield."

"Well," I said, "here goes nothing."

I hit a ball into the air toward center, keeping it a little to Edgar's left because I didn't want the A.S.P.C.A.[3] coming out after me for hitting an animal with a baseball.

Joe, standing nearby, yelled, "Wow!"

He yelled because the minute the ball hit the bat, Edgar started to run, white mane bouncing as he loped in the direction of the ball. Then, as easy as can be, he caught the ball in his mouth and kept going over to where Tarp Mudweller was standing. He dropped the ball into Tarp's hand. Tarp winged it back to the infield, so I could see pretty quick how the throwing problem was solved.

"Boy!" Joe gasped.

Ab Sneed called, "Nice goin', Edgar."

I stood there, holding the fungo stick in my hand and looking out at that horse, trying to convince myself that it hadn't happened. But it had.

"Try another one," Joe said. "Maybe he was just lucky."

"It's not luck," I told him, "when a horse catches a baseball in his teeth."

I hit one to Edgar's right this time and I hit it deep, but Edgar put on a little more speed, circling to catch the ball and then going to drop the ball into Boone McCloud's hand.

---

[2] fungo stick: a bat designed for hitting practice balls

[3] A.S.P.C.A.: the American Society for the Prevention of Cruelty to Animals

After five minutes, both Joe and I had to agree that Edgar was easily as good as any of our outfielders, and a lot better than most. He covered more ground than anyone, and the throwing wasn't nearly the problem I thought it would be, because all of our outfielders had scatter arms[4] anyway, and maybe it was better that one of them hold onto the ball a little longer.

"What can we use him for?" I asked Joe. "He can't get up there and bat. And he just can't play the outfield without batting."

"He's good for shock purposes," Joe told me. "Maybe in the last inning or two we can put him in if we need a good defensive outfielder and the other team is beginning to tee off on the ball. Imagine the reaction when they see a white horse in center field!"

Joe had a point, but it was a point upon which one could hardly be rational.

When Tarp came in from the outfield, he said, "What do you think, Bud?"

I swallowed and said, "OK, he made the team."

That night I got on the phone, and I arranged a few games with nearby town teams. The first game to be played was at Three Corners, a town thirty miles away and about three times as big as Smokey Bellows—that is, it had three houses instead of one.

Joe said to me, "You think old Tarp will ride Edgar to Three Corners, Bud?"

"Well," I said, "that's one way two players can get there as cheaply as one."

Tarp brought Edgar up to Three Corners in his truck, and of course nobody there had any idea what a white horse was doing at a ball game. Tarp tied Edgar in under the trees off the first-base side of the field, and then everybody forgot about him for the first seven innings of the game.

---

[4] scatter arms: said of weak-throwing fielders who can't control where the ball goes: they *scatter* their throws around the field.

I was doing the pitching for the Smokey Bellows Anvils, even though I wasn't much of a pitcher. But there wasn't anybody else on the team who could put the ball over the plate, so I nominated myself.

Joe was at third base. We had Tarp in right field and Ab Sneed at first. The other Smokey Bellows boys were scattered here and yonder. There were a few uniforms among us, but not too many. Tarp wore overalls in right field, and heavy work shoes—which could be kind of slippery on long grass. One thing I could say about Edgar. He wouldn't be slipping around in the outfield, not with four hoofs digging into the turf.

The Three Corners team was about as good as our Anvils, which was to say that they were somewhat worse than mediocre. It was a 6–6 game going into the eighth inning, and the Three Corners' runs were not exactly earned, our team having made seven errors. Most of the errors had been made in the outfield on misjudged fly balls. Boone McCloud had made three.

In the eighth, Joe hit a triple, and I brought him in with a single, which gave us a one-run lead. I guessed it was about time to use Edgar. I said to Tarp, "We're putting Edgar in center field now."

Tarp just nodded, like it was an every day occurrence. He walked over to the grove where he'd tied his horse. I walked over to the Three Corners bench and said to their scorekeeper, "Edgar is now in center field for us instead of Snodgrass."

"Edgar who?" asked the scorekeeper.

"Just Edgar," I told him.

There must have been about 150 fans sitting on a few rickety benches and standing around in the infield, all farm people watching this game. Everybody started to laugh when Tarp rode Edgar out to center field. When Tarp slid off Edgar's back and trotted over toward right, leaving nobody in center but Edgar, the crowd got kind of quiet.

I was out on the mound, taking my warm-up pitches, and I noticed that the umpire was standing off to one side, looking out toward center.

I said to him, "We're ready to go, Jack."

"You ain't got no center-fielder," the umpire said, walking halfway down the lane.

I said, "We have a horse in center field."

He looked at me, a kind of smile on his face. "Whadda you mean, a horse?" he asked.

"You see him," I said. "He's in the lineup now."

The Three Corners manager, a big, rawboned farmer in his forties playing first base, came out toward the mound and said, "You have to get that hoss off the field, son."

I turned to look out at Edgar, and I noticed that he was nibbling away at the grass, as usual, which was what he always did until he heard the crack of the bat.

I said, "The horse is in the lineup. I just made the change with your scorekeeper."

Mr. Baylis looked at me and then at the umpire and then out at the horse. Then he called to the scorekeeper, who came running out with his book.

"Edgar," Mr. Baylis said. "You got an Edgar out in center field, Arch?"

"That's right," Arch said. "Only he ain't there yet."

Mr. Baylis had a red nose and a scrawny red neck. He scratched the back of his neck and then his nose. "That's Edgar in center field?" he asked.

"That's right," I said.

"Where?" Arch asked.

The umpire said, "There must be a rule about horses playin' baseball."

"There's no rule," I said. "Edgar is our center-fielder. He's playing."

"Where is he?" Arch asked. He hadn't heard what the umpire had said.

Mr. Baylis said patiently, "Just go back to the bench an' mark the score, Arch. They're playin' now with eight men an' a horse."

"A what?" Arch gaped.

"Just go back to the bench an' mark the score," Mr. Baylis said. He looked at me again and then shook his head and walked back to the bench.

The crowd started to talk again because we still had no center-fielder, except for this white horse nibbling on the grass.

In the eighth inning, though, nothing happened. The Three Corners team went down in order, two ground balls to the infield and a pop to Ab Sneed at first. He was mighty lucky to catch it.

We had a little trouble getting our center-fielder off the field between innings. It seems the grass out there was pretty good. Tarp had to pull and push before he got Edgar over the sidelines, with the crowd whooping it up.

We still had our 7–6 lead at the last half of the ninth inning, with Edgar back in center field and very happy with the grass out there.

Joe said to me, "Three to go, Bud."

Then a ground ball went right through Joe's legs. "Nice going," I said.

"Still three to go," he said.

Three Corners had a man on first base with nobody out. I got the next man on a pop to our catcher, but then I walked the following player, which wasn't very smart of me. I got mad then, and bore down hard, striking out one of the farmers. This gave us two outs.

The next Three Corners player hit a ground ball to second, which should have been an easy out, but the ball was kicked around, which made everybody safe.

I was a little disgusted because the next batter coming up was Mr. Baylis, and he was their slugger, having hit two long balls to the outfield, one for a triple.

"One to go," Joe said from third.

I watched Mr. Baylis in the batter's box, batting left-handed. Mr. Baylis didn't have a uniform. He wore a checked shirt, old-fashioned short knickers that he'd dug out of a trunk somewhere and a painter's white cap. The bat he lugged up to the plate must have weighed well over fifty ounces, and he had a lot of power in that big, rawboned body.

I got a strike on him, and then I fed him two wide ones. He fouled a pitch, which made it 2–2. Everybody was yelling for Mr. Baylis to clout one. I tried to fool him with an inside pitch, but he wouldn't bite, and the umpire called it a ball. It was a 3–2 count now, with the bases loaded and everybody ready to run on the next pitch.

Joe said from third, "Don't let it worry you, Bud, boy."

I wasn't going to let Baylis worry me, and I wasn't going to walk him either, and force in that tying run. I reared back and I let him have a fast one, putting everything I had behind it.

The ball went in shoulder high. When Mr. Baylis swung his bat, the ball went out about twice as fast as it had gone in. Everybody started yelling like crazy as that white ball sailed out toward center field, heading for a grove of trees about five hundred feet from home plate.

"Edgar!" I yelled, but I didn't have to yell, because our center-fielder was already on the move.

I never saw a center-fielder run the way Edgar did. Of course, four hoofs are better than two feet but, even for a horse, Edgar could really run when he heard that bat crack.

The ball was hit high and far, farther than I'd ever seen a ball hit before. Edgar was galloping like a race horse, tail swishing behind him. The base-runners were scooting around the bases, and I was thinking, as I watched from the mound, that no outfielder in the world could catch that ball. But Edgar was not an ordinary outfielder.

As the ball fell, Edgar suddenly turned his head and reached up and caught that ball just as nice as could be. The noise suddenly stopped. Mr. Baylis, who had been rounding first, pulled up like he'd run into a stone wall in one of his fields.

The umpire had taken off his mask, and he came walking out toward the mound, lips moving, but no sound coming out. Then he said, in a shaky voice, "The batter is out. I mean you, Mr. Baylis."

Mr. Baylis stood there watching Edgar swing around, come back, and drop the ball into Tarp Mudweller's hand.

They said four people fainted after the catch, one of them being an old fellow who'd once had a tryout with the Chicago Cubs.

When Tarp and Edgar came in, I said, "Nice going, Edgar."

Edgar played in quite a few games for us that year. I won't say he starred in all of them, and once he even dropped an easy fly ball, which lost us a game. This stuff you hear about him batting .350 and all that is the bunk. He couldn't steal bases, either, but he could play the outfield. As a matter of fact, he was the best outfielder we had, and I guess the best horse-outfielder this country has ever seen. He couldn't talk, though. Don't let anybody kid you about that!

THINK IT OVER

1. *Why do you think that Bud, the narrator, says that other stories about Edgar are likely to be exaggerated?*

2. *How does Edgar know when to catch the ball?*

3. *How does Edgar help the Anvils when they play Three Corners?*

4. *If you were on a baseball team, and the opposing team brought a horse out to play, what would you say or do?*

WRITE

In what ways is Edgar a good baseball player? In what ways is he a poor player? List his strong and weak points.

SPORTS LEGENDS AND LAUGHERS

FROM *AMAZING BUT TRUE SPORTS STORIES*
BY PHYLLIS AND ZANDER HOLLANDER

ILLUSTRATED BY JAY LEACH

GOING, GOING, GONE

They say that what goes up must come down. Well, not always.

There was this major-league game on May 4, 1984, at the Hubert H. Humphrey Metrodome in Minneapolis. Oakland was playing the Minnesota Twins.

With two out in the fourth inning, Minnesota pitcher Frank Viola threw a low fastball to Dave Kingman. The batter they called "King Kong"—because of his size and mighty wallops—hit what appeared to be a routine high pop-up over the infield.

Minnesota shortstop Houston Jiminez and third baseman John Castino stood behind the mound, gazing upward. Jiminez called for the ball. He waited. Then he waited some more.

"When nothing was coming down, I got scared," Jiminez said. "I covered my head. Never in my life had I seen anything like this. It was amazing."

Castino said, "It was the most helpless feeling. We just waited and waited . . . three, four, five seconds."

The ball, it turned out, had disappeared through a drainage hole in the bottom layer of the Metrodome's fabric ceiling, about 180 feet above home plate.

Umpire Jim Evans gave Kingman a ground-rule double, citing as precedent the double he had once granted when a ball lodged in a rooftop speaker in Seattle's Kingdome.

RUNNING *A G A I N S T* CUSTOM

There was no hint of the unusual when the starter signaled the beginning of the sixty-ninth Boston Marathon in 1967. Run over a 26-mile, 385-yard course between Hopkinton and Boston, Massachusetts, it was the oldest and then-largest marathon in the United States, where more than 100,000 spectators lined the course.

Suddenly, the crowd was startled to see Will Cloney, director of the race, chasing after one of the contestants. His target, K. Switzer, was to say later, "I was crying like a maniac. I was being spun around by the shoulder. . . ." Actually, Cloney was trying to rip the number off Switzer's shirt and chase the runner off the course.

But the 21-year-old Syracuse University student, eluding the official, managed to continue and finish the race, marking the start of something much bigger than that one competition. K. Switzer, it turned out, was a woman who had made a daring entry into the traditionally all-male marathon. Kathrine Switzer had filled in her entry blank simply as K. Switzer, leading officials to assume she was male.

Such was the gravity of her boldness that the AAU[1] officially barred women from all competition with men in these long-distance events. It took a long, hard, five-year battle for the barrier to be dropped, and in 1972 women were allowed to compete with the men in the same race. A year later, a separate division was established for women competing in the Boston Marathon, and by 1984 the ultimate was achieved when women ran the marathon for the first time at the Los Angeles Olympics.

---

[1] AAU (Amateur Athletic Union): an organization that supervises competitions for nonprofessional athletes

CALLED
ON ACCOUNT OF
GRASSHOPPERS

A horde of grasshoppers, numbering in the millions, invaded the Texas League baseball park in Midland, Texas, during the second game of a doubleheader between Midland and Amarillo.

The grasshoppers hit in such numbers that they dimmed the lights. Fans screamed, players swung their bats, and everyone clawed at the insects covering the playing field, the stands, and the mercury vapor lights.

The umpires were forced to suspend the game.

Health Department officials said a cool weather front that had pushed into the area might have brought the invasion.

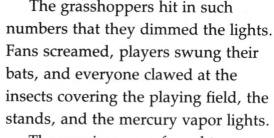
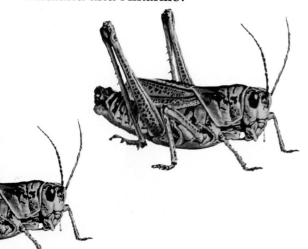
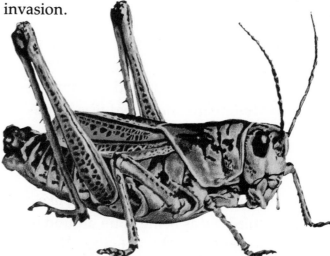

"LEAPING LIZARD"

As a five-year-old, Lynette Woodard watched in horror as an Air Force jet plunged from the sky into her Wichita, Kansas, neighborhood—killing 30 residents and just narrowly missing her home. Apart from the everlasting memory of the tragedy, the event would change her whole life.

Five years later in 1970, across the street from her house on the site of the crash, a basketball court was built. It was there at Piatt Park that Lynette became "hooked on hoop," playing pickup games daily with the neighborhood youngsters. "Soon the guys would pick me before their friends," she proudly remembered.

In high school, Lynette starred for the women's team that won state championships in 1975 and 1977, and as a student at the University of Kansas she continued to rule the court. Though the "Leaping Lizard," as she was called, didn't get to compete in the 1980 Olympic Games because of the U.S. boycott, she did make the Olympic team. Before graduation from the University of Kansas in 1982, Lynette was elected to their Hall of Fame as the top career-scorer—man or woman—with a record 3,649 points.

In 1984, the 5-foot-11 guard seemingly topped her career by leading the U.S. Olympic basketball team to a gold medal as its captain.

Her career as a basketball player was figured to be over after the Los Angeles Olympics. Whereas Lynette's male counterparts could embark on professional careers in the NBA, there seemed to be no future in women's professional basketball.

But in the fall of 1985, twenty-six-year-old Lynette found another way to keep dribbling. The newspaper headlines said it: HARLEM GLOBETROTTERS SIGN A WOMAN.

The woman was Lynette Woodard. She would be the first of her sex to play for the famous Harlem Globetrotters—a team that has appeared before tens of millions, live and on television, around the globe.

"MR. SQUARE TOE"

The first thing anyone notices about Tom Dempsey is what fate decreed: He has half of a right foot and only a stub for a right hand—the results of a birth defect.

But that didn't keep him from a playing career in the National Football League.

His father encouraged the handicapped Dempsey to compete in youth athletic programs and in high school sports at Encenitas, California, where Tom played defensive end. When he arrived at Palomar Junior College in San Marcos, California, Dempsey became a kicker.

"I simply tried it one day in practice and discovered I could do it," he said.

At first he used a specially-made shoe. But he discovered that he could kick higher and farther without a shoe.

Dempsey's place-kicking so impressed the New Orleans Saints, they gave him a contract in 1969. He was no longer a barefoot kicker and was able to get clearance from the NFL to use a custom-made shoe. It had no metal, the only aid being a one-and-three-quarter-inch leather boost on the "sawed-off" kicking surface.

Early in the season he drilled a 55-yard field goal against the Los Angeles Rams, one yard shy of the NFL record.

The New Orleans fans and his teammates were enthusiastic and encouraging, and he didn't mind his nicknames of "Mr. Square Toe" and "Elevator Foot."

On November 8, 1970, Dempsey kicked the field goal against the Los Angeles Rams that put him into the NFL record book. It was a 63-yarder. Nobody has been able to match it.

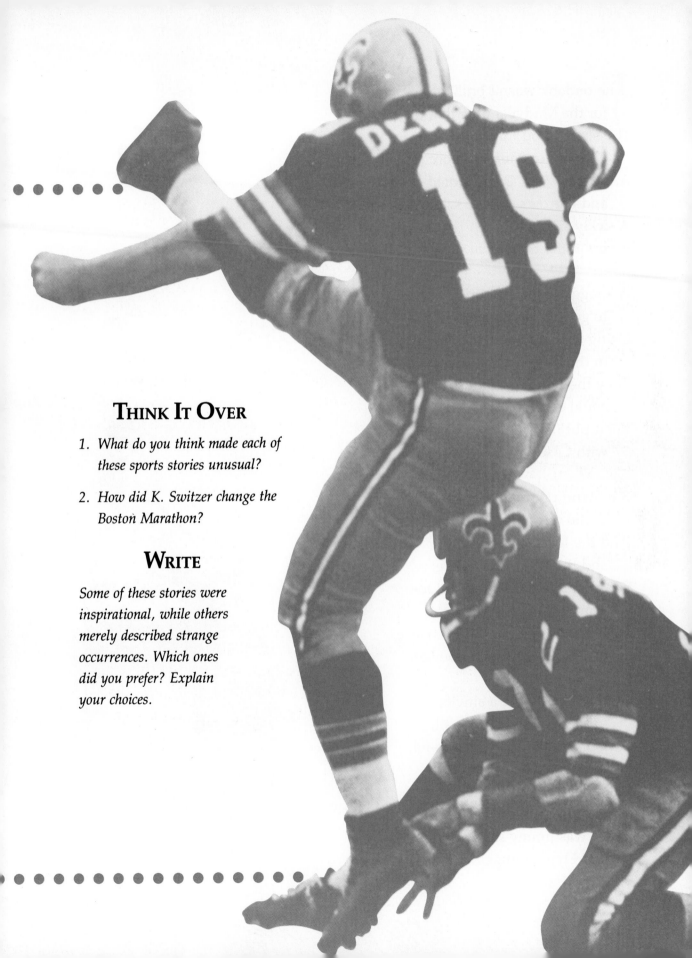

THINK IT OVER

1. *What do you think made each of these sports stories unusual?*

2. *How did K. Switzer change the Boston Marathon?*

WRITE

Some of these stories were inspirational, while others merely described strange occurrences. Which ones did you prefer? Explain your choices.

The outlook wasn't brilliant
    for the Mudville nine that day:
The score stood four to two
    with but one inning more to play.
And then when Cooney died at first,
    and Barrows did the same,
A sickly silence fell
    upon the patrons of the game.

A straggling few got up
    to go in deep despair. The rest
Clung to that hope which springs eternal
    in the human breast;
They thought if only Casey
    could but get a whack at that—
We'd put up even money now
    with Casey at the bat.

But Flynn preceded Casey,
    as did also Jimmy Blake,
And the former was a lulu
    and the latter was a cake;
So upon that stricken multitude
    grim melancholy sat.
For there seemed but little chance
    of Casey's getting to the bat.

But Flynn let drive a single,
    to the wonderment of all,
And Blake, the much despis-ed,
    tore the cover off the ball;
And when the dust had lifted,
    and the men saw what had occurred,
There was Jimmy safe at second
    and Flynn a-hugging third.

CASEY AT THE BAT

Ernest Lawrence Thayer

MUDVILLE NINE

illustrated by Ken Bachaus

Then from 5,000 throats and more
	there rose a lusty yell;
It rumbled through the valley,
	it rattled in the dell;
It knocked upon the mountain
	and recoiled upon the flat,
For Casey, mighty Casey,
	was advancing to the bat.

There was ease in Casey's manner
	as he stepped into his place;
There was pride in Casey's bearing
	and a smile on Casey's face.
And when, responding to the cheers,
	he lightly doffed his hat,
No stranger in the crowd could doubt
	'twas Casey at the bat.

Ten thousand eyes were on him
    as he rubbed his hands with dirt;
Five thousand tongues applauded
    when he wiped them on his shirt.
Then while the writhing pitcher
    ground the ball into his hip,
Defiance gleamed in Casey's eye,
    a sneer curled Casey's lip.

And now the leather-covered sphere
    came hurtling through the air,
And Casey stood a-watching it
    in haughty grandeur there.
Close by the sturdy batsman
    the ball unheeded sped—
"That ain't my style," said Casey.
    "Strike one," the umpire said.

From the benches, black with people,
    there went up a muffled roar,
Like the beating of the storm-waves
    on a stern and distant shore.
"Kill him! Kill the umpire!"
    shouted someone on the stand;
And it's likely they'd have killed him
    had not Casey raised his hand.

With a smile of Christian charity
    great Casey's visage shone;
He stilled the rising tumult;
    he bade the game go on;
He signaled to the pitcher,
    and once more the spheroid flew;
But Casey still ignored it,
    and the umpire said, "Strike two."

"Fraud!" cried the maddened thousands,
    and echo answered fraud;
But one scornful look from Casey
    and the audience was awed.
They saw his face grow stern and cold,
    they saw his muscles strain,
And they knew that Casey
    wouldn't let that ball go by again.

The sneer is gone from Casey's lip,
    his teeth are clenched in hate;
He pounds with cruel violence
    his bat upon the plate.
And now the pitcher holds the ball,
    and now he lets it go,
And now the air is shattered
    by the force of Casey's blow.

Oh, somewhere in this favored land
    the sun is shining bright;
The band is playing somewhere,
    and somewhere hearts are light,
And somewhere men are laughing,
    and somewhere children shout;
But there is no joy in Mudville—
    mighty Casey has struck out.

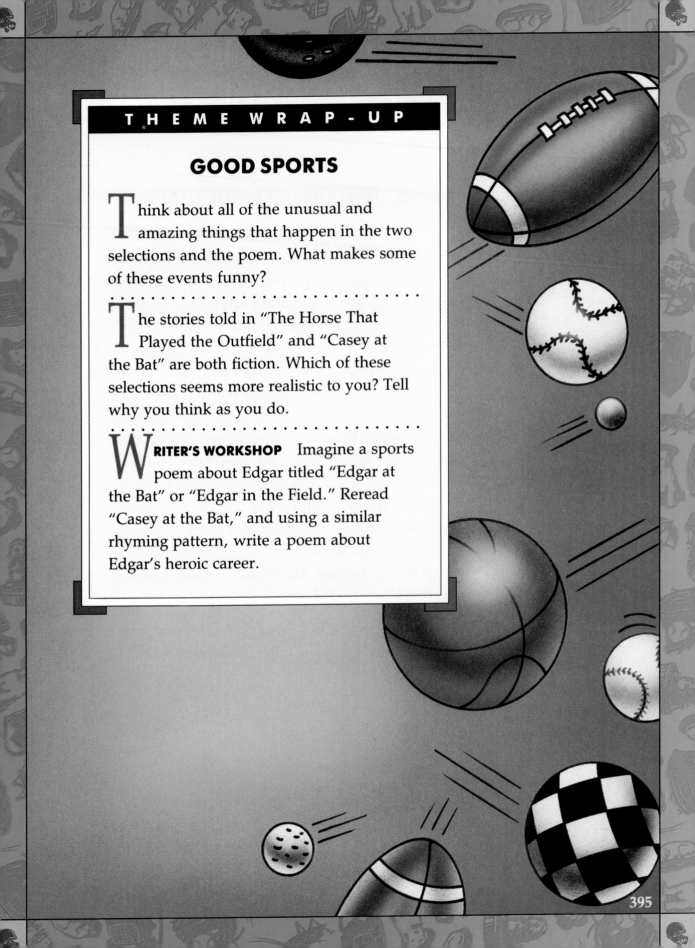

GOOD SPORTS

Think about all of the unusual and amazing things that happen in the two selections and the poem. What makes some of these events funny?

· ·

The stories told in "The Horse That Played the Outfield" and "Casey at the Bat" are both fiction. Which of these selections seems more realistic to you? Tell why you think as you do.

· ·

WRITER'S WORKSHOP Imagine a sports poem about Edgar titled "Edgar at the Bat" or "Edgar in the Field." Reread "Casey at the Bat," and using a similar rhyming pattern, write a poem about Edgar's heroic career.

CONNECTIONS

AMERICA'S ALL-AROUND ATHLETE

One of America's great sports legends was a man named Jim Thorpe. Thorpe was an Olympic gold medalist and one of the first professional football players. He was also a Native American.

Thorpe was born on a ranch in Oklahoma in 1888. Even as a young boy he showed great athletic ability. Once he ran home from school without stopping—a distance of 18 miles!

As a college football player, Thorpe led his team to victory over much larger and more famous schools. Many people called him the nation's top football player.

In 1912 Thorpe competed in the Olympic Games in Sweden, where he won two gold medals in track and field. After that he became a star player in professional baseball and football. Many still consider him the greatest all-around athlete in American history.

■ *Have a "Sports Day" in class. If you have a favorite sports star, bring information on his or her background and achievements to share.*

MATH CONNECTION

FOOTBALL STATISTICS

During his fifteen-year career in the early 1900s, Jim Thorpe was one of the leading running backs in professional football. The chart below lists rushing statistics for modern running backs. Use your math skills to figure out the average yards per carry for each runner. Then fill in a copy of the chart.

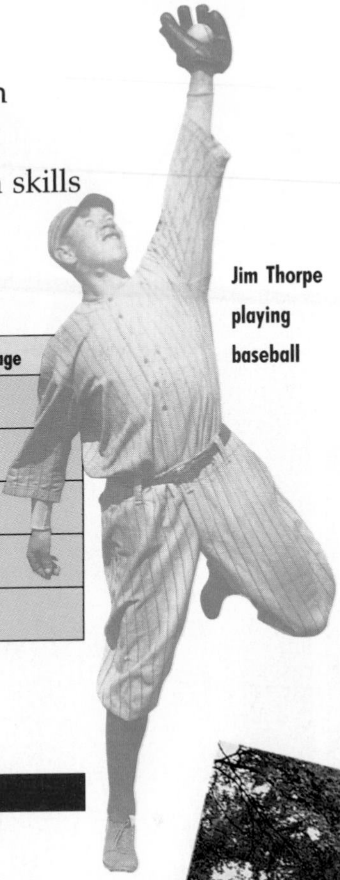

Jim Thorpe playing baseball

RUSHING STATISTICS (1990)	Number of Carries	Total Yards	Average
Barry Sanders (Detroit)	255	1304	
Thurman Thomas (Buffalo)	271	1297	
Marion Butts (San Diego)	265	1225	
Earnest Byner (Washington)	297	1219	
Bobby Humphrey (Denver)	288	1202	

SOCIAL STUDIES CONNECTION

FAMOUS NATIVE AMERICANS

Jim Thorpe is just one of many well-known Native Americans. With a partner, research another famous Native American, such as Sequoyah, Billy Mills, Wilma Mankiller, or Chief Seattle. Then present an oral report, using visual aids if possible.

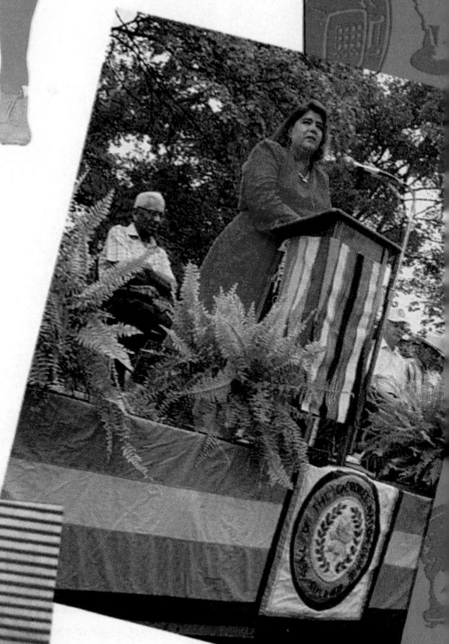

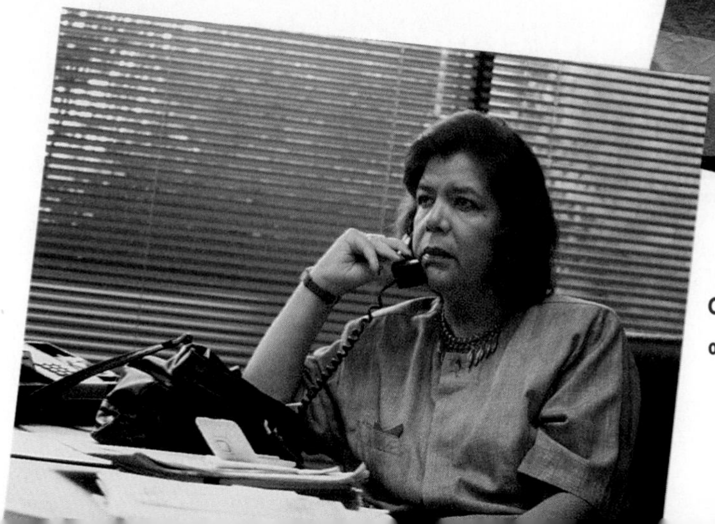

Chief Wilma Mankiller of the Cherokee Nation

UNIT FIVE

OCEANS

I must go down to the seas again,
To the lonely sea and the sky. . . .
John Masefield

People have always been drawn to the
sea. Some, like this poet, love the sea
for its beauty, mystery, and excitement.
Others, including the peoples of the Pacific
islands and the Inuit, or Eskimos, value and
respect the sea because for centuries it has
provided their livelihood. Develop your
own appreciation of the sea as you read
about the power and mystery of the earth's
oceans.

THE FROZEN OCEAN
· ·
402

THE AMAZING DOLPHIN
· ·
434

FOLLOWING THE WHALES
· ·
460

399

BOOKSHELF

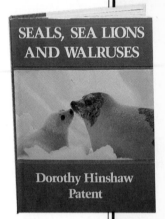

SEALS, SEA LIONS AND WALRUSES

BY DOROTHY HINSHAW PATENT

Wonderful photographs illustrate a wealth of information about these appealing animals. The book also tells how people are moving to protect them, and why this is important. OUTSTANDING SCIENCE TRADE BOOK FOR CHILDREN

HBJ LIBRARY BOOK

MEETING THE WHALES

BY ERICH HOYT

Will whales and humans ever communicate? Scientists study the huge brains of whales and closely observe their behaviors. Stunning photographs show whales and scientists in action.

LIFE IN A TIDAL POOL
BY ALVIN AND VIRGINIA SILVERSTEIN

The little pools you find along the seashore are like miniature oceans. The authors show you what to look for as you explore these fragile environments.

SHADOW SHARK
BY COLIN THIELE

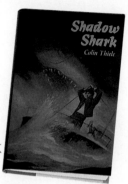

Twelve-year-old Joe barely escapes being killed by a huge shark called Scarface. But the hunt for Scarface off the Australian coast brings even more danger. ALA NOTABLE BOOK

HOW TO BE AN OCEAN SCIENTIST IN YOUR OWN HOME
BY SEYMOUR SIMON

If you've ever wondered what makes waves and tides, or how seawater might be made drinkable, this is the book for you. It's full of experiments you can do to find out! OUTSTANDING SCIENCE TRADE BOOK FOR CHILDREN

THE FROZEN OCEAN

Everyone believed the gigantic ocean liner was unsinkable. Then late one evening, the *Titanic* met another titan of the sea—one even larger and more powerful. In the following selections, you'll learn how these two giants met and how the result of their tragic meeting still fascinates people today.

CONTENTS

A Rendezvous with
ICE

from *Earth's Changing Climate* by **Roy A. Gallant**
illustrated by **Catherine Farley**

A LAND OF "PERMANENT" SNOW

Greenland is a gleaming land of snow capped with an ice
sheet that began to form some 100,000 years ago. Today this
ice sheet is nearly 3 kilometers (about 2 miles) thick in places.
But Greenland has not always been ice-covered, nor will it
always be. Each day giant chunks of ice "calve," or break, off
the west coast of Greenland's ice cap and plunge into the sea
as mammoth icebergs. Every year an estimated 500 cubic
kilometers (125 cubic miles) of ice plunges into the frigid
waters of Baffin Bay along Greenland's west coast. In only a

few minutes Rink Glacier, for example, may dump 500 million tons of ice into Baffin Bay. Some of this ice forms icebergs a mile or more long and towering 100 meters (300 feet) above the water. In a very active year, from 10,000 to 15,000 icebergs may break loose from Greenland's frigid shores.

The Voyage of Iceberg X

Perhaps it was on Tuesday, June 8, 1909, that one such giant slab of ice calved off the end of one of Greenland's numerous glaciers and plunged into the dark waters near Melville Bay. A mammoth iceberg was born. Although we can compute a date for this event, no one will ever know the *exact* place or the date when this event occurred, but occur it did.

At a pace of about four kilometers (2.5 miles) a day, this small mountain of ice began drifting southward on a three-year journey that was to shock the world. First it drifted across Baffin Bay toward the east coast of Baffin Island, a journey taking about six months. Here it was caught up and moved along a little faster by the cold, southward-flowing Labrador Current, which flows down out of the Arctic Ocean. Six months later it had been carried down through the Davis Strait and into the Labrador Sea off the north coast of Newfoundland. Two years from the time it had started its journey, it was a few hundred kilometers due east of Gander, Newfoundland. By this time it had traveled a total of some 3,000 kilometers (1,800 miles). Though it had lost much of its bulk through melting, it was still a floating mountain of ice, a pilotless "ship" passively moving southward ever nearer the busy North Atlantic shipping lanes.

There we will leave our titan of ice and turn to a titan of a different sort.

The world's newest, largest, and most luxurious ocean liner sailed on her maiden voyage from Southampton, England, on April 10, 1912. She was the White Star liner *Titanic*, 274 meters (883 feet) long and displacing 66,000 tons of water. She was described as "a Victorian palace afloat." According to a London *Times* editorial, "everything had been done to make the huge vessel unsinkable, and her owners believed her to be so."

On leaving Southampton, she crossed the English Channel to France and then steered a course for Newfoundland. Aboard her were 1,315 passengers and 885 crew, although there is some confusion about these exact numbers. Her skipper was 60-year-old Edward J. Smith, a veteran of 40 years at sea. He was to retire after the *Titanic*'s maiden voyage.

For several weeks before the *Titanic* had sailed, the United States Navy's Hydrographic Office in Washington had been aware of large fields of ice drifting southward from Greenland and into the shipping lanes which the *Titanic* had now entered. The first alarm about icebergs crackled into the *Titanic*'s radio room at 9:00 A.M., Sunday, April 14: "WESTBOUND STEAMER *CARONIA* REPORTS BERGS AND FIELD ICE IN 42°N FROM 49° to 51°W APRIL 12. COMPLIMENTS." The *Titanic* was on course only a few kilometers south of that position. The ship's chief radio operator acknowledged the message. At 11:45 A.M. the *Amerika*, another liner, informed the *Titanic* it had just passed "two large icebergs" just south of the position reported by the *Caronia*. Again the *Titanic* acknowledged. At 1:42 P.M. the Greek steamer *Athenia* reported seeing icebergs directly along the *Titanic*'s course. Then at 9:40 P.M. the steamer *Mesaba* advised the *Titanic* of "much heavy pack ice and great numbers of large icebergs."

In spite of these several warnings, neither the owner of the *Titanic*, who was among the passengers, nor others on board showed much concern. They finally held to their belief that this

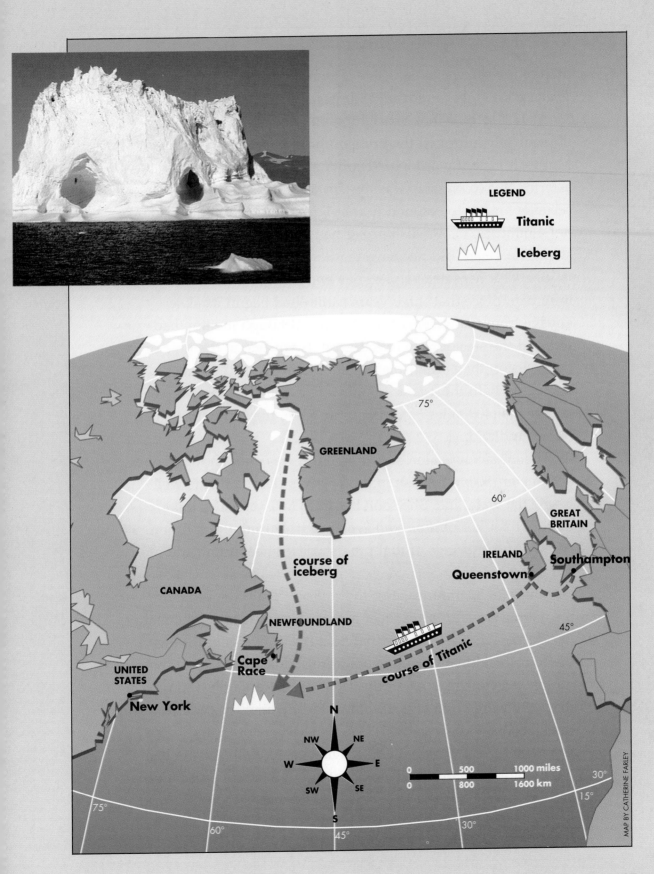

LEGEND

Titanic

Iceberg

75°

GREENLAND

60°

GREAT BRITAIN

IRELAND

Southampton

course of iceberg

Queenstowns

45°

CANADA

NEWFOUNDLAND

course of Titanic

Cape Race

UNITED STATES

New York

N

NW   NE

W   E

SW   SE

S

0   500   1000 miles
0   800   1600 km

30°

15°

75°

60°

45°

30°

MAP BY CATHERINE FARLEY

titan of the sea was unsinkable. The night was clear and the *Titanic* continued to plow ahead, nearly at top speed.

At 11:40 P.M. a lookout sighted an iceberg dead ahead and immediately informed the bridge officer. Chief Officer William M. Murdoch instantly ordered "Hard a-starboard! Engines full astern!" But so massive was the *Titanic* that it would take 30 seconds for her to respond to full right rudder. It would also take her 4 minutes, over a distance of half a nautical mile, to come to a stop. The *Titanic* did not have that kind of time on her side.

She kept her fated rendezvous and collided with that mountain of ice that three years earlier had begun its slow voyage from the waters of Baffin Bay. Although melting had reduced the size of Iceberg X during its voyage, at the time of the collision the berg displaced an estimated 200,000 tons compared with the *Titanic*'s 66,000. The collision took place 650 kilometers (400 miles) south of Cape Race, the southern tip of Newfoundland.

The impact was almost gentle, but it was enough to cut open a 93-meter (300-foot) gash in the *Titanic*'s starboard side well below the waterline. She soon began to take on water more rapidly than her pumps could remove it. During the collision, chunks and shavings of that prehistoric ice heap tumbled onto her decks.

Not until 30 minutes after the collision did Captain Smith, recovering from utter disbelief over the seriousness of the matter, decide to radio for help. By that time it was five minutes past midnight, and many passengers were still below decks in their rooms. Several ships heard the *Titanic*'s distress calls and replied that they were on their way to her. Meanwhile, the order to man the lifeboats was given, with "women and children first." The fact is that there were not enough lifeboats for all, so sure had her owners been of her unsinkability, and many of those lifeboats launched were filled to only half their capacity.

At 2:20 A.M., Monday, April 15, the unsinkable *Titanic* slipped beneath the calm, black sea. First her bow nosed under, then for a brief moment she was poised with her stern straight up, as though in one last salute. People in lifeboats reported seeing her that way, her propellers plainly visible. Then she silently slipped beneath the calm sea to the bottom, where she remains to this day.

The *Carpathia* was first to arrive on the scene. By this time it was 3:30 A.M. and the frigid waters had claimed those unable to swim to the lifeboats helplessly standing by. Of the total of 2,201 on board the *Titanic*, 700 were saved. By the time the rescue ships had done all they could and left with the handful of survivors, all that remained was scattered debris and a small mountain of ice with a chip taken out of its side, a relic of the past formed some tens of thousands of years ago.

THINK IT OVER

1. *What makes the sinking of the* Titanic *seem unbelievable?*

2. *How do icebergs form in Greenland?*

3. *What was Iceberg X, and where was it headed?*

4. *Why does the author of this selection describe the iceberg as "a pilotless ship"?*

WRITE

Imagine that you are a survivor of the Titanic *disaster. Write a business letter to the builders of the liner, explaining what they did wrong.*

Sea Slant

On up the sea slant,
On up the horizon,
This ship limps.

The bone of her nose fog-gray,
The heart of her sea-strong,
She came a long way,
She goes a long way.

Flying Cloud by J.E. Buttersworth. Private Collection

by Carl Sandburg

On up the horizon,
On up the sea-slant,
She limps sea-strong, fog-gray.

She is a green-lit night gray
She comes and goes in the sea fog.
Up the horizon slant she limps.

AWARD-WINNING
POET

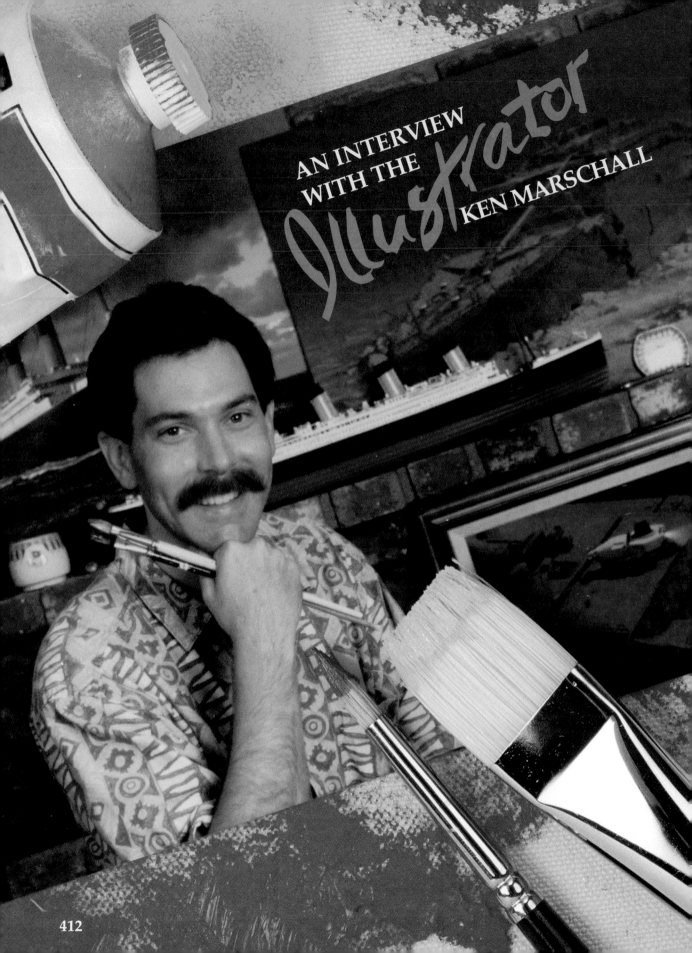

AN INTERVIEW
WITH THE
Illustrator
KEN MARSCHALL

Ken Marschall is an artist who has spent years painting his own visions of the Titanic. *Writer Ilene Cooper spoke with him about his fascination with that great ship and about his work featured in* Exploring the Titanic.

COOPER: *You did your first painting of the* Titanic *in 1968 when you were just a teenager. What piqued your interest?*

MARSCHALL: I saw a movie about the *Titanic* on television. The story seemed like the height of fiction, yet it actually happened. The largest ship in the world on its maiden voyage. A glassy, smooth ocean. Sailors who had been at sea for twenty-five years had never seen a sea as mirror clear as it was that night. And then, out of nowhere, a rogue iceberg. Even after all these years, I'm still captivated by the story.

I'm also very interested in passenger vessels, and not just ships but trains and planes as well. The *Titanic* was like a civilization gone to sea, with restaurants, laundries, switchboards, post offices. All the human things that collectively make this beehive work are interesting to me. The size, the power, the construction, the leap forward she was in design and luxury—those were the lures.

COOPER: *Has anything else grabbed you the way the* Titanic *did?*

MARSCHALL: I worked on a book about the sinking of the *Bismarck,* but that was a naval vessel, so it did not have the same attraction for me. I also became totally wrapped up in and appreciative of the design of the *Lusitania.* I'm working on a book about the sinking of the *Andrea Doria* too. I'm also interested in ships without the disaster aspect, like the *Queen Mary.* But as far as the disaster ships go, I think I'm so interested because these wonderful ships were cheated. They didn't get to live their lives out like other ships—something as beautiful as the *Andrea Doria* or as intricate as the *Lusitania,* as magnificent as the *Titanic* on her maiden voyage, and their lives were just cut short.

413

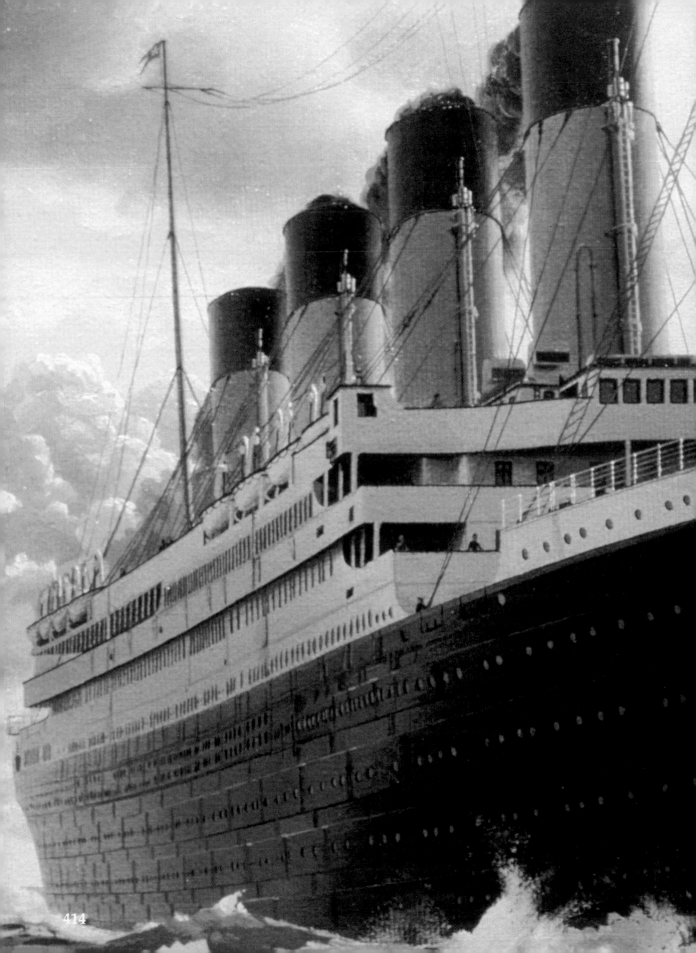

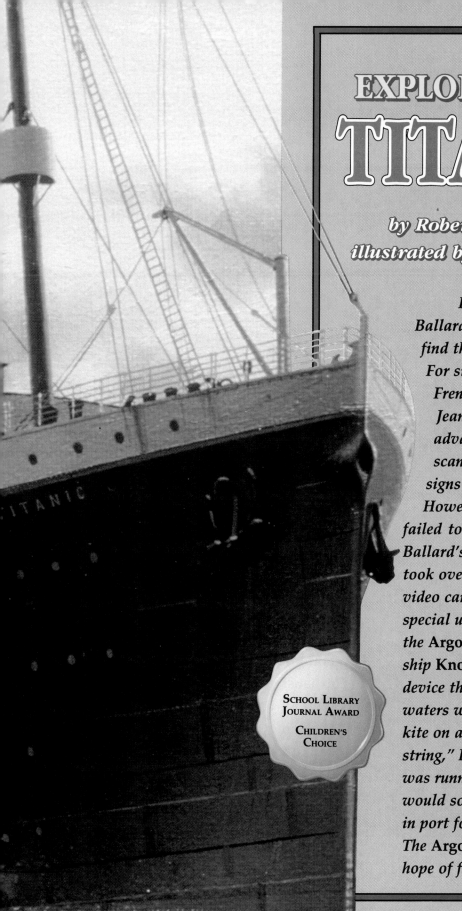

EXPLORING THE
TITANIC

by Robert D. Ballard
illustrated by Ken Marschall

In 1985, Dr. Robert D. Ballard led an expedition to find the wreck of the Titanic. For six weeks, a team of French researchers led by Jean-Louis Michel used advanced sonar devices to scan the ocean floor for signs of the great ship. However, their search failed to turn up any clues. Ballard's American team then took over the search using video cameras mounted on a special underwater sled called the Argo. Using the research ship Knorr to haul such a device through the deep ocean waters was "like towing a kite on a two-and-a-half mile string," Ballard said. Time was running out. The Knorr would soon have to be back in port for another expedition. The Argo provided their best hope of finding the lost ship.

SCHOOL LIBRARY
JOURNAL AWARD

CHILDREN'S
CHOICE

Discovery

Towing *Argo* was a delicate balancing act. If the *Knorr* went too fast, *Argo* would lift too high off the bottom for its cameras to see anything. If the ship's speed was too slow, *Argo* might crash to the bottom. Keeping a tight balance between *Knorr* and *Argo* was very tough and very tiring work. And it went on hour after hour, day after day.

Then we had only five days left to go. The crunch had come. Suddenly the ocean seemed huge, and our doubts began to grow. Was the *Titanic* really in our carefully plotted search area? If so, surely something would have shown up on our monitor screens by now. Were we looking in the wrong place? Would we return empty-handed? I began to feel a rising panic.

In a last-ditch effort, we decided to check out a tiny portion of ocean bottom that Jean-Louis and his SAR[1] sonar system had missed because of strong currents. We headed to that spot ten miles away.

[1] SAR: The French sonar system, Sonar Acoustique Remorqué [sō · när′ ä · kōōs · tēk′ rə · môr · kā′]. A device that locates and takes pictures of underwater objects by sending out sound waves and picking up their echoes with a microphone.

But as we began to tow *Argo* back and forth across the new search area, our hopes really began to fade. There was nothing down there. By now the routine inside our control room had become mind-numbing: hour after hour of staring at video images of flat bottom mud. On top of that, we were exhausted. The strain of it all was getting to us, and the boredom was becoming unbearable. Then, with a bad turn in the weather and only four days left, we reached our lowest point. I began to face total defeat.

Just after midnight on September 1, I went to my bunk for some rest, and the night shift led by Jean-

Louis manned their stations. About an hour into their watch, one of the team members asked the others, "What are we going to do to keep ourselves awake tonight?" All they'd seen so far was mud and more mud, endless miles of nothing. Stu Harris, who was busy flying *Argo,* didn't answer. His eyes were glued to the *Argo* video monitor.

"There's something," he said, pointing to the screen. Suddenly every member of the sleepy watch was alive and alert. No one could believe it wasn't just another false alarm, or a joke. But, no, there on the screen were clear images of things man-made. Stu yelled, "Bingo!" The control room echoed with a loud "Yeah!" from the whole team, and then wild shrieks and war-whoops. All sorts of wreckage began to stream by on the screen. Then something different appeared—something large and perfectly round. Jean-Louis checked in a book of pictures of the *Titanic.* He came across a picture of the ship's massive boilers, used to burn coal and drive the engines. He couldn't believe his eyes. He looked from book to video screen and back again. Yes, it was the same kind of boiler!

I scrambled out of my bunk when I got the news and ran to the control room. We replayed the tape of the boiler. I didn't know what to say. I turned to Jean-Louis. The look in his eyes said everything. The *Titanic* had been found. We'd been right all along. Then he said softly, "It was not luck. We earned it."

Our hunt was almost over. Somewhere very near us lay the R.M.S.[2] *Titanic.*

Word had spread throughout the ship. People were pouring into the control room. The place was becoming a madhouse. Everyone was shaking hands and hugging and slapping each other on the back.

---

[2] R.M.S.: Royal Mail Steamer

It was now almost two in the morning, very close to the exact hour of the *Titanic's* sinking. Someone pointed to the clock on the wall. All of a sudden the room became silent.

Here at the bottom of the ocean lay not only the graveyard of a great ship, but of more than 1,500 people who had gone down with her. And we were the very first people in seventy-three years to come to this spot to pay our respects. Images from the night of the disaster—a story I now knew by heart—flashed through my mind.

Out on the stern of the *Knorr*, people had started to gather for a few moments of silence in memory of those who had died on the *Titanic*. The sky was filled with stars; the sea was calm. We raised the Harland & Wolff flag, the emblem of the shipyard in Belfast, Ireland, that had built the great liner. Except for the shining moon overhead, it was just like the night when the *Titanic* had gone down. I could see her as she slipped nose first into the glassy water. Around me were the ghostly shapes of lifeboats and the piercing shouts and screams of passengers and crew freezing to death in the water.

Our little memorial service lasted about ten minutes. Then I just said, "Thank you all. Now let's get back to work."

In the short time remaining, I planned to get as many pictures of the wreck as possible. I wanted to show the world what condition the *Titanic* was in after seventy-three years on the bottom. A million questions flew through my mind. Would the ship be in one piece or broken up? Were the funnels still standing upright? Would the wooden deck be preserved in the deep salt water? And, a darker thought—would we find any remains of the people who had died that night? Photographs would give us the answers.

We started to make our first run with *Argo* over the major piece of wreckage we'd just found. But there were dangers lurking below. If *Argo* got caught in tangled wreckage, it would take a miracle to free it. It could mean the end of our mission.

As *Argo* neared the bottom, no one moved in the control room. Not a word was spoken. Now *Argo* was passing over the main hull of the *Titanic*. It was time to take a close look.

"Take it down farther. Go down to sixteen feet."

"Roger."

On the video screen, I could see the dim outline of a hull. "It's the side of the ship. She's upright!"

Suddenly, out of the gloom the Boat Deck of the ship came into view.

"Keep your eyes peeled for funnels."

But there were only gaping holes where funnels had once stood. Then as we crossed over the middle of the ship, we could see the flattened outline of the bridge. Was this where Captain Smith had stood bravely to the end?

Before we knew it, *Argo* had safely passed over the wreck and back into the empty murk. We had made it safely after all. All at once the crowded control room exploded. People were whooping, hugging, and dancing around while Jean-Louis and I quietly stood there thinking about what we had just seen. We now knew that the *Titanic* had landed on the bottom upright, and that a major piece of her appeared to be intact.

I wanted to make more passes over the wreck with *Argo*, but first it was time to clear the control room. I needed my team as rested as possible for the next sixty-four hours, which was all the time we had left. "Hey, we've got too many people up. You'll all be exhausted when your watch comes up. Let's get some of you back in bed. This is a twenty-four hour operation."

During the rest of that afternoon and evening, we managed only two more *Argo* passes over the wreck because of bad weather. But we did discover to our surprise and sadness that the ship was broken in two—her stern was missing. Where the back of the ship should have been, our video images faded into a confusing mass of twisted wreckage.

By now the storm had reached its peak. We could no longer use *Argo*. For ten hours the wind howled across our rolling deck as the *Knorr* pitched and heaved in the rough sea. Well, I thought finally, if we can't use *Argo* and the video system, then we'll work with ANGUS.

ANGUS was quite like *Argo*, except that it was an older camera sled that took still photographs instead of video as it was towed over the sea floor. Our nickname for ANGUS was the "dope on a rope." Now we would bring our old friend to the rescue. After all, I had used ANGUS in rougher seas than this.

But our first runs over the wreck with ANGUS only produced blurry images. The cameras were working properly, but we had come over the wreck too high to get good pictures. We were now down to our final hours, and I felt victory slipping away. At that moment I just wanted to go home. My leg was sore from a fall on the deck and I hadn't slept in days. We had found the *Titanic*. Wasn't that good enough? Who said we had to bring home pretty pictures?

But somehow I found the strength

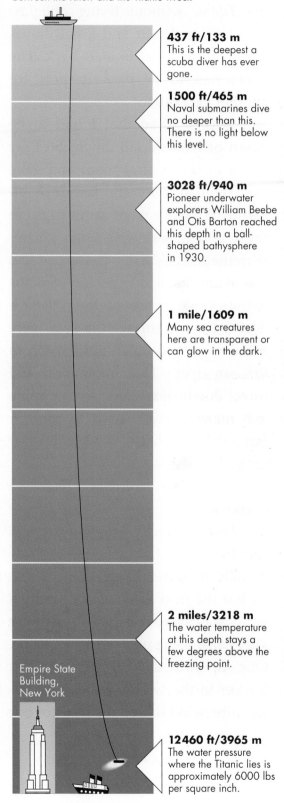

Scale drawing shows the enormous distance between the Knorr and the Titanic wreck

437 ft/133 m
This is the deepest a scuba diver has ever gone.

1500 ft/465 m
Naval submarines dive no deeper than this. There is no light below this level.

3028 ft/940 m
Pioneer underwater explorers William Beebe and Otis Barton reached this depth in a ball-shaped bathysphere in 1930.

1 mile/1609 m
Many sea creatures here are transparent or can glow in the dark.

2 miles/3218 m
The water temperature at this depth stays a few degrees above the freezing point.

Empire State Building, New York

12460 ft/3965 m
The water pressure where the Titanic lies is approximately 6000 lbs per square inch.

to continue. I was not going to leave the *Titanic* without trying one last time. We had four and a half hours left before we had to start back. The *Knorr* had to be back in port for another expedition.

I was so tired that I had to lie down or I would fall down. So I lay down in the control room and gave the commands for the last-ditch attempt. What we were about to do in these rough seas was even crazier than the risky ANGUS passes we had just made. We had to get our cameras within close range of the *Titanic*'s decks. On the surface the seas were heaving up and down at least ten to thirteen feet. That motion would travel down our 12,500 feet of cable and make ANGUS hard to control. But what the heck, it was now or never.

"Down to thirteen feet," I croaked.

"Thirteen feet? Are you crazy?" said the pilot.

"Thirteen feet," I repeated.

For the next three hours hardly a word was spoken as we made pass after hair-raising pass over the *Titanic*. One slip and ANGUS would be lost forever in the wreckage below. Outside, the wind rattled the walls of our control room as the storm blew itself out. Then, at about six in the morning, a simple message boomed over the *Knorr*'s intercom from the captain: "You have to start up now."

Right on time, ANGUS was pulled back on deck. A few hours later, news came from our photo lab that we had good, clear photographs of the *Titanic*. We'd made it! By a whisker.

Now, finally, I went to my bunk to get some sleep. When I awoke, it was nighttime, and the good ship *Knorr* was steaming quietly and steadily to our home port.

On the clear, warm morning of September 9, 1985, as we steamed down Nantucket Sound, Massachusetts, the *Knorr* was mobbed by helicopters, small planes, and pleasure craft running circles around us and blowing their horns. News of our discovery of the *Titanic* had made headlines around the world.

Then a small boat with a welcoming party including my wife and two sons, Todd and Douglas, approached our ship. Having my family there was really important to me. They had paid a big price over the years during my long months away from home, but they'd never once complained.

As we came into port, I couldn't believe my eyes. The dock was a mass of people filling every square inch of space. There was a platform bristling with television cameras and reporters. Banners were flying, a band was playing, schoolchildren hung on to balloons, and a cannon boomed out a salute.

What a victory welcome!

Exploring the Great Ship

With a big grin, I turned and gave the "thumbs up" sign for good luck to the crew standing on the deck of our new research ship, *Atlantis II*. In stocking feet I began to climb down the ladder inside *Alvin*, our tiny submarine. It was July 13, 1986, almost a year after our French-American expedition had first found the *Titanic* and taken photographs of her. Unfortunately, our French colleagues were not able to join us this year. I would miss my friend Jean-Louis.

We had steamed out to where the *Titanic* lay in the treacherous North Atlantic. Now it was time to take a closer look at her.

Our goal was to dive two and a half miles into the pitch-black freezing depths to where the *Titanic* lay. Then we would try to land *Alvin* on her decks. If all went well, we would be the first human beings in seventy-four years to see the legendary ship at close range.

We closed *Alvin*'s hatch, and I exchanged glances with my pilot and co-pilot as we felt our submarine gently rocking back and forth. We knew that meant we were now dangling half over the deck of *Atlantis II* and half over the water—one of the most dangerous moments of a dive. Should the sub suddenly fall, we could all get badly hurt.

But we hit the water safely. Then our lift line was released, and divers swarmed over the sub checking everything, including *Jason Junior*, or *JJ*. *JJ* was our remote-controlled underwater robot, who was attached to the outside of *Alvin* in a special garage. He operated on a long cable attached to our sub and was equipped with still and video cameras. With his help we hoped to explore inside the wreck below.

The three of us were crammed into the tiny cabin, our inner space capsule. Hemmed in by panels of instruments, we had no room to stretch out or stand up. We were like three sardines in a spherical can. It was warm and stuffy, but the ice-cold water outside would soon cool *Alvin*'s hull, both outside and inside.

Daylight began to fade into deeper and deeper blues as our sub reached its maximum descent speed of 100 feet per minute. It would take us two and a half hours to reach the bottom. There was little talking as we fell swiftly into utter darkness. Soft music played on the sub's stereo.

Suddenly, a white-tipped shark appeared outside my window and disappeared just as quickly. Sharks often swim by *Alvin* to investigate the noise. It was comforting to know that two inches of metal protected us. I remembered the time a swordfish had attacked *Alvin* and got its sword stuck in the sub.

The long fall to the bottom is usually a lulling experience. The interior gets darker and darker and begins to cool until, after less than fifteen minutes, the sub has reached a depth of 1,200 feet and total darkness. To conserve power, *Alvin*'s outside lights are left off. The only illumination inside comes from three small red lights.

But this time we had technical problems to worry about. First, we discovered that *Alvin*'s sonar had stopped working. Probably either the cold seawater or the increasing pressure had damaged it. Sonar guided us by bouncing electronic sound waves off anything in our path. Without sonar we couldn't see beyond a few yards. Our surface navigator on board *Atlantis II* would have to guide us to the *Titanic* with his sonar and our sub-to-ship telephone.

A few minutes later, at about 2,000 feet, we passed through what is known as a deep-scattering layer, because it shows up like a cloudy blur on sonar. In fact, the cloud is made up of thousands and thousands of tiny creatures that live at this depth of the ocean. Many of them glow in the dark, their small bodies exploding like fireworks as they become aware of our presence. When I first saw these creatures, they reminded me of a tiny passenger train with lighted windows passing by at night.

By the time we had passed 5,000 feet, almost one hour into our dive, it was getting cold in the sub. We put on our first layers of extra clothing. I was wearing a wool hat from my sons' hockey team to keep my head warm. During the long hours in the tiny cabin, my legs often fell asleep, and sometimes I'd get a bad cramp in my hip. At times like that, *Alvin*'s cabin was more like a torture chamber than a space capsule.

Ten minutes later, at 6,000 feet, our pilot noticed that the instrument panel was showing a saltwater leak into the battery banks that power the sub. Our time on the bottom of the ocean would have to be awfully short today. And to make things even worse, the surface navigator's sonar suddenly stopped working. That meant we were now almost completely blind.

Our lights pierced the blackness as the ocean bottom slowly emerged from the dark-green gloom below us.

We'd arrived. The only trouble was, we didn't know where we were. All we could see through the portholes was our own shadow cast by *Alvin*'s lights, and some gently rolling ground covered with mud.

So close and yet so far away. The ship lay somewhere near us, probably no more than 400 feet—the length of two city blocks. But when you're more than two miles down in black murk, a few hundred feet without any guiding sonar might as well be a thousand miles.

I couldn't believe it. I'd waited thirteen long years for this moment, and now, a stone's throw away from my dream, I was trapped inside a sardine can on my hands and knees staring at nothing but mud.

Suddenly, a head-splitting alarm buzzer pierced the silence inside our tiny sub. The leak in our battery was

getting to the critical point. We had very little time left if we were to get back to the surface without damaging *Alvin*. Quickly, we decided to guess where the *Titanic* might be and blindly go there in a last-ditch throw of the dice.

Alvin now gently touched the bottom with its single runner, like a one-legged skier, and we began to inch along. The shrill alarm was starting to drive us crazy, and the tension in the sub was heavy. Our time was running out fast. It was going to be a very close call if we hoped to see the *Titanic*.

Then our surface navigator called in on the telephone with the good news that his sonar was working again, and that "the *Titanic* should be about fifty yards west of us."

We turned the sub and strained our eyes to see out the portholes.

Now the bottom began to look strange. It began to slope sharply upward, as though it had been bulldozed into place. My heartbeat quickened.

"Come right," I said to the pilot. "I think I see a wall of black just on the other side of that mud mound."

Then, directly in front of us, there it was: an endless slab of rusted steel rising out of the bottom—the massive hull of the *Titanic*! I felt like a space voyager peering at an alien city wall on some empty planet. Slowly, I let out my breath; I didn't realize I had been holding it.

But one look at the fabulous wreck was all I got. Our pilot quickly dropped *Alvin*'s weights, clicked off that horrible alarm, and we went hurtling toward the surface. One moment longer on the bottom, and *Alvin*'s power system would have been in extreme danger.

All we had to show for six hours' work was a brief glimpse of the *Titanic*. But my dream had finally come true.

I was in a grim mood when I stepped out of the sub onto the deck of the *Atlantis II.* "I saw the ship for about ten seconds," I said. "But we've got a sick puppy here, and we've got to fix it." If we wanted to dive the next day, we had to take care of our growing list of technical problems.

While I slept, our team of experts worked through the night to cure our sick submarine.

Luckily it was all systems go the next morning, and we were full of confidence as we began a second dive. Our goal was to check out possible landing sites for *Alvin* on the decks of the *Titanic*.

Our second view of the *Titanic* was breathtaking. As we glided soundlessly across the ocean bottom, the razor's edge of the bow loomed out of the darkness. The great ship towered above us. Suddenly it seemed to be coming right at us, about to run us over. My first reaction was that we had to get out of the way. But the *Titanic* wasn't going anywhere. As we gently brought our sub closer, we could see the bow more clearly. Both of her huge anchors were still in place. But the bow was buried more than sixty feet in mud, far too deep for anyone to pull her out of the ooze.

It looked as though the metal hull was slowly melting away. What seemed like frozen rivers of rust covered the ship's side and spread out over the ocean bottom. It was almost as if the blood of the great ship lay in pools on the ocean floor.

As *Alvin* rose in slow motion up the ghostly side of the ship, I could see our lights reflecting off the still-unbroken glass of the *Titanic*'s portholes. They made me think of cats' eyes gleaming in the dark. In places the rust formations over the portholes looked like eyelashes with tears, as though the *Titanic* were crying. I could also see a lot of reddish-brown stalactites of rust over the wreck, like long icicles. I decided to call them "rusticles." This rust turned out to be very fragile. If touched by our sub, it disappeared like a cloud of smoke.

As we rose further and began to move across the mighty forward deck, I was amazed at the sheer size of everything: giant bollards and shiny bronze capstans that were used for winding ropes and cables; the huge links of the anchor chains. When you were there on the spot, the ship was truly titanic.

I strained to get a good look at the deck's wood planking, just four feet below us. Then my heart dropped to my stomach. "It's gone!" I muttered. Most of the *Titanic*'s wooden deck had been eaten away. Millions of little wood-eating worms had done more damage than the iceberg and the salt water. I began to wonder whether the metal deck below the destroyed wood planking would support our weight when *Alvin* landed.

We would soon find out. Slowly we moved into position to make our first landing test on the forward deck just next to the fallen mast. As we made our approach, our hearts beat quickly. We knew there was a real risk of crashing through the deck. The sub settled down, making a muffled crunching noise. If the deck gave way, we'd be trapped in collapsing wreckage. But it held, and we settled firmly. That meant there was a good chance that the *Titanic*'s decks would support us at other landing sites.

We carefully lifted off and turned toward the stern. The dim outline of the ship's superstructure came into view: first B Deck, then A, finally the Boat Deck—the top deck where the bridge was located. It was here that the captain and his officers had guided the ship across the Atlantic. The wooden wheelhouse was gone, probably knocked away in the sinking. But the bronze telemotor control to which the ship's wheel had once been attached stood intact, polished to a shine by the current. We then safely tested this second landing site.

I had an eerie feeling as we glided along exploring the wreck. As I peered through my porthole, I could easily imagine people walking along the deck and looking out the windows of the ship that I was looking into. Here I was at the bottom of the ocean looking at a kind of time capsule from history.

Suddenly, as we rose up the port side of the ship, the sub shuddered and made a clanging noise. A waterfall of rust covered our portholes. "We've hit something!" I exclaimed. "What is it?"

"I don't know," our pilot replied. "I'm backing off." Unseen overhangs are the nightmare of the deep-sub pilot. Carefully, the pilot backed away from the hull and brought us slowly upward. Then, directly in front of our forward porthole, a big lifeboat davit slid by. We had hit one of the metal arms that held the lifeboats as they were lowered. This davit was one of the two that had held boat No. 8, the boat Mrs. Straus had refused to enter that night. She was the wife of the owner of Macy's department store in New York. When she had been offered a chance to save herself in one of the lifeboats, she had turned to her husband and said, "We have been living together for many years. Where you go, I go." Calmly, the two of them had sat down on a pile of deck chairs to wait for the end.

Now, as we peered out our portholes, it seemed as if the Boat Deck were crowded with passengers. I could almost hear the cry, "Women and children first!"

We knew from the previous year's pictures that the stern had broken off

431

the ship, so we continued back to search for the severed end of the intact bow section. Just beyond the gaping hole where the second funnel had been, the deck began to plunge down at a dangerous angle. The graceful lines of the ship disappeared in a twisted mess of torn steel plating, upturned portholes, and jumbled wreckage. We saw enough to know that the decks of the ship had collapsed in on one another like a giant accordion. With an unexpectedly strong current pushing us toward this . twisted wreckage, we veered away and headed for the surface.

We made more trips down to the *Titanic*. At the end of the final dive, I knew I had visited the great ship for the last time. Two and a half hours later when we reached the surface, everybody on the *Atlantis II* prepared to head for home. Later that night there would be a party on board, but through it all I was still thinking about the *Titanic*: of the people who built her, sailed on her, and died when she went down.

THINK IT OVER

1. *Would you have liked to be aboard* Alvin *when its crew explored the* Titanic? *Explain your answer.*

2. *What did the crew members do when they first discovered the wreckage?*

3. *How did the crew members confirm that the wreck was the* Titanic?

4. *What did Dr. Ballard and his team hope to find? Did their findings live up to their expectations?*

5. *What did Dr. Ballard mean when he said that exploring the wreckage of the* Titanic *was like looking at "a kind of time capsule from history"?*

WRITE

The scientists devoted a great deal of time to discovering and exploring the Titanic. *Do you think the expedition was worthwhile? Write a paragraph explaining your opinion.*

THE FROZEN OCEAN

Compare the information you learned about the *Titanic* in "A Rendezvous with Ice" with what you discovered in "Exploring the *Titanic*." Why was it helpful to gain different perspectives?

Look at Ken Marschall's painting of the *Titanic* sinking in "Exploring the *Titanic*." What does the painting make you feel about the ship, its passengers, and the cold ocean?

WRITER'S WORKSHOP What do you think about the idea of trying to retrieve the *Titanic* from the bottom of the ocean? Dr. Ballard's expedition raised that question. Many people felt that the ship and its contents were like a graveyard and should be left in peace. Others felt that the ship and the lost valuables on it would be worth a lot of money and should be recovered. The topic was much debated, and people on both sides had strong opinions. Write a paragraph expressing your opinion.

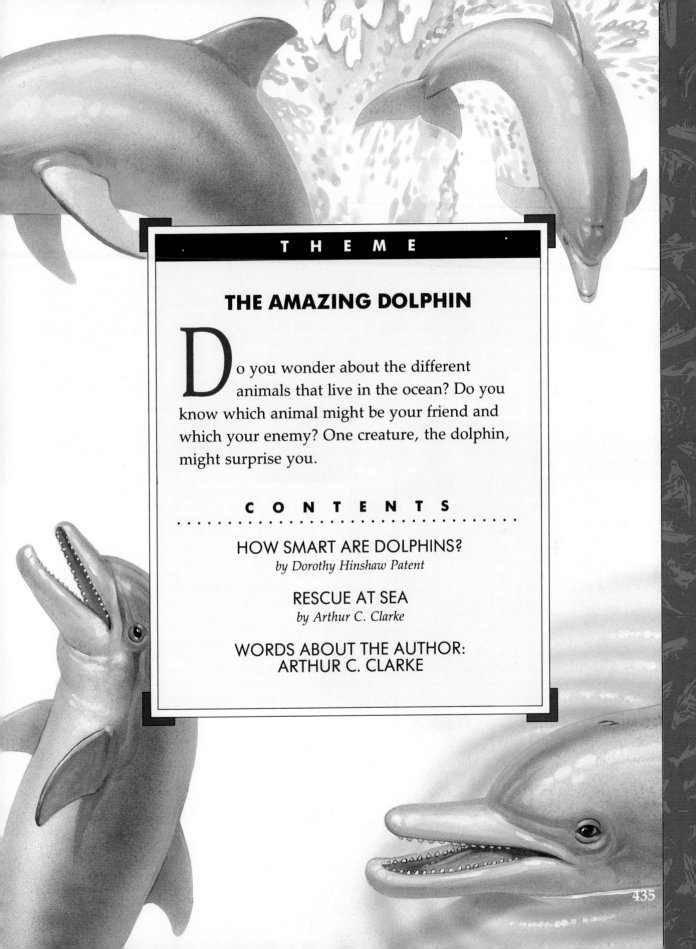

THE AMAZING DOLPHIN

Do you wonder about the different animals that live in the ocean? Do you know which animal might be your friend and which your enemy? One creature, the dolphin, might surprise you.

C O N T E N T S

HOW SMART ARE ANIMALS?

DOROTHY HINSHAW PATENT

AWARD-WINNING AUTHOR

HOW SMART
ARE DOLPHINS?

from *How Smart Are Animals?* by Dorothy Hinshaw Patent

Dolphins are favorite animals, entertaining thousands of people every day in marine parks around the world. They show their intelligence by their rapid learning, something that can be easily evaluated by science. But they have other traits, too, that may indicate brain power beyond easy learning.

Playing may at first not seem like intelligent behavior. But a quick look at the animal kingdom will show that only mammals and some birds appear to indulge in play. When young animals play, they are strengthening their muscles and learning how to put pieces of behavior together to form the sequences necessary for fighting, hunting, and escaping from danger. But when adult animals play in an apparent attempt to relieve boredom, play takes on a different significance.

In the wild, dolphins, like other animals, spend most of their time on vital activities such as the search for food. But they may also play. Researchers have watched as dolphins toss bits of seaweed about and catch it in their mouths. Wild dolphins near shore may play on mud banks, rushing toward the shore and sliding up out of the water. The animals repeat the behavior over and over again. Dolphins also ride the bow waves of ships and play about in the wakes made by whales.

In captivity, dolphin play can result in frustration for their keepers. People who work around dolphins know not to leave a tool or another important object where a dolphin can get it. The night watchman at one marine park once made the mistake of leaning over a night-darkened tank and shining his flashlight onto the water, looking for the dolphin. In a moment, the animal appeared and snatched the flashlight from his hand. The man tried to use a net to retrieve his light, but the dolphin kept pushing it just out of reach. When he finally got it back, the flashlight was completely ruined. During visiting hours this same animal would lie in wait with a ball, offering it to passing humans in play, much like a golden retriever would on land.

Dolphins are also very interested in the activities around them. At Marineland of Florida, a pilot whale (actually a kind of dolphin) entertained herself by watching the bottle-nosed dolphins next door perform. As the days went by, she pulled her body farther and farther out of her tank to get a better view. One day, she inched herself up too far and fell over the edge, out of the water. Worried attendants checked her over and were relieved that she hadn't injured herself. They got her back into the water and put up a guard rail so she couldn't fall out again.

Dolphins in marine parks often watch while others train or perform and in several cases have learned an entire performance just by watching. In one case, two dolphins that were trained in completely different routines were mixed up by the trainers. Although their performances were nervous and sloppy, each animal managed to carry out the routine of the other. Only later did the trainers realize their mistake.

Dolphins can also imitate the behavior of other species. One captive bottle-nosed dolphin amused itself by copying the swimming movements of a seal in its tank. Dolphins normally swim by holding their flippers out to the side and moving their bodies up and down in a "dolphin kick." When the dolphin was copying the seal, however, it held its tail still and moved its flippers back and forth like a seal. It also scratched itself with its flippers like a seal, something dolphins don't normally do. This same dolphin also copied the movements of turtles, penguins, and even of a human diver cleaning the tank. It imitated the diver cleaning a tank window, making noises like the air flow valve the diver used and releasing a stream of bubbles like the diver. It used a bit of broken tile to scrape the bottom of the tank, copying the diver using a vacuum hose.

Killer whales are actually large dolphins, and they also show creativity in finding entertainment in the unstimulating world of the oceanarium. At the Vancouver Aquarium in British Columbia, killer whales have taken to taming sea gulls. A whale will hold a bit of fish in its mouth, sticking its head out of the water. The birds have learned that the whales won't hurt them, and they come right up to a whale holding a fish and take it straight from the giant animal's mouth.

THINK IT OVER

1. *Do you think dolphins are intelligent animals? Explain your answer.*

2. *What have scientists learned by watching dolphins in captivity play?*

WRITE

Imagine that you are a dolphin trainer. List three things you would do to keep your dolphins from becoming bored.

RESCUE AT SEA

from *Dolphin Island* by **Arthur C. Clarke**

illustrated by **Murray Kimber**

In the twenty-first century, the whistling roar of a hovership means adventure in faraway lands. Sixteen-year-old Johnny Clinton is used to hearing the giant land-sea freighters flying past his house. Then one night the hovership *Santa Anna* breaks down near Johnny's house. He decides to get a closer look at the ship. As he climbs a ladder leading up one side of the ship, the giant freighter begins to vibrate. Johnny safely reaches the inside of the ship just before it takes off, continuing its journey out to sea. Johnny is scared but also excited by the prospect of adventure. Nervous about being caught, he hides inside a storage compartment. Johnny drifts off to sleep but is jarred awake by an explosion. Suddenly the ship is sinking, the lights have gone out, and Johnny is left in total darkness.

It was the first time in his life that Johnny had ever felt utter, unreasoning panic. His limbs had turned to jelly; he could hardly breathe for the weight that was pressing on his chest. It seemed that he was already drowning—as indeed he might soon be unless he could escape from this trap.

He had to find the way out, but he was surrounded by crates and packing cases, and soon lost all sense of direction as he blundered among them. It was like one of those nightmares when you tried to run and couldn't; but this was no dream—it was all too real.

The pain and shock of crashing against some unseen obstacle jarred him out of his panic. It was no good losing his head and stumbling around in the dark. The thing to do was to keep moving in the same direction until he found the wall. Then he could work along it until he came to the door.

The plan was excellent, but there were so many obstructions that it seemed an age before he felt smooth metal in front of him and knew that he had reached the wall of the compartment. After that, the rest was easy, and he almost cried with relief when he found the door and jerked it open. For the corridor outside was not, as he had feared, also in darkness. The main lights had failed, but a dim blue emergency system was operating, and he could see without difficulty.

It was then that he noticed the smell of smoke, and realized that the *Santa Anna* was on fire. He also noticed that the corridor was no longer level—the ship was badly down at the stern, where the engines were. Johnny guessed that the explosion had breached the hull, and that the sea was coming in.

Perhaps the ship was in no danger, but he could not be sure. He did not like the way she was listing, still less the ominous creaking of the hull. The helpless ship was rolling and pitching in a most unpleasant manner, and Johnny felt a sensation in the pit of his stomach that he guessed must be the first sign of seasickness. He tried to ignore it and to concentrate on the more important matter of staying alive.

If the ship was sinking, he had better find his way to the lifeboat as quickly as possible; that would be where everyone else would be heading. The crew would be surprised to find another passenger, and he hoped there would be enough room for him.

But where was the lifeboat section? He had been there only once, and though he was sure he could find his way if he had plenty of time, this was just what he lacked. Because he was in such a hurry, he took several wrong turnings and had to retrace his footsteps. Once he found his way blocked by a massive steel bulkhead which, he was certain, had not been there before. Smoke curled around its edges and Johnny could hear, quite distinctly, a steady crackling sound from the far side. He turned and ran as fast as he could, back along the dimly lit passageway.

He was exhausted and desperately frightened when he finally got back on the correct track. Yes, this was the right corridor—there would be a short flight of stairs at the end, and that would lead to the lifeboat section. He started to run, now that he was near his goal and had no need to conserve his strength.

His memory had not played him false. The stairs were there, just as he had expected. But the boat was gone.

The hull was wide open, and the davits were slung outward with their empty pulley blocks waving as if to tantalize him. Through the huge gap that had been opened to pass the lifeboat, fierce gusts of wind were blowing, bringing flurries of spray. The taste of salt was already bitter in Johnny's mouth; soon he would know it only too well.

Sick at heart, he walked to the opening and looked out over the sea. It was night, but the Moon that had seen the beginning of his adventure still shone upon its ending. Only yards below, an angry sea was smashing against the side of the ship, and ever and again a wave came climbing up the hull and went swirling around his feet. Even if the *Santa Anna* was not shipping water elsewhere, she would soon be doing so here.

Somewhere, not far away, there was a muffled explosion, and the emergency lights flickered and died. They had served him just long enough, for he could never have found his way here in the darkness. But did it matter anyway? He was alone, in a sinking ship, hundreds of miles from land.

He peered out into the night, searching for some sign of the lifeboat, but the sea was empty. The launch could, of course, be standing by on the other side of the *Santa Anna*, and he would be unable to see it. This seemed the most likely explanation, for the crew would hardly have left the area while the ship was still afloat. Yet they had certainly wasted no time, so they must have known that the situation was serious. Johnny wondered if the *Santa Anna* was carrying a cargo of explosives or inflammables—and if so, just when it would go up.

A wave slapped against his face, blinding him with spray; even during these few minutes, the sea had crept appreciably higher. Johnny would not have believed that so large a ship could go down so quickly; but hoverships, of course, were very lightly built and were not designed for this sort of treatment. He guessed that the water would be level with his feet in about ten minutes.

He was wrong. Suddenly, without any warning, the *Santa Anna* checked her slow, regular wallow and gave a great lurch, like a dying animal trying to get to its feet for the last time. Johnny did not hesitate; some instinct told him that she was going down and that he had better get as far away as he could.

Bracing himself for the chill, he hit the water in a smooth, clean dive. Even as he went under, he was surprised to experience not cold, but warmth. He had forgotten that during these last few hours he had passed from winter into summer.

When he came to the surface, he started swimming with all his might, in his clumsy but effective overarm stroke. Behind him he heard monstrous gurglings and crashings, and a roaring sound as of steam escaping from a geyser. Abruptly, all these noises ceased; there was only the moaning of the wind and the hissing of the waves as they swept past him into the night. The tired old *Santa Anna* went down smoothly, without any fuss, and the backward suction that Johnny had feared never arrived.

When he was sure that it was all over, he started to tread water while he surveyed the situation, and the first thing that he saw was the lifeboat, less than half a mile away. He waved his arms and shouted at the top of his voice, but it was quite useless. The boat was already leaving; even had anyone been looking back, it was unlikely that he would have been spotted. And, of course, no one would have dreamed that there was another survivor to be picked up.

Now he was alone, beneath a yellow, westering Moon and the strange stars of the southern skies. He could float here for hours; the sea, he had already noticed, was much more buoyant than the fresh-water creeks in which he had learned to swim. But however long he stayed afloat, it would make no difference in the end. There was not one chance in a million that anybody would find him; his last hope had vanished with the departing lifeboat.

Something bumped into him, making him yelp with surprise and alarm. But it was only a piece of debris from the ship. The water around him, Johnny noticed, was full of floating objects. The discovery raised his spirits a little, for if he could make a raft, that would improve his chances considerably. Perhaps he might even drift to land, like those men who had ridden the Pacific currents on the famous *Kon-Tiki*, almost a century ago.

He began swimming toward the slowly swirling debris, and found that the sea had suddenly become much smoother. Oil oozing from the wreck had calmed the waves, which no longer hissed angrily, but rose and fell in sluggish undulations. At first their height had scared him, but now as he bobbed up and down with their passage, he found that they could do him no harm. Even in his present predicament, it

was exciting to know that one could rise safely and effortlessly over the biggest wave.

Presently he was pushing his way among floating boxes, pieces of wood, empty bottles, and all sorts of small flotsam. None of this was any use to him; he wanted something big enough to ride on. He had almost given up all hope of finding it when he noticed a dark rectangle rising and falling in the swell, about fifty feet away.

When he reached it, he was delighted to find that it was a large packing case. With some difficulty, he scrambled aboard and found that it could carry his weight. The raft was not very stable, and had a tendency to capsize, until Johnny spread himself flat across it; then it rode the waves with about three inches to spare. In the brilliant moonlight, Johnny could read the stenciled letters across which he was lying. They said: "PLEASE STORE IN A COLD, DRY PLACE."

Well, he was hardly dry, but he was certainly getting cold. The wind blowing across his wet clothes was making him feel

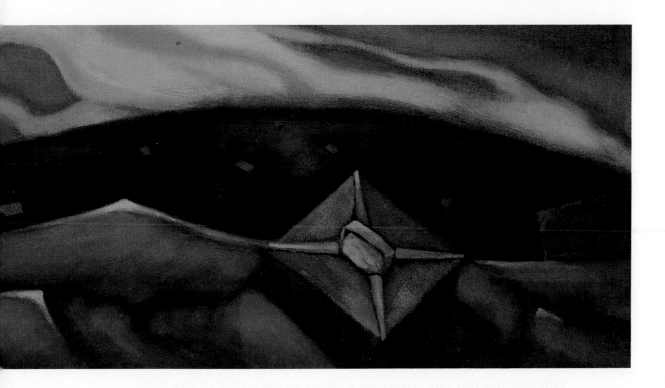

uncomfortably chilly, but he would have to put up with this until the sun rose. He looked at his watch and was not surprised to see that it had stopped. Even so, the time it showed made no sense; then he remembered that he must have crossed many time zones since he stole aboard the ill-fated *Santa Anna*. By now, his watch would be at least six hours fast.

He waited, shivering on his little raft, watching the Moon go down and listening to the noises of the sea. Though he was worried, he was no longer badly frightened. He had had so many narrow escapes that he had begun to feel that nothing could harm him. Even though he had no food or water, he was safe for several days. He refused to think further ahead than that.

The Moon slid down the sky, and the night grew darker around him. As it did so, he saw to his astonishment that the sea was ablaze with floating particles of light. They flashed on and off like electric signs, and formed a luminous lane behind his drifting raft. When he dipped his hand in the water, fire seemed to flow from his fingers.

The sight was so wonderful that for a moment he forgot his danger. He had heard that there were luminous creatures in the sea, but he had never dreamed that they existed in such countless myriads. For the first time, he began to glimpse something of the wonder and mystery of the great element that covered three quarters of the globe, and which now controlled his destiny.

The Moon touched the horizon, seemed to hover there for a moment, and then was gone. Above him the sky was ablaze with stars—the ancient ones of the old constellations, the brighter ones that had been put there by man in the fifty years since he had ventured into space. But none of these were as brilliant as the stars that flashed beneath the sea in such billions that the raft appeared to float upon a lake of fire.

Even when the Moon had set, it seemed ages before the first sign of dawn. Then Johnny saw a faint hint of light in the eastern sky, watched eagerly as it spread along the horizon, and felt his heart leap as the golden rim of the sun pushed up over the edge of the world. Within seconds, the stars of sky and sea had vanished as if they had never existed, and day had come.

He had barely time to savor the beauty of the dawn when he saw something that robbed the morning of all its hope. Heading straight toward him out of the west, with a speed and purpose that chilled his blood, were dozens of gray, triangular fins.

As those fins sliced toward the raft, cutting through the water with incredible speed, Johnny thought of all the gruesome tales he had read about sharks and shipwrecked sailors. He drew himself up into as little space as possible, at the center of the packing case. It wobbled alarmingly, and he realized how small a push would be needed to turn it over. To his surprise, he felt little fear, only a kind of numbed regret and a hope that, if the worst came to the worst, it would all be over quickly. And it seemed a pity, too, that no one would ever know what had happened to him. . . .

Then the water around the raft was full of sleek, gray bodies, switchbacking along the surface in a graceful roller-coaster motion. Johnny knew almost nothing about the creatures of the sea, but surely, sharks did not swim in this fashion. And these animals were breathing air, just as he was; he could hear them wheezing as they went by, and he caught glimpses of blowholes opening and closing. Why, of course —they were dolphins!

Johnny relaxed and no longer tried to hide himself in the middle of his raft. He had often seen dolphins in movies or on television, and he knew that they were friendly intelligent creatures. They were playing like children among the wreckage of the *Santa Anna*, butting at the floating debris with their streamlined snouts, making the strangest whistling and creaking noises as they did so. A few yards away, one had reared its head completely out of the water and was balancing a plank on its nose, like a trained animal in a circus act; it seemed to be saying to its companions, "Look at me—see how clever I am!"

The strange, unhuman but intelligent, head turned toward Johnny, and the dolphin dropped its plaything with an unmistakable gesture of surprise. It sank back into the water, squeaking with excitement, and a few seconds later, Johnny was surrounded by glistening, inquisitive faces. They were smiling faces, too, for the mouths of the dolphins seemed to be frozen in a kind of fixed grin—one so infectious that Johnny found himself smiling back at them.

He no longer felt alone; now he had companionship, even though it was not human and could do nothing to help him. It was fascinating to watch the leathery, dove-gray bodies moving around him with such effortless ease as they hunted among the debris of the *Santa Anna*. They were doing this, Johnny soon realized, purely out of playfulness and fun; they were more like lambs gamboling in a spring meadow than anything he had ever expected to find in the sea.

The dolphins continued to bob up and to look at him from time to time, as if making sure that he had not run away. They watched with great curiosity as he pulled off his sodden clothing and spread it to dry in the sun, and they seemed to be giving the matter careful thought when Johnny asked them solemnly: "Well, what shall I do now?"

One answer to that question was obvious: he had to arrange some shelter from the tropical sun before it roasted him alive. Luckily, this problem was quickly solved; he was able to build a little wigwam from some pieces of driftwood which he lashed together with his handkerchief and then covered with his shirt. When he had finished, he felt quite proud of himself, and hoped that his audience appreciated his cleverness.

Now he could do nothing but lie down in the shade and conserve his strength while the wind and the currents carried him to an unknown fate. He did not feel hungry, and though his lips were already dry, it would be several hours before thirst became a serious problem.

The sea was much calmer now, and low, oily waves were rolling past with a gentle, undulating motion. Somewhere Johnny had come across the phrase, "Rocked in the cradle of the deep." Now he knew exactly what it meant. It was so soothing, so peaceful here that he could almost forget his desperate position; he was content to stare at the blue sea and the blue sky, and to watch the strange yet beautiful animals that glided and swooped around him, sometimes hurling their bodies clear out of the water in the sheer joy of life. . . .

Something jolted the raft, and he awoke with a start. For a moment he could hardly believe that he had been sleeping and that the sun was now almost overhead. Then the raft jerked again—and he saw why.

Four dolphins, swimming side by side, were pushing the raft through the water. Already it was moving faster than a man could swim, and it was still gaining speed. Johnny stared in amazement at the animals splashing and snorting only inches away from him; was this another of their games?

Even as he asked himself that question, he knew that the answer was No. The whole pattern of their behavior had changed completely; this was deliberate and purposeful. Playtime was over. He was in the center of a great pack of the animals, all now moving steadily in the same direction. There were scores, if not hundreds, ahead and behind, to right and left, as far as he could see. He felt that he was moving across the ocean in the midst of a military formation—a brigade of cavalry.

He wondered how long they would keep it up, but they showed no signs of slackening. From time to time, one of the dolphins would drop away from the raft, and another would immediately take its place, so that there was no loss of speed. Though it was very hard to judge how fast he was moving, Johnny guessed that the raft was being pushed along at over five miles an hour. There was no way of telling, however, whether he was moving north, south, east, or west; he could get no compass bearing from the almost vertical sun.

Not until much later in the day did he discover that he was

heading toward the west, for the sun was going down in front of him. He was glad to see the approach of night, and looked forward to its coolness after the scorching day. By this time he was extremely thirsty; his lips were parched and cracked, and though he was tantalized by the water all around him, he knew that it would be dangerous to drink it. His thirst was so overpowering that he did not feel any hunger; even if he had some food, he would be unable to swallow it.

It was a wonderful relief when the sun went down, sinking in a blaze of gold and red. Still the dolphins drove on into the west, beneath the stars and the rising Moon. If they kept this up all through the night, Johnny calculated, they would have carried him the best part of a hundred miles. They *must* have a definite goal, but what could it be? He began to hope that there was land not far away, and that for some unknown reason these friendly and intelligent creatures were taking him to it. But why they were going to all this trouble he could not imagine.

The night was the longest that Johnny had ever known, for his growing thirst would not allow him to sleep. To add to his distress, he had been badly sunburned during the day, and he kept twisting and turning on the raft in a vain attempt to find a comfortable position. Most of the time he lay flat on his back, using his clothes to protect the sore spots, while the Moon and stars crept across the sky with agonizing slowness. Sometimes the brilliant beacon of a satellite would drift from west to east, traveling much more swiftly than any of the stars, and in the opposite direction. It was maddening to know that up on the space stations were men and instruments that could easily locate him—if they bothered to search. But, of course, there was no reason why they should.

At last the Moon went down, and in the brief darkness before dawn the sea once more came alight with phosphorescence. The graceful, superbly streamlined bodies all around

the raft were outlined with fire; every time one of them shot into the air, the trajectory of its leap was a glowing rainbow in the night.

This time Johnny did not welcome the dawn; now he knew how pitiful his defenses were against the tropical sun. He re-erected his little tent, crept beneath it, and tried to turn his thoughts away from drink.

It was impossible. Every few minutes he found himself picturing cold milk shakes, glasses of iced fruit juice, water flowing from faucets in sparkling streams. Yet he had been adrift for not more than thirty hours; men had survived without water for much longer than that.

The only thing that kept up his spirits was the determination and energy of his escort. The school still drove on into the west, carrying the raft before it with undiminished speed. Johnny no longer puzzled himself about the mystery of the dolphins' behavior; that was a problem that would solve itself in good time—or not at all.

And then, about midmorning, he caught his first glimpse of land. For many minutes he was afraid that it was merely a cloud on the horizon—but, if so, it was strange that it was the only cloud in the sky and that it lay dead ahead. Before long he could not doubt that it was an island, though it seemed to float clear of the water, and the heat haze made its outlines dance and shimmer against the skyline.

An hour later, he could see its details clearly. It was long and low and completely covered with trees. A narrow beach of dazzling white sand surrounded it, and beyond the beach there seemed to be a very wide, shallow reef, for there was a line of white breakers at least a mile out at sea.

At first Johnny could see no signs of life, but at last, with great relief, he spotted a thin stream of smoke rising from the wooded interior. Where there was smoke there were human beings—and the water for which his whole body was now craving.

He was still several miles from the island when the dolphins gave him a bad shock; they were turning aside as if to by-pass the land that was now so close. Then Johnny understood what they were doing. The reef was too great an obstacle; they were going to outflank it and approach the island from the other side.

The detour took at least an hour, but Johnny's mind was at rest, now that he felt sure that he was nearing safety. As the raft and its untiring escort swung around to the western side of the island, he saw first a small group of boats at anchor, then some low white buildings, then a collection of huts with dark-skinned people moving among them. There was a fairly large community here, on this lonely speck in the Pacific.

Now at last the dolphins seemed a little hesitant, and Johnny got the impression that they were reluctant to go into the shallow water. They pushed the raft slowly past the anchored boats, then backed off as if to say, "It's up to you now."

Johnny felt an overwhelming impulse to say some words of thanks, but his mouth was too dry for speech. So he stepped quietly off the raft, found himself in water only waist deep, and waded ashore.

There were people running along the beach toward him, but they could wait. He turned toward the lovely, powerful creatures who had brought him on this incredible journey, and waved them a grateful farewell. Already they were turning back toward their home, in the deep water of the open sea.

THINK IT OVER

1. *What is your impression of Johnny and the way he handles the situation he is in?*

2. *How is Johnny successful in escaping the sinking hovership, even in his exhausted and frightened state?*

3. *What are some of the hardships Johnny faces during his journey on the raft?*

4. *What does Johnny do to protect himself from the tropical sun while floating on the raft?*

WRITE

Why do you suppose the dolphins take Johnny all the way to the island? Write what you think is a possible explanation.

W**O**RDS ABOUT THE AUTH**O**R:

ARTHUR C. CLARKE

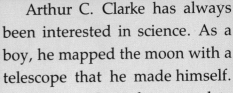

Arthur C. Clarke has always been interested in science. As a boy, he mapped the moon with a telescope that he made himself. Later he wanted to study science in college but couldn't afford to go at that time, so in 1936 he took a job as an auditor. (He eventually received a degree in physics and pure and applied mathematics from King's College at Cambridge University in England.) Ironically, it was his job as an auditor that allowed him to develop his interest in outer space and space travel. The job gave him enough free time to devour science fiction magazines and the books of Jules Verne and H. G. Wells, which dealt with the wonderful possibilities of scientific exploration.

AWARD-WINNING
AUTHOR

He later joined a group that called itself the British Interplanetary Society, whose members shared his interests; they were early science fiction fans who would meet to talk about the newest scientific discoveries and read the latest American magazines on the subject. When the group launched a newsletter, Clarke became a frequent contributor. He also began publishing science fiction stories.

In 1941 Clarke enlisted in the Royal Air Force and became a radar instructor. The work was interesting, but what he really enjoyed were the hours he spent in the evening perfecting his mathematical theory about satellites, which seemed at that time like science fiction to most people. Clarke wrote an article for *Wireless World* magazine in 1945 that predicted in detail a satellite system that would relay radio and television signals all over the world. Most people didn't believe it. Just twenty years later, however, the Early Bird satellites were launched.

Though some people like to think of Clarke as a predictor of future technologies, he thinks of himself as a writer, and he has a great body of work to prove him right. He has written more than 600 essays, articles, and books. His best-known work started as a short story titled "The Sentinel." Film director Stanley Kubrick read it, contacted Clarke, and told him, "We're going to write the best science fiction movie of all time." Together they wrote the screenplay for the movie *2001: A Space Odyssey*.

Clarke now makes his home in Sri Lanka, where he continues to write.

THE AMAZING DOLPHIN

Given what you learned about dolphin behavior from the first selection, does the dolphin rescue in "Rescue at Sea" seem believable? Explain your answer.

. . . .

Imagine that you wanted to recommend that a classmate read these selections. Which would you tell him or her to read first? Why?

. . . .

WRITER'S WORKSHOP   What do you think will happen when Johnny reaches the island? Write a brief scene that tells of Johnny's first encounter with the island's inhabitants.

459

FOLLOWING THE WHALES

Have you ever heard the call of a baby whale or seen a bowhead whale "sky hop"? Let author Jean Craighead George take you on journeys through the undersea world. You are bound to surface with a newfound respect for the mighty whales that roam the ocean depths.

C O N T E N T S

THE BIG SPRING

SPRING COMES to the OCEAN

JEAN CRAIGHEAD GEORGE

FROM *SPRING COMES TO THE OCEAN*
BY JEAN CRAIGHEAD GEORGE

ILLUSTRATED BY JULIAN MULOCK

Off the coast of Bandon, Washington, a gray whale surfaced. Her seven-inch-long nostrils emerged first and blew a spout of air and water fifteen feet into the air. The column swooshed with a roar that could be heard for half a mile. Having exhaled, she then inhaled, and the breath came into her lungs with a whine, like wind rushing into a tunnel. Her nostrils closed over this salty gasp. A low wall of muscle arose around the nostrils like a frown and kept the water out. She submerged.

Four seconds later, her nose, which was on the top of her head, came up again. She gave four strong blows. The waves clapped around her. She snorted at them, then headed down into the corridors of the Pacific Ocean.

The female gray whale was 43 feet long. She weighed 34 tons. She was one of a group of animals that are the largest ever to live on this earth. Like all whales she was also hostess to many small beasts. On her back and over her mountain of a belly lived thousands of barnacles. They pulled their feet in and stopped kicking food into their mouths when their great hostess surfaced to breathe. They adjusted to her rising and diving, just as we adjust to the moods of the earth as it circles the sun.

This city-block-of-an-animal plunged forward for a thousand feet. Then she surfaced and peered over the ocean. She had no language, she made no vocal sounds, but she spied now and then to make sure her kinsmen were traveling with her.

Beside her swam her son, a 20-foot baby. He had been born in January in the California Bay, and now the two of them were on their way north to the Bering Sea—a long journey of 7,000 miles.

The mother plunged down into the green spring ocean and looked around. She was following a familiar canyon wall that she knew as well as you know your own street, for she had traveled along it every year for 20 years of her life. The submarine canyon was gray and dark, and lay like a great highway up the continental shelf. The whale knew exactly where she was.

Ahead of her loomed a sand barrier. She quickened her pace for she knew she was coming to a cove. Once more she blew and looked around. She saw no other gray whales and sensed she was behind the main migration. At the sand bar she tasted the silt of Coos Bay and, because she could not feel the currents from her baby, slowed down, then stopped.

Her son was looking at a giant squid. The mother attracted his attention by crunching her wide teeth, the only sound she could make, but an effective one. The baby spurted to her side. He was eager and energetic. He whooshed friskily to the surface and peered around. He saw boats and lighthouses. This was his first trip to the summer rendezvous of the gray whales—the Bering Sea. His mother was teaching him the underwater landmarks, for in the fall he would have to travel back alone in the manner of the gray whale. Their migration was not a social affair. Each whale made the exhausting trip by itself.

The mother whale swung over the delta at the mouth of the bay and crunched her teeth again. Her son came down to her. She was taking the water from the bay in and out of her mouth. He did likewise, and the taste of the bay was forever imprinted on his senses. Each bay and cove and canyon had to be memorized in this manner, by taste, by sight, and by currents that eddied and pulled, for each was different in every inlet along the great California coast.

The mother plunged over the sand bar. The whale child followed. For a moment they lingered in the different water pressures, feeling all the details of this place with their throat grooves, the openings under their necks that were sensitive to pressures, to currents and eddies.

The mother delayed long here as if to impress this particular spot on the youngster. From here they would take out to sea, and the underwater world of the continent would be replaced by the deeps of the Pacific. From here on it would be all pressure memories. The whale child circled gently, biting the sand, filtering the water in and learning.

Then they hurried on—a thousand feet at a run. They

swam to the edge of the continental shelf.

Suddenly the whale child looked back. He whirled in panic. Coos Bay appeared different from the north. He turned and flipped back to the sand bar, tasting the salts and minerals once more, feeling the texture of the water, trying to learn well. When he was satisfied with his impressions he tailed out to meet his mother. But she was gone.

The life of the gray whale is silent for the most part, a grind on their plankton-filtering teeth, a noisy blow. Over the sea canyon walls, ticking and rasping like the beat of a tin cup on a wooden table, came the rare "distress" sound made by the clicking teeth of the baby whale.

He was lost. He surfaced, blew a great column of air and water and pulled himself skyward so high his whole chest was out. All he saw was a trawling boat harvesting the bottom-dwelling fish. He saw no mother. He glanced at the boat again. It was big, it might be a whale. He headed for it, spying tentatively as he went.

The boat was gray like his mother and covered with barnacles. Rising and blowing he came up to the object. But the whale child drew back. The wooden whale was too small, the wrong design, the wrong scent, and the water that surrounded it was not warmed by the mammal body. Oil seeped from it.

The young whale fled in terror, diving into unfamiliar hills and valleys. His eyes rolled as he searched. Schools of fish felt him on their lateral lines and wheeled away. He plunged on, but saw no sand barrier, tasted nothing familiar.

He cried into the ocean, tapping out his bleat that traveled swiftly for hundreds of yards and then faded against the coastal reefs.

As the sun went down, lopsided as it reached the horizon, the giant child circled and circled the empty waters. He spied out and looked until he was tired. Finally he slept. His flippers, once the feet of his land-walking ancestors, hung down into the sea. His tense nostrils were barely above the surface.

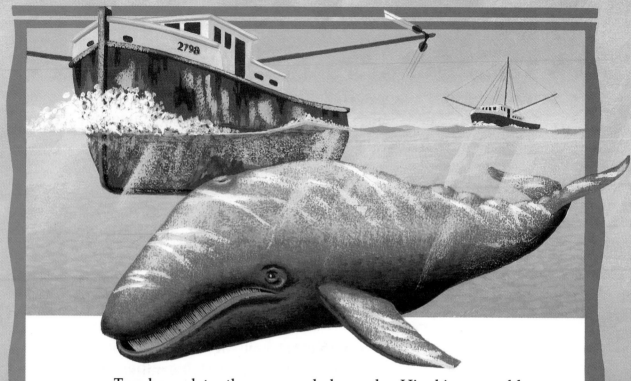

Two hours later the young whale awoke. His skin was cold and he turned sleepily to nurse. Then he remembered his mother was not around. He swirled in panic. He breached, head in the air, fins out. He saw the land, and knew this was where he must begin to retrace his steps. He swam south.

No adult gray whales eat on the long eight-month migration, nor do they eat in the bays where they give birth to their young and remate. No other beast can go so long without eating and still be active. Woodchucks, ground squirrels, bears feed all summer, and starve all winter; but they sleep during their starvation and do not use much energy. Not the gray whale. This beast swims constantly while starving, with the exception of the babies that nurse on the trip north.

And so, the giant whale child sucked in the ocean because he was hungry and weak. He filtered out the plankton through odd rows of baleen teeth that were more like sieves than teeth. Then he rolled southward in fear and fright.

At noon he found Coos Bay. He knew its taste. His mother had taught him this. Swimming to the familiar barrier he tapped his jaws together and called. There was no answer in all the vast ocean. The young whale drifted into the cove. It was familiar. He had been born in a cove, in the low hot waters of the California Bay where flats shone white in the dry land. The young whale spied upon the shore. It was different from his first home; there were tall trees and lush plants. The strangeness alarmed him, and he submerged for his ten minutes underwater. The bars, the shallows, the light that flickered from the sun down into the bay were comforting. But he saw no whales. There had been thousands in the bay of his birth. This was a desolate cove.

The young whale felt strong instincts pulling him, and occasionally he swam to the mouth of the bay and looked north, for gray whales work on appointments with their needs. They must give birth to calves in the protected lagoons. They must depart on schedule to travel the 7,000 miles to the only food they eat—the plankton of the Bering Sea—and they must get there on time, or they starve to death. Again in the fall they must leave on schedule in order to reach the bays in time to have their babies in the protected waters. Any interference with this timing means death to the whales.

The young whale child tapped his teeth and circled Coos Bay. He had been born in January, a magnificent male of sixteen feet. Upon his arrival in the whale world, he had been immediately nuzzled by his giant mother, who, without arms or feet with which to hug him, expressed her love by circling him. She led him to the surface to blow; then, tipping her body, she showed him where to find her milk.

The rest of the two months in the lagoon were reassuring to the young whale child. Hundreds of other whales slept and rolled with him, each one awakening instinctively before the tide went out and beached him, an event which means certain death to a whale, for they are helpless on the land. The whale child learned to tell when the tide was leaving, and how to avoid being stranded. He met other young whales, and by meeting them, knew what he was.

In March there were fewer and fewer of his kind in the bay, for the great migration had started north. Finally his mother beat her tail, crunched her teeth and led him around sand bars, over hills, and out into the sea. He stayed close to her big side. She paused beyond the bay channel to teach him the tastes and pressures of his birthplace. Then she spanked him forward to keep her schedule with the burst of spring in the Bering Sea.

The young whale felt pressures and tastes in Coos Bay similar to those he knew as an infant, and so he lingered, blowing and swirling over the bottom. By night he would swim toward the shore, and by day he would surge to the entrance, feeling the pull of his species toward the dark waters of the north. But he did not know how to go.

And so he stayed where he was.

The days passed. His mother did not return. The huge child grew weak with longing and hunger. He could not know that they had lost each other as she had spurted forward to drive a killer whale from their path. Killer whales never kill adult gray whales, but they compete for the same waters; and so to protect their rights, they molest the young. Over the eons the gray whale has learned peace by avoidance. They keep to the bottom. The killers keep to the surface.

But all life is chance. A killer whale and the whale child's mother had met, and she responded to an old instinct. She chased him. From that moment on their separation became greater as the mother moved instinctively north searching for her child in an effort to keep her schedule with June in the Bering Sea. And the child, following the instincts of the young, looked for familiar waters.

A week later the tired whale child came up to the shores of Coos Bay where people moved and boats were tied. In loneliness he watched the boats. They were almost as big as his mother. One night he nuzzled one. And close beside its purring motors he fell asleep.

But as he slept he breathed like a wind tunnel. The owner of the yacht heard the strange sound, and came out to see if a storm were brewing.

He looked down into the water and saw the young whale sleeping happily against his ship. He stared again to make sure, then paced the entire length of his deck until he came to the end of the baby. An unmistakable whale tail lay under the water. He radioed the Marine Laboratory and he radioed the Fish and Wildlife Service.

At dawn the lost whale child was a captive.

The excitement was great. During the night the men had enclosed him in a great wire fence, and they all stood and stared at him as he snapped and rolled.

Gray whales had almost become extinct in the Pacific Ocean during the whaling years in the nineteenth century, but with laws prohibiting their killing, they had increased in numbers. Nevertheless the ships and boats on the Pacific often frightened them and diverted them from keeping their precise schedules with the plankton and the bays. And these delays spelled their death.

So the scientists in Coos Bay were thrilled to be able to study a live gray whale. They measured and weighed him. They noted the movements of the whale child, they put microphones in the water to record any sounds he might make, and they watched him judge the tide and swim to the deepest pocket of the cage when it went out. They took his temperature and analyzed his blood.

To feed him they poured nutrients into the water that were similar to the nutrition in the plankton. The formula came from studies made on the stomachs of other gray whales that had washed ashore in the past. The scientists were coming to a new understanding of this remarkable beast, and they were excited.

Meanwhile the remarkable beast grew weaker and weaker, for the plankton formula was not what he needed. He needed his mother's milk. He cried at night, and eyed the men by day.

Then one night a small craft, sailing out into the ocean, was rocked by an enormous object just off the sand bar at the lighthouse. The boat was thrown off course by the swell. Its crew peered into the water to see if they had struck anything, but the sea was black. Only a trail of phosphorescent animals told them something big had passed down the channel into the bay. They gave the incident little thought, for their boat righted itself quickly and purred on out to sea.

The next morning when the scientists came to take a cardiograph of the young whale, they were distressed to find the fence crunched as if it were paper—and the whale child gone.

Far out at sea a mother whale and her son blew four times and submerged to follow green currents in the depths of the Pacific Ocean. The mother lingered to teach her son the pressure and weight of these bleak waters. She was very patient, and her child was serious and obedient.

A school of sharks circled them as they plunged over the edge of the continental shelf and thundered north, for the belly of the female bore toothlike gashes—as if raked by a wire fence.

As they followed the watery highways, known only to the gray whales, the "roadsides" were spangled with the signs of spring. Diatoms[1] bloomed, copepods[2] glittered among the diatoms, fish glimmered as they tossed their silver eggs to the sea, and clams siphoned the bright water in and out of their valves; for it was springtime in the ocean.

---

[1] diatoms [dī'ə·tomz]: any of various tiny, single-celled plants with hard cell walls found in fresh or salt water

[2] copepods [kō'pə·pädz]: any of various tiny animals having a tough outer shell and found in fresh or salt water

---

THINK IT OVER

1. *In what ways does the author reveal the strong bond between the mother whale and her baby?*

2. *The mother whale teaches her baby to recognize underwater landmarks. Does this information help the baby? Explain your answer.*

3. *How does the baby whale become a captive? How does it regain its freedom?*

WRITE

Do you think it was right for the scientists to capture the baby whale? Write an opinion paragraph explaining your answer.

WORDS ABOUT
THE AUTHOR

Jean Craighead George

In her book *Beastly Inventions: A Surprising Investigation into How Smart Animals Really Are*, Jean George wrote about her childhood. She says that she was not a scientist like her father and her brothers, "but without knowing it at the time, I was beginning a long search for unique animals of all kinds. It was not to be as organized a quest as theirs, but rather a hopscotch trip into worlds stretching well beyond my imagination."

AWARD-WINNING
AUTHOR

473

*J*ean George was born in Washington, D.C., in 1919. Her father was an entomologist; he studied insects. Her whole family enjoyed nature and being outdoors. When she went to college, Jean George studied science and English. Later she studied art and modern dance. After she finished school, she had several jobs, all of which had to do with writing or art. She worked as a newspaper reporter, a magazine artist, and a teacher. Then she became an editor and reporter for *Reader's Digest* magazine. Her experiences at the *Reader's Digest* gave her many ideas for her work as an author and illustrator.

Jean George's specialty is writing about nature and natural history, and she writes both books and magazine articles about nature and animal life. Her first books, which she wrote as her three children were growing up, were animal stories for children. At first she wrote and illustrated all her books by herself, but after writing *Summer of the Falcon* in 1962, she decided to have other illustrators do the pictures for her books.

To get ready for her writing, Jean George studies and travels, spending time in libraries and museums. She explores places like the Colorado River or the sea ice off Alaska and takes notes on what she sees. Doing such extensive research is a difficult job, but she makes good use of her work. She typically uses what she has learned about a subject to write both a nonfiction magazine article and a fiction book for young people.

When Jean George writes, she mixes natural history with good stories. Sometimes her stories are about the customs and backgrounds of people from different parts of the world. Although most of her books are written for and are usually about young people, she has written one or two books for adults. Her most famous book is *My Side of the Mountain*, which is about a boy who spends a winter surviving alone in the woods. Paramount Pictures made the story into a movie in 1969. Her own favorite, however, is *Spring Comes to the Ocean*, which she wrote in 1965. The American Library Association liked the book too. It put *Spring Comes to the Ocean* on its list of Notable Children's Books.

Jean George doesn't like to repeat the subjects she writes about. She has written about many things, including animals, nature, weather, cities, and regions of the earth. In 1982 she wrote her autobiography. She has even written a cookbook.

Whatever she writes, one thing is always the same: Jean George keeps searching. Even though she has learned a lot about nature and the world around her, she knows there is always more to discover.

illustrated by Wayne McLoughlin

WATER SKY

Jean Craighead George

• • •

Weir Amaogak is among the last of the old Eskimo whale hunters. In his time, the number of whales passing by the Alaskan coast has dropped sharply because commercial whaling ships have taken too many. The giant bowhead whales are endangered to such an extent that the Eskimos are now limited by the government to catching just a few each year. The Eskimo people believe in taking from the ocean only what they need to survive. They depend on the whales for food, shelter, and fuel for their fires.

Weir is on his way to the camp of another hunter, Vincent Ologak. Weir and Vincent share the Eskimo belief that whales give themselves to the hunters. The two men believe that a bowhead will soon present itself to them.

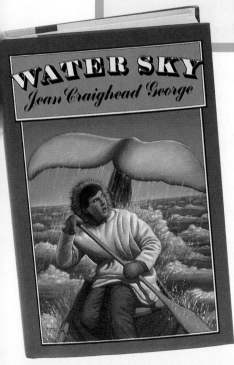

AWARD-WINNING AUTHOR

Iñupiat words in Water Sky

agviQ (ahg' vik): bowhead whale
aiviQ (eye' vik): walrus
Ataata (ah · ta' ta): grandfather
boyer (boi' yər): boy
Iñupiat (in · you' pea · it): Eskimo people and language
Nukik (noo' kik): "strength"
piayaaq agviQ (pie · ya · ahk' ahg' vik): a young whale
umiaq (oom' me · ak): a boat made of animal skins

Weir Amaogak was somewhere in the white barrens between Wainwright and Barrow, humming as he pulled his graceful basket sled with a borrowed snow machine. He was coming along the coast on his way to join the Vincent Ologak crew. He glanced back to check on his thirteen-year-old grand-daughter, Ukpik. She was tucked in the furs on the old-style sled Weir had made of bent willow limbs from the foot of the Brooks Range. She sat with her feet straight out like a sitting bear's. Her nose and eyes peeked out of her blowing wolverine ruff. Weir Amaogak smiled to see his favorite person in all the world riding through the ice-bound wilderness with him. This was the second time he had taken her whaling, and he was glowing with thoughts of whales and this helpful grandchild.

Ukpik sat on a box that held Weir's harpoon, whale lance, ice saws and block and tackle. The harpooner had spent three weeks cleaning, sharpening and oiling the equipment out of respect for the whale. Everything must be perfect for the perfect animal.

Weir Amaogak was the last traditional harpooner. He used a harpoon to which was attached a pre-white-man sealskin float. When the harpoon was embedded in the whale, the float brought the animal to the surface and slowed it down so Weir could take it mercifully and honorably with his lance. He did not use the modern harpoon and shoulder gun that are equipped with bombs, for Weir did not use modern equipment. He used his old and primitive tools, his own knowledge of the anatomy of whales and his strength. He never missed.

He was also one of the last Eskimos in the Arctic to own a dog team. He had borrowed a friend's snow

machine for this trip, leaving his lively huskies at home out of consideration for his beloved friend Vincent Ologak. Dogs require a lot of food, and Vincent was no longer wealthy.

Also on the sled were survival supplies. The harpooner traveled his Arctic homeland with a stove, pots, food, gun, ammunition and skins. He carried these in the summer and winter, on five-hundred-mile trips as well as on two-mile excursions. He was alive because he took the same precautions his ancestors had taken when they traveled—he carried a home with him. No modern technology, which had changed so much of the North Slope and Eskimo life, could change the weather at the top of the world. As far as Weir was concerned, it was as dangerous and unpredictable as it had been when the Eskimos had migrated to the Arctic twenty thousand years ago.

Weir drove at a steady pace on the smooth ice along the beach. He noted the caribou on the land, the eider ducks out over the ice and, here and there, the graceful little Arctic foxes. This was a dangerous time for the foxes. It was spring, and they were anticipating the gray landscape of summer. Their fur was changing from white to gray. This, together with their black eyes and noses, made them more visible to enemies on the white snow and ice.

Weir checked on Ukpik again, and this time she pointed to her mouth to say she was hungry. Gladly he slowed down and stopped. He had been driving

for many hours and was ready for a rest. He reached into a skin bag, brought out the paniqtaq—dried fish and seal meat—and carried it to her.

"How much longer?" she asked.

"Less than half a sleep to go."

She slid off the sled, stretched her arms and hopped up and down to exercise her legs and toes. Ukpik was a petite young lady whose small nose and large black eyes gave her the wondrous look of natchiagruk, the baby seal. Her skin was like golden silk, and her red cheeks knotted into little apples when she smiled. Ukpik was very beautiful.

Ukpik means snowy owl in Iñupiat. Although her English name was Patsy, she preferred to be called Little Owl.

Little Owl was studying her native tongue in school. She also studied English, mathematics and American and English history, and took a course in corporate law. This was in preparation for her dual way of life as an American citizen and an Eskimo. The native villages of Alaska are incorporated. They invest their percentage of the oil taken on their land and spend the profits on their people. Schoolchildren are given a hundred dollars apiece by the North Slope School District to invest in their own school corporations. The children make and sell Eskimo doughnuts, charge for dances and invest the money they raise. Some graduate and manage the village corporations. Little Owl enjoyed her complicated education and was an excellent student.

She sat down on the snow machine beside Weir to finish her seal meat.

"What is Vincent Ologak's new apprentice like, Ataata?" she asked her grandfather.

"The what?"

"The new boyer, Vincent Ologak's relative from the outside? I heard you talking to Bertha about him."

"The new boyer. Yes, yes, that would interest you. I am getting old. Let me see, Bertha says he has not so much Eskimo in him and that he is very strong."

"Oh, Ataata, that's not what I'm asking. Did she say he was handsome? How old is he?"

"He is young. He is a piayaaq agviQ—a whale who has just left his mother."

"I mean how many years, silly Ataata."

"So young that his blubber is soft, like a young whale's."

She stopped pursuing that subject. "Do you think he'll be angry with me?"

"Be angry with you? Why would he be?"

"Because I will be paddling the umiaq with you when you go out to harpoon the whale."

"Yes, I want you. You are a strong paddler. But why should the boyer care?"

"Well, don't you think a boyer from the lower forty-eight would resent that? Me, a girl, in the boat and him in the kitchen?"

"Oh, he will be in the boat all right. Vincent Ologak says Nukik, the whale, will give himself to this boy."

"Vincent Ologak said that?" Her eyes widened. "Then it must be so."

Weir Amaogak pushed back his parka hood to better see the frozen ocean. A thick cap of silver-gray hair tumbled around his face and neck. Bold lines ran from his nose to the corners of his mouth, calling attention to his broad full lips. The half-moon eyes were permanently squinted from a lifetime of watching the ice and the wildlife. He blew on his bare hands and studied the horizon.

"Water sky, Ukpik," he said. "Want to ride out and see if the whales are passing through that lead?"

"I love to watch whales."

"The second wave of whales is late. Maybe we can learn something."

Weir Amaogak unhitched the sled. Little Owl swung onto the backseat of the snow machine and hugged her grandfather around the waist. They started out across the land-fast shore ice that forms in coves and is smoother than the open-sea ice. In a short distance the ice roughened, and Weir was bumping the machine through valleys and over pressure ridges beyond the cove. The water sky grew darker and darker until it hung like a rainstorm above them.

"We are here," Weir said, pulling around a blue-green ice mound and stopping beside a lake of open water in the continent of ice.

"Whale puddle," he said of the lake.

Its edges sparkled with a covering of thin clear ice that was forming in the calm. Weir studied the open water in the middle of the puddle while Little Owl observed the shores.

"AiviQ," she said, pointing to a monstrous brown walrus sitting like a pompous king on the edge of the whale puddle. His ivory tusks, which came down to the middle of his chest, were blunted by years of fighting bulls for his harem. The light gleamed on the wire-thick whiskers that jutted out of his puffy lips. He stared stone faced at Little Owl.

"Is he giving himself to us?" Ukpik asked. "He sits so still."

Weir did not answer. He was concentrating on the new ice near the east end of the whale puddle. Ukpik turned back to the walrus.

"Go home, aiviQ," she called. "We do not need you."

"Whale!" whispered Weir, pointing to a black slick at the far end of the lake. "AgviQ—see him?"

The slick moved and the black blowhole of an enormous whale lifted into the air.

Whoosssfff. The giant shot a geyser into the sun. Although Weir and Ukpik had seen hundreds and hundreds of whales, they watched as if this were their very first—in awed silence.

The whale went under, came up, breathed out and in, went under again. He did this seven times, then he sounded—dived deep and stayed down for thirteen minutes.

The thin ice that had formed in front of Weir and Little Owl buckled up into a huge air-filled dome. A whale could be seen inside it taking a breath. Weir dropped onto his stomach. Little Owl lay down beside him. They waited. The whale vanished.

Presently it blew in the open water, then lifted itself up until its twenty-foot head was in view. It turned one eye on the man and the girl. Thrashing its flukes, it rose yet higher.

"Sky hopping!" Weir whispered. "That's higher than a breach. The whale is excited." Little Owl held her breath. The giant was no more than thirty feet away and as big as the Wainwright church. The profile of its mouth curved up, then down, and ended just below its thoughtful eye. Water poured out between the rows of baleen in the great smile. It stood on end for a long moment, then threw itself onto the new ice and shattered it. Pieces shot out in all directions like glass spears. They tinkled as they fell back. Green and purple waves rolled up from the fall, breaking more ice. The whale spiraled onto its belly and, with a graceful twist, put its head in the water. Its back came into view. A flipper whirled and the tail stock, which seems too narrow for the bowhead bulk, curved above the water. Slowly the huge flukes lifted. They were white.

"Nukik!" Weir said softly.

A chill ran down Little Owl's spine. The leviathan was, indeed, looking for someone. She had seen his humanlike eye scanning Weir, then herself. The intelligence behind it had been dissatisfied or perhaps not interested. Nukik, she knew in her heart, was searching for Vincent Ologak's camp and the boyer. The white teachers at school did not believe whales gave themselves to people.

Another whale surfaced and blew far out in the whale puddle, and close at hand a female with a baby at her side came up to breathe. The mother lifted her youngster to the surface with a flipper. He took a breath, peered around and saw Little Owl. He lifted his head higher and wiggled his long gray-blue body, as if he knew another youngster when he saw one. Little Owl clapped her mittens over her mouth to keep from crying out in glee. The baby splashed and waved its flippers; then the mother scooped him up and dove with him. They left whale tracks, great swathes of smooth water on the surface outlined with turbulent bubbles.

"Oh, Ataata," Little Owl whispered. "I wish I could swim under the water with them. We land creatures can never really know the whales—only their blowholes and tails."

"Perhaps I can help you, Little Owl," Weir said, getting to his feet. "I sometimes feel that I am part whale. Sit down, little granddaughter. I will tell you what Nukik is doing.

"The water where he swims is green. Spears of gold light come down from the top of the water. They are the glowing lamps that lead Nukik to air. He looks for these bright guides that tell him where the leads are when he travels under the ice. It is pretty in Nukik's world. Fish flash around him, the ice shines, the kelp on the bottom of the sea dances and reaches up to him.

"The mother and baby have followed Nukik to the east end of the puddle. They are resting now." Weir sat very still, waiting for Nukik to do something else.

"Nukik is leading them under the ice."

Seven minutes passed without Weir speaking.

"Nukik has found a crack in the ice beyond the puddle, and the mother and baby are breathing there. They hang at the surface. They are comfortable and safe.

"Nukik is listening to the ice and current. He learns from the screeching of ice against ice that the leads are closed for miles and miles ahead. He and his pod of friends and relatives cannot travel their ancestral route along the shore." Weir suddenly smiled.

"Close your eyes, Little Owl. Can you see Nukik? He is very big and very fat. His head is slightly pointed. White scars mark his black skin. He is pocked with many holes and bumps. He is an old whale.

"He must be my age, Little Owl. Whales are like people. They have a long childhood, and like people they don't have babies until they are in their teens. They grow wise and old like us, and some, like some people, become good leaders. Nukik is one of these.

"And like us, whales grow old and die. Nukik's life is run. He is ready to complete the cycle and live again in our spirits and our bodies." Weir's voice was reverent and low.

"Much of this knowledge I know from my father and grandfather, who learned it from their fathers and grandfathers as far back as there have been Eskimo whalers. And I have added some new knowledge of my own."

"The whales must know about the Eskimos," Little Owl said. "Do you think, Ataata?"

"They probably know a lot about us," answered Weir. "And they probably know individual Eskimos as we know individual whales. I have seen Nukik of the white fluke many times. I am sure he knows me. One spring I saw him off Point Hope, when I harpooned for Ernie Fellow. Nukik waved a flipper. Last spring I saw him when I was with Vincent Ologak. He sky hopped for us, but he would not give himself to us. We were not the person he was looking for."

Weir stopped talking and read the sun as if it were a clock in the sky. He started the snow machine and drove back to the sled. Little Owl did not get on it.

"Don't go yet, Ataata," she said. "Nukik and

his friends are in trouble. Please tell me what he is doing now."

Life in the Arctic cannot be rushed, as every Eskimo knows, so Weir sat down. Passing on knowledge to the young is the most important thing an elder can do, and Weir took his responsibilities seriously.

He closed his eyes.

"Nukik has left the mother and baby resting in the crack. He pumps his whole body up and down and swims under the pack ice. He is watching for the lamps in the gloom. He sees only purple darkness, and far behind him the glow of the whale puddle like a moonrise under the sea."

Little Owl felt as if she were under the water at last. She closed her eyes.

"Now Nukik uses his senses. He hears the cracks and tastes the air pockets. They taste of sun. He finds an area where there are many cracks.

"Ahead is a mountain range of pack ice that reaches almost down to the ocean floor. It is jagged in some places, smooth in others. It is yellow and blue and green. The water pressure tells Nukik that the barrier goes on and on. The baby cannot dive deep enough to get under it or hold its breath long enough to find the air pockets.

"Nukik takes his kind of compass reading on this location. He photographs the shapes on his brain and notes the taste of the water. He returns to his pod and leads them to the breathing cracks under the pack ice. Now he returns to the mother and baby."

Apparently there was a lull in the events in the ocean, for Weir was silent. Little Owl thought of a question while they waited.

"Where did Nukik come from?" she asked.

"In the winter Nukik and his pod live with the sun in a secret place in the Bering Sea. Almost two weeks ago the lengthening day and the warming waters told them it was time to migrate to their summer home. They swam east with the second wave of a thousand or more whales.

"The first wave is made up of adolescents and young adults. They left the Bering Sea in early April and are now in their summering grounds. The third wave, of assorted sizes and ages, will pass Barrow in late May and early June.

"Nukik's wave is made up of mothers, their babies and youngsters, pregnant females and old whales like himself. Why the whales break up into these waves is known only to the whales.

"Nukik's wave swam until they came to the Bering Straits. There they were stopped by an ice jam that blocked the narrow pass.

"They were delayed many days. Finally, the sun warmed the water, the ice jam melted and floated away and Nukik and his pod continued. They swam past the Point Hope whalers without giving themselves. They swam by the Wainwright whalers without giving themselves and were stopped today by that wall of pack ice. So happily we came upon them." Weir's eyes opened and closed again. "Nukik is active."

"What is he doing now, Ataata?"

"He is circling the mother and baby. He slows down, for he hears something. He listens. A walrus is calling; his voice sounds like a church bell ringing underwater. The walrus is on his way to the bottom to dig in the mud for clams. Seals are whistling like chirruping birds. One shoots up from the depths, passes Nukik and pops up into her blue iglu. But now he is not listening for walrus and seals.

"Nukik usually pays attention to the seals. They feed on the fish that feed on the plankton. By joining the seals he finds the plankton.

"He also listens for the chirps of the beluga whales. They, too, eat the fish that feed on the plankton. But these voices do not interest him now." Weir cocked his head to one side, and the creases in his dark face smoothed as he concentrated.

"Nukik is listening for the voice of a bowhead, a deep lugubrious moo. He heard it once. He knows who it is, and the whale's call is urgent."

Little Owl clasped her hands together.

"Ataata, what is happening?"

"Nukik is back to the whale puddle. He finds the whale. She is a pregnant female. Nukik sounds, swims toward her and with grace breaches and looks around.

"There is no midwife or attendant with the female. Whales need help with their newborns. A friend usually lifts the baby to air as soon as it is born and while the mother recovers.

"Most whales are born in the water, but this mother throws her tail up on a thick piece of new ice. Her abdomen contracts with great force. Nukik sky hops, rising to the base of his tail stock. The female gives a long, low moo and delivers a fifteen-foot baby onto the ice."

"A baby whale has been born? Ataata, how lovely." Little Owl leaned closer, for Weir's eyes were scrunched tight and his voice was low.

"The infant snorts air, and the mother gently nudges him into the sea with her tail. She holds him up on her flipper to breathe. She lets him sink. She lifts him up. She lets him sink. At last the baby has learned the rhythm of breathing. Nukik swims quietly up to the little whale.

"He noses his granddaughter affectionately."

"Ataata, Ataata." Little Owl clapped her hands. "Nukik has a granddaughter. She will be good to him and love him." Weir squeezed Little Owl's hands and got to his feet. He glanced at the sun, then back at his granddaughter.

"Nukik will not lead his pod on. They will swim east without him. Nukik will stay with his daughter and granddaughter and the other mother and baby. He will teach them about the sea. He will breach and splash for them.

"And then, when the shore leads open again, Nukik will lead them to Vincent Ologak's camp. There he will leave them forever."

THINK IT OVER

1. *What knowledge and wisdom about whales does Weir pass on to his granddaughter?*

2. *How do you know Weir respects whales?*

3. *In what ways does Little Owl live in two worlds?*

WRITE

What kind of animal is special to you? Write a short poem that describes the animal. Try to show your feelings about it.

FOLLOWING THE WHALES

In "Water Sky," Little Owl says, "We land creatures can never really know the whales—only their blowholes and tails." How do the two selections support or disprove this statement?

· ·

Describe the difficulties and dangers that are faced by the whales in these selections.

· ·

WRITER'S WORKSHOP   Think of an animal you have observed or read about. Imagine what the animal does all day. Then write a suspenseful story with the animal as the main character.

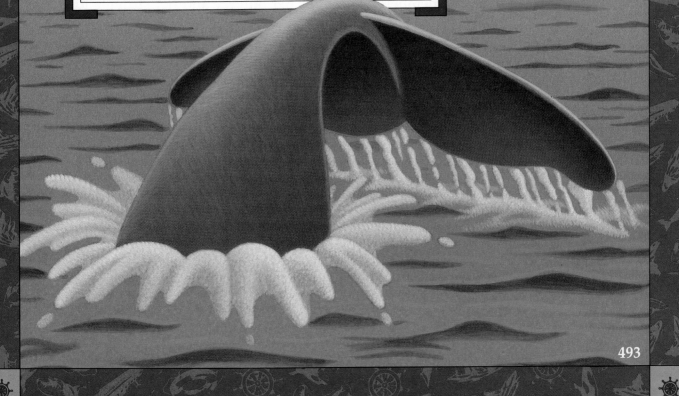

493

CONNECTIONS

LIFE IN THE SOUTH SEAS

Long ago, the people of the South Seas sailed the Pacific Ocean in giant canoes. They traveled great distances and settled thousands of islands, including Hawaii. Today these islands are known as Oceania. The 25,000 islands in Oceania are very small, and only a few thousand are inhabited.

Hawaii is a state of the United States. It is the only state that was once an independent monarchy. The last monarch was Queen Liliuokalani, the only woman ever to rule Hawaii. Liliuokalani tried to maintain the independence of her people. However, in 1893, she agreed to give up her throne to protect her followers from threats by sugar planters. Queen Liliuokalani is remembered today for her bravery and her struggle to keep Hawaii from being taken over by foreign settlers.

■ *Have a "South Seas Day" in class. Bring pictures or examples of South Seas island life and culture, and share them with classmates. Discuss what life might be like on a South Seas island.*

Queen Liliuokalani

ISLAND ENVIRONMENT

There are two main types of islands in the South Pacific: high islands and low islands. Research the origins and features of each type, and share this information with your classmates.

ISLAND CHART

With a partner, find out about one of the islands or island groups in Oceania. Make a chart like the one below, and list your findings. Display your chart, and be prepared to answer questions from your classmates.

(NAME OF ISLAND)		
Land/Climate:	(map)	Society/Culture:
Government:		Economy:

495

DAYS·GONE·BY

People from all over the world helped build the United States. From Native Americans and early European settlers to the most recent immigrants from Asia, every group has contributed to our nation. Consider the African American and Mexican cowhands who helped open the great American West. Those pioneer days required hard work and dedication. As you read the next selections, set in historical times, marvel at the strength and determination of those who built our country.

THEMES

FRONTIER DAYS
. . . .
500

HUNGRY FOR LEARNING
. . . .
524

CIVIL WAR DAYS
. . . .
552

BOOKSHELF

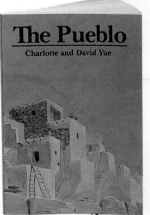

THE PUEBLO
BY CHARLOTTE AND DAVID YUE

This book brings to life the busy, apartmentlike villages of the Pueblo Indians and explains how their way of life was tied to the land. SCHOOL LIBRARY JOURNAL BEST BOOK, NOTABLE CHILDREN'S TRADE BOOK IN THE FIELD OF SOCIAL STUDIES

HBJ LIBRARY BOOK

OLD YELLER
BY FRED GIPSON

While Travis's father is away on a trail drive, Travis must defend his mother and little brother from the perils of frontier life. But he has help from an ugly yellow dog. NEWBERY HONOR BOOK, ALA NOTABLE BOOK

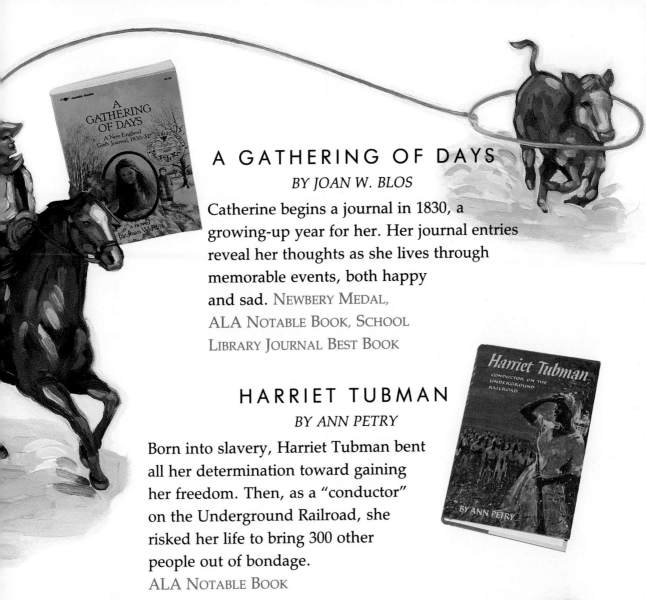

A GATHERING OF DAYS

BY JOAN W. BLOS

Catherine begins a journal in 1830, a
growing-up year for her. Her journal entries
reveal her thoughts as she lives through
memorable events, both happy
and sad. NEWBERY MEDAL,
ALA NOTABLE BOOK, SCHOOL
LIBRARY JOURNAL BEST BOOK

HARRIET TUBMAN

BY ANN PETRY

Born into slavery, Harriet Tubman bent
all her determination toward gaining
her freedom. Then, as a "conductor"
on the Underground Railroad, she
risked her life to bring 300 other
people out of bondage.
ALA NOTABLE BOOK

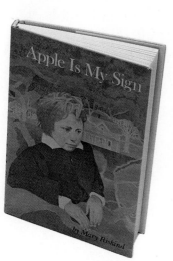

APPLE IS MY SIGN

BY MARY RISKIND

Harry's father has
always kept his deaf
family apart from their
hearing neighbors. But
when Harry returns
from his special school,
his new outlook
changes all their lives.
ALA NOTABLE BOOK

FRONTIER DAYS

Through pictures and stories we can journey back to days gone by. In the next selections you will discover the taste of a real chuckwagon stew and cross a raging river on a cattle drive.

CONTENTS
· ·

502

CHUCKWAGON DAYS

FROM *HUNTER'S STEW AND HANGTOWN FRY*
BY LILA PERL

ILLUSTRATED BY TERRY SHOFFNER

During the Civil War years, the Texas rangelands became heavily stocked with cattle. Some of the new ranchers of the 1850s had brought herds of English shorthorns and Herefords west with them, as both were superior in beef-producing quality to the half-wild Spanish longhorns. Whatever their breed, the animals flourished on the Texas grasses. Yet they could not be safely or conveniently shipped to market while hostilities between the states continued.

Once the war ended, a great era of railroad building began, and it became possible to transport the animals from America's new cattlelands to packing houses and consumers in St. Louis, Chicago, and points east via the recently completed rail lines. However, a distance of some 600 to 700 miles lay between the Texas range and the railheads in the Kansas "cow towns" of Wichita, Abilene, and Dodge City. For this portion of the journey, the cattle had to be driven on the hoof, an operation known as the "long drive," from which sprang some of the most colorful cowboy lore of nineteenth century America.

The perils of the trail were considerable. The herds frequently numbered close to 3000, and the most serious danger was that of a stampede, for the Texas longhorns were a temperamental and unpredictable lot. The cowhands had to be wary, skillful, and rugged. Other hazards of the weeks' or even months' long trek were Indian raids, attacks by rustlers or wild animals, and the spread of cattle diseases like the dreaded tick fever. Yet the journey could not be hurried, for the more slowly the beasts moved across northern Texas, the territory of Oklahoma, and southwestern Kansas, and the more thoroughly they fed on the rich grasses of the summer plains, the fatter they were when they arrived at the cow town markets to be weighed up and purchased by cattle buyers and shipped east in freight cars.

On the trail, food had to be provided for the trail boss and the dozen or so cowhands he had carefully selected, so the choice of an able cook or "pot wrangler," usually dubbed "cookie" by the rest of the men, was a serious matter. Unlike their charges, the cowboys could not be expected to eat off the country. Their hours were long and their duties exhausting. Even after making camp at night, they usually bedded the cattle down and sang them to sleep, lulling them with mournful ballads that eventually built into a well-known repertory of cowboy songs.

The remarkable rolling kitchen out of which the pot wrangler did his cooking was called a chuckwagon. Colonel Charles Goodnight, a pioneer cattleman of the Texas Panhandle, is credited with having invented it. Actually, the chuckwagon was an ordinary-looking covered wagon with a tall box that had a large drop door built onto the back of it. The box was a traveling pantry with shelves holding staples like flour, cornmeal, rice, salt, sugar, coffee, dried beans, lard, raisins, cured pork, and other nonperishables.

When the trail outfit came to a halt, the cook simply let down the hinged drop door of the pantry and, supported by a couple of hinged-on legs, it converted into a work table for

504

mixing biscuits, cornbread, and hotcakes, and preparing stews, beans, and coffee. Food was cooked over an open fire in one of cookie's huge kettles or iron skillets. Steaks from the steers slaughtered en route were coated with flour and salt and fried in sizzling beef fat or lard. "Chuckwagon stew" consisted of chunks of beef plus parts like tongue, heart, liver, kidneys, and brains, well seasoned with onions, salt, and chili powder. Occasionally the monotony of beef would be varied with venison, wild turkey, prairie chicken, or even buffalo.

The nearest thing to a vegetable dish was dried beans, usually the pinto beans of the Southwest. Oddly speckled, like birds' eggs, with spots of brown on beige, the beans turned a rich, warm, all-over brown when cooked. This food was the heritage of the Indians, passed on to the cowboys of the Southwest just as the first Indian cowhands had taught the skills of the *vaquero*, in roping and branding cattle, to the newcomers from the east. The dish known as "chuckwagon beans," eaten frequently on the long cattle drives, reflected both Indian and Spanish influences, for it included onions, garlic, and salt pork or bacon, as well as chili powder.

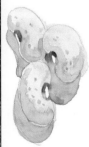

The cooking time could be reduced somewhat by soaking the beans in water first, although long, slow cooking guaranteed firmer beans. Chuckwagon beans made a meal in themselves, the creamy bean liquid mopped up with freshly made biscuits "baked" over an open fire in a well-heated, covered iron pot.

Trail biscuits were made to rise by the use of sourdough "starter," a fermented mixture that produced gas bubbles and so acted as a substitute for yeast. The trail cook's greatest treasure was his small wooden cask of sourdough that he kept warm and well-replenished, even taking it to bed with him on cold nights. Once a cask of sourdough got working—through the addition of sugar or molasses to flour, water, and salt—it could go on for years. So each time the chuckwagon cook added some sourdough starter to his biscuit dough or hotcake batter, he made sure to add some more flour, water, and salt to the cask to ferment. Gold prospectors in California and, after the turn of the century, in Alaska also carried sourdough starters with them. Alaskan miners even came to be nicknamed "sourdoughs."

The biggest cooking problem on the trail, beyond that of keeping the water cask well filled, was finding adequate fuel. Twigs, dried grasses, and any other dry vegetable matter that would burn was carefully collected as the outfit moved along. But often the cooking fire had to be made with dried cow chips, just as the Indians of the Great Plains made their cooking fires with dried buffalo chips.

Coffee was a round-the-clock beverage for the trail gang, and a pot was kept hot, sitting in the embers of the fire, all through the night as the cowhands came off their watches. Meals were pretty much the same whether they were breakfast, lunch, or dinner; fried steak, stew, or beans was as likely at one as at the other. Desserts were rare, but sometimes cookie would prepare "spotted pup," a dish of cooked rice and raisins sweetened with brown sugar.

The heyday of the long cattle drives across Oklahoma, from Texas to Kansas, lasted less than twenty years. As the homesteaders came onto the Great Plains during the 1860s and 1870s, more and more buffalo grass was plowed under for the planting of wheat fields. The invention of barbed wire in 1874 gave the homesteaders a means of fencing in their fields and, at the same time, fencing out the herds of cattle passing through to graze. Skirmishes often took place between the cattlemen and the farmers, and the former sometimes cut the metal fences claiming that the barbs injured their cattle. By the early 1880s, the days of the open range were clearly numbered.

THINK IT OVER

1. *Why did long cattle drives come to an end?*

2. *What were some of the perils and problems the cowboys and the pot wrangler faced during the long drive?*

WRITE

Using the foods described in this selection, write a menu for breakfast, lunch, and dinner.

RED RIVER CROSSING

from *TRAIL BOSS IN PIGTAILS*
by MARJORIE FILLEY STOVER

■ ▬ ■

illustrated by WENDELL MINOR

> In the 1850s, the Burke family of Illinois moved to Texas to
> start their own cattle ranch. However, the hot, dry climate
> took its toll on Pa Burke's health. Three years later, with
> Pa too sick to run the ranch, the Burkes have decided to
> return to Illinois. They are taking along their herd of
> longhorn cattle, which they hope to sell in Chicago. Pa died
> suddenly along the trail, and now the family must depend on
> Emma Jane, the oldest child, to lead them onward. Her sister
> Easter and her brother Martin do their best to help. Ma Burke
> is kept busy watching the younger children, Matt, Martha,
> and Phoebe. Many times on the long trip north, Emma Jane
> has to think and act quickly to keep the cattle moving.

Emma Jane stirred in her bedroll and clung to its warmth for a
few more precious minutes. She could hear Ma stirring outside and
the breakfast fire crackling. Emma Jane sat up and fished for her
boots in the half-darkness of the tent. The other children were not
stirring yet. She spooled her bedroll, automatically brushing off
any grass that stuck to the tarpaulin, which protected her blankets
against moisture and prickers. She thrust a loop of rope around it,
and pulling it tight with a quick hitch, ducked out of the tent and
stowed it in the wagon. Her bed was made.

"Mornin', Ma." Emma Jane sloshed a little water into the washbasin from the water barrel on the side of the wagon.

Ma greased the bake oven with a bacon rind and began to slide in the little balls of biscuit dough. "Mornin', Emma Jane. Going to be a nice day."

"We can use a little sunshine after two days of rain—and with all that rain, I'm afraid the river's going to be up." Emma Jane hooked up the milk pail and headed for Daisy, who was staked nearby. Squatting down beside the cow, Emma Jane sent two white jets of milk singing into the bottom of the pail.

By the time the milking was finished, the little camp was buzzing with activity. The tent flaps were pulled back, and Easter was helping Phoebe spool her bedroll. Martha stumbled toward the wagon, barely able to see over her bedroll, which Easter had plopped into her outstretched arms.

Matt had dumped his roll by the wagon step and squirreled up onto the seat. His sharp eye spied a lizard scuttling through the grass, and he swooped down to chase it. Oblivious to all else, he dived in front of the half-blinded Martha and slithered under the wagon after his quarry.

Martha shrieked, swayed, and came tumbling down, sputtering indignantly. "Matthew Burke, don't you *ever* look where you're goin'?"

"Let's get the tent down," called Emma Jane.

Emma Jane piled her tin plate with hominy grits, fried side meat, and sourdough biscuits. She partly filled her cup with a dipper of fresh milk and then poured a stream of steaming black from the coffeepot until brown bubbles frothed about the rim of the cup. She ate her breakfast in hurried mouthfuls, stuffed a couple of extra biscuits into her pocket, and shoved her tin plate, cup, and eating irons into the waiting kettle of hot water.

Emma Jane let the cattle drift in the direction of the trail. She could see the hustle-bustle of breaking camp. The dishwater was poured over the embers of the fire. Matt, Phoebe, and Martha scooted back and forth carrying things to Ma, who packed them in the wagon.

Martin brought up the oxen one at a time and stood them in place. He helped Ma with the heavy yoke and lifted the bow up under Pete's throat and pushed the ends through the holes in the yoke. Then he slid the wooden bow pin through one end of the bow to hold it. Ma was pushing the other bow under Pepper's throat and fastening it with its bow pin. The yoke was chained to the wagon tongue.

Easter mounted Fanny and rode off to help Emma Jane. Easter did not like to herd. She would rather sit in the wagon and tat. But this was Martin's chance to crawl inside for a nap.

Ma cracked the whip, and Pete and Pepper strained forward. Nothing happened. Emma Jane, hanging back from the herd, was afraid that the heavy wagon was stuck in the soft earth. But the oxen heaved harder, and the wagon lurched forward. Once more the Burke family was on its way.

Emma Jane relaxed in the saddle. Mules might be faster, she thought, but the oxen were powerful heavers, and when the ground was soft, their split hooves pulled out of the mud easier than mules'.

The sun climbed higher in the sky. Nothing warmed up faster than a Texas morning. The sun was rapidly drying the ground. It was easy herding on the prairie. Flat as a man's hand, the land stretched, now and again rising in a gentle swell or dipping to the brighter green of a watercourse.

By four in the afternoon they were outside of Preston Bend, a flourishing village because of the Red River and its Rock Bluff Crossing nearby. But as Emma Jane had feared, the river had spilled over its banks. They must set up camp till the river went down.

A week dragged by. From the rocky bluff, Emma Jane gazed across the roiling waters and moodily traced a pattern with her forefinger on Star's neck. The water was down some, but the low,

gentle slope on the other side, which made it easy for the cattle to come out, was still licked by the flood. She was itchy to be on the move again.

She thought wryly of her spunky reply to Captain Ross that if the rivers flooded, all they had to do was make camp and wait for the water to go down. Well, they were waiting. Once again she measured the distance with her eye, and her fingers drummed on the saddle pommel as she studied the turbulent river. The ferry was operating again, making a dent in the backed-up traffic, but to swim a herd—

A horse reined up beside her. In the saddle sat a man with a bright red beard and hair to match, bristling from beneath his broad-brimmed hat. He gave a low whistle. "The Red's big swimming, I see."

Emma Jane flicked the ends of the reins across her open palm. "Been that way the past week. Rains up the river keeping it full, I reckon."

The man pushed back his hat and studied the sky. "'Pears to me we may git a few more bucketfuls tonight."

"Could be." Emma Jane snapped the leather ends of the reins so hard that they reddened her palm, but she didn't notice.

The man pulled his hat down again and went on talking, more to himself than to Emma Jane. "If the Red floods its bank again, there's no tellin' how long we might have to squat here waitin' to push across."

"Nothin' else to do." Emma Jane's voice was flat.

The newcomer rubbed his red beard and sucked speculatively on his lips. "She's full, but I've been across worse."

The restless flicking of the reins stopped. Emma Jane's gaze focused squarely on man and mustang in alert appraisal. "You aimin' to swim a herd across, Mister?"

"Yep. Got seven hundred critters comin' up the trail an hour behind me."

■ ▬ ■

Emma Jane didn't wait to think twice. "If you're aimin' to cross, Mister, would you let us crowd our herd of eighty-two longhorns in behind yours? We'd sure like to get travelin' again."

"*Your* herd?" Bushy red eyebrows lifted in surprise.

"Yes, sir. Our whole family is goin' back to Illinois. We aim to sell them in Chicago."

Blue eyes appraised her sharply for a moment. "Oh—those your cattle I saw a couple of kids herdin' back aways?"

"I reckon."

The bushy brows pulled together. "Well, I can't see as there'd be any harm shovin' your steers in behind mine—long as you've got a good hand followin' 'em. That river's not gonna be any child's play. Tell your pa he's welcome to try the big swim if he wants—but he better have someone waitin' on t'other side to help cut them out."

Emma Jane's eyes gleamed. "Thanks, Mister. Thanks a heap! I know—uh—Pa—uh, we'll have to break camp, but we'll be there. Just tell your drag men to be watchin' for us." With a kick of her heels and a wave of her hand, Emma Jane wheeled Star and galloped off.

"And I know it's just what Pa'd want," she told herself. "Pa said he knew I could do it, and I can."

She stopped by the herd to get Martin. He would have to be on the other side to help her. They left Easter with the longhorns and drove Pete and Pepper and Daisy ahead of them in an unwilling trot.

Emma Jane planned as they rode. "Daisy is a family cow, and she'll have to go on the ferry with the family. The river's too wild for her. You'll have to get some money from Ma for the ferry. Then hightail it to the landing as fast as you can. Alone on horseback you ought to make the next boat."

Martha and Phoebe were playing under an oak tree with their corncob dolls and a set of acorn cups and saucers when Martha looked up and saw them coming with the oxen. She jumped up, sending the acorn cups tumbling. "Has the Red gone down? Are we leaving?"

Phoebe heard nothing, but she took her cue from Martha and jumped up after her.

Matt abandoned the anthill he was watching. "Are we goin'? Are we goin'?"

"We're leaving Texas," said Emma Jane, as Ma hurried from the tent. Even while Emma Jane's excited words spilled out the story, Ma was reaching into an inner skirt pocket for the black leather purse.

"Wait a minute, don't go yet," she told Martin as she handed him a coin. "You'll need a packet of food."

Emma Jane organized the children. She and Martha spooled the bedrolls, while Matt and Phoebe carried them to the wagon.

Emma Jane pulled a rope tight around a bedroll. "The man says we can just drive our cattle right in behind his, and it won't be any extra trouble at all to get them across, Ma—ours is such a small herd."

Ma was stuffing corn pone and dried beef into a clean salt sack. "It'll be good to get goin' again. Here, Martin—be careful now." They waved him off.

Camp was nearly broken. Ma was yoking the oxen when Emma Jane put her foot in the stirrup and swung into the saddle.

Ma shoved a bow pin into place. "You and Easter come on soon as you're sure the cattle are making it across with no trouble."

Emma Jane waved to show Ma that she had heard. She was only too well aware that Ma was under the impression that the cowboys from the other herd were going to swim the Burke cattle across for them, and she was thankful Ma had been too rushed to have time to wonder why she had sent Martin ahead, instead of going herself.

She was also aware that the red-bearded trail boss had assumed that the man of the family would be there to swim after the herd. Right now she didn't want to enlighten either one of them. She had faith in Star to swim any river that any other horse could swim, and if Star could swim it, she reckoned she could make it on Star's back.

By the time Emma Jane joined Easter, she could hear the bellowing and trampling of the approaching herd. She deliberately kept her own cattle back from the trail. It would be better, she figured, if she did not talk to that trail boss again on this side of the river. She saw him riding point, his red beard flaming over his brown shirt. When he spotted her, he gave a beckoning signal. She acknowledged it and then looked off toward camp, shading her eyes as if watching for someone. Almost at once she turned back with an affirmative wave, indicating that they would join the drag of his herd.

The trail boss rode on, pushing his steers along. It was easier to keep them from balking at the water's edge if they were carried into the river by the force of their own momentum.

Emma Jane and Easter watched until the drag hove into view. Then they turned their longhorns toward the trail and swung in at the tail of the big herd.

A lanky cowboy, riding drag, blinked at the girls from under sandy lashes. His crooked teeth flashed. "Thought your trail boss was going to follow 'em across."

Emma Jane leaned forward pretending to pull a cocklebur from Star's mane. "Sure thing. Everything's all set. We're still half a mile from the river banks."

The cowboy shrugged. Plenty of time for the trail boss of this pint-sized herd to join them. He turned back to his own cattle.

Emma Jane straightened in the saddle. Her spirits soared in relief. Across the tossing horns, she saw Easter staring at her with open mouth. Emma Jane set her lips in the stubborn line the Burke family knew so well. Then her lips quirked, and she rolled her eyes. Her shoulders rose in a careless shrug as if to say, "Well, what can I do about it, if *that's* what he thinks?"

Easter grinned.

As they neared the edge of the bluff, they could see the leaders of the herd swimming across. Only their heads were out of the water, and their great horns rocked gently back and forth like so many rocking chairs upon the water. The succeeding waves of closely packed animals stepped docilely into the surging flood, obediently following their leaders.

Down between the sides of the rocky chute went the Burke eighty-two. Emma Jane had counted on the fact that the cowboys ahead would be too busy watching their own cattle to pay any attention to her, and she was right.

The lanky cowboy at the drag glanced back just before he shoved in the last of his steers. But even though he saw no trail boss, he had no time to question now. After all, it made no difference to him whether or not this pint-sized herd crossed the river. If their trail boss was late, he'd missed his chance.

Emma Jane watched anxiously. With a snort, Colonel plunged into the muddy river and the others followed. The two girls converged upon the reluctant Patches and forced him in. Then Star was in the water. Emma Jane gave her an encouraging pat. "Atta girl, you can make it."

Easter's tremulous voice followed them. "Good luck, good luck!"

The water was colder than Emma Jane had expected, and swifter as they neared the middle of the channel. Much swifter. Once the lanky cowboy looked back. She saw his amazed jerk of consternation and thought she caught a nasal groan. "Holy Cow!" But she was too busy to be sure. She mustn't let Patches decide to turn around in the middle of the Big Red.

Star swam like a veteran, steadily and strongly. Emma Jane watched her herd with pride as they unwaveringly answered the challenge of the river. Soon they were clambering, dripping and snorting, out on the other side. It had all gone as smoothly as a greased sourdough biscuit.

For a moment, Star's foot slipped as she scrambled up the

519

slippery bank, but in an instant she found firm footing, and they were safe on the other shore. They were across! They were in Indian Territory in the land of the Choctaws.

Emma Jane turned and waved to Easter, watching from the top of the bluff. As she did so, a big tree trunk, its tangled branches still outspread, floated gently by. Emma Jane felt a shudder run clear to her toes as she realized the churning maelstrom of panic-stricken cattle that bobbing tree could have created had it arrived a few minutes earlier.

Giving herself a quick shake, she turned back to the herd and found herself looking directly into the glaring blue eyes of the man she had met by the river. His red beard bristled with indignation as he thundered, *"Where* is your trail boss? Of all the danged silly things I ever saw, this beats 'em all—to let a mite of a gal like you swim across a swift rampagin' river—where in tarnation is your trail boss?"

The water was still running in muddy rivulets down Emma Jane's pants, and her shirt and face were spattered, but she pulled herself tall in the saddle and met his gaze straight on. *"I'm* the trail boss, Mister."

"You're the trail boss!" Emma Jane had heard that same note of incredulity before. "But your pa—you told me your whole family was goin' back to Illinois!"

"That's right." Emma Jane was meekly polite. "Ma's driving the covered wagon with the little ones. Martin, Easter, and I take care of the herding—and *that's* all the family we've got now, Mister."

He stared at her in open-mouthed amazement. "Well, I'll be danged! How far you come like this?"

"Waco. We left in mid-April."

"Clear from Waco—well, I'll be danged—and plannin' on goin' clear to Chicago—well, I'll be—! But this is no job for a mite of a gal!" The roar rose again and the red beard flashed. "You can't do that!"

"Oh, yes, I can! I'm *doin'* it, Mister."

For a moment, the red beard shook in fiery agitation. Then the quivering thatch of red quieted. A look of admiration swept away the anger in the man's face.

"By the great horn spoon, I guess you are! You've got plenty of spunk. With a bit of luck you may make it at that. You may make it at that!"

"Thanks, Mister. Pa said he *knew* I could do it. And I reckon I will."

∎ ▬ ∎

THINK IT OVER

1. *How does Emma Jane meet the challenge of crossing the Red River?*

2. *What stops Emma Jane from crossing the river immediately?*

3. *Why doesn't Emma Jane want to talk to the red-bearded trail boss until she is on the other side of the river?*

4. *How does the red-bearded trail boss react after Emma Jane has crossed the river?*

WRITE

Do you think Emma Jane does the right thing by swimming after the herd herself? Express your opinion in a letter to Emma Jane.

Whoopee Ti Yi Yo, Git Along, Little Dogies

Traditional Cowboy Song

As I walked out one morning for pleasure,
    I spied a cowpuncher a-ridin' along;
His hat was throwed back and his spurs was a-jinglin',
As he approached me a-singin' this song,

Whoopee ti yi yo, git along, little dogies,
It's your misfortune, and none of my own.
Whoopee ti yi yo, git along, little dogies,
For you know Wyoming will be your new home.

Early in the spring we round up the dogies,
Mark 'em and brand 'em and bob off their tails;
Round up our horses, load up the chuck-wagon,
Then throw the dogies upon the old trail.

It's whooping and yelling and driving the dogies;
Oh, how I wish you would go on!
It's whooping and punching and "Go on little dogies,
For you know Wyoming will be your new home."

Your mother she was raised way down in Texas,
Where the jimson weed and sandburs grow;
Now we'll fill you up on prickly pear and cholla
Till you are ready for the trail to Idaho.

Whoopee ti yi yo, git along, little dogies,
It's your misfortune, and none of my own.
Whoopee ti yi yo, git along, little dogies,
For you know Wyoming will be your new home.

Cattle Stampede
by Robert Lindneux
American, born 1871

FRONTIER DAYS

What three modern-day kitchen appliances would have been most useful during the settling of the Wild West? How would these appliances have changed life on the frontier for the characters in "Red River Crossing"?

. . . .

How did the information in "Chuck-wagon Days" help you become better acquainted with the setting of "Red River Crossing"?

. . . .

WRITER'S WORKSHOP   Imagine Emma Jane from "Red River Crossing" singing "Whoopee Ti Yi Yo, Git Along, Little Dogies" during her long drive. How do the words of the song apply to Emma Jane's experience? What is missing? Write a verse that Emma Jane might add to this song about her experience as a trail boss.

THEME

HUNGRY FOR LEARNING

What if your greatest desire was to learn to read, but you were forbidden to do so? What if the only education you could have was what you taught yourself? Two young boys who lived early in the last century faced these challenges, yet they grew up to be among the most famous men of their time.

CONTENTS

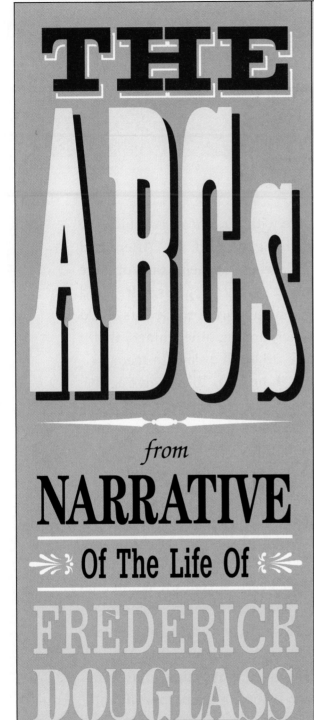

THE ABC's

from

NARRATIVE

Of The Life Of

FREDERICK DOUGLASS

by
Frederick Douglass

Born into slavery in 1818, Frederick Douglass was a brilliant young man who took many risks in his struggle to become free. After escaping from his master in 1838, Douglass went to Massachusetts and became a leading spokesman against slavery. He recruited soldiers for the Union Army during the Civil War, and later held a number of posts in the United States government. He died in Washington in 1895. In the excerpt from his autobiography, you will read how the twelve-year-old Douglass risked his life to learn how to read.

Very soon after I went to live with Mr. and Mrs. Auld, she very kindly commenced to teach me the A, B, C's. After I had learned this, she assisted me in learning to spell words of three or four letters. Just at this point of my progress, Mr. Auld found out what was going on, and at once forbade Mrs. Auld to instruct me further, telling her, among other things, that it was unlawful, as well as unsafe, to teach a slave to read.

To use his own words, further, he said, "If you give a slave an inch, he will take an ell.[1] A slave should know nothing but to obey his master—to do as he is told to do. Learning would *spoil* the best slave in the world. Now," said he, "if you teach that slave (speaking of me) how to read, there would be no keeping him. It would forever unfit him to be a slave. He would at once become unmanageable, and of no value to his master. As to himself, it could do him no good, but a great deal of harm. It would make him discontented and unhappy." These words sank deep into my heart, stirred up sentiments within that lay slumbering, and called into existence an entirely new train of thought. It was a new and special revelation, explaining dark and mysterious things, with which my youthful understanding had struggled, but struggled in vain. I now understood what had been to me a most perplexing difficulty—to wit, the white man's power to enslave the black

---

[1] ell [el]: a unit of length equal to 45 inches

man. It was a grand achievement, and I prized it highly.

From that moment, I understood the pathway from slavery to freedom. It was just what I wanted, and I got it at a time when I the least expected it. Whilst I was saddened by the thought of losing the aid of my kind mistress, I was gladdened by the invaluable instruction which, by the merest accident, I had gained from my master. Though conscious of the difficulty of learning without a teacher, I set out with high hope, and a fixed purpose, at whatever cost of trouble, to learn how to read. The very decided manner with which he spoke, and strove to impress his wife with the evil consequences of giving me instruction, served to convince me that he was deeply sensible of the truths he was uttering. It gave me the best assurance that I might rely with the utmost confidence on the results which, he said, would flow from teaching me to read.

What he most dreaded, that I most desired. What he most loved, that I most hated. That which to him was a great evil, to be carefully shunned, was to me a great good, to be diligently sought; and the argument which he so warmly urged, against my learning to read, only served to inspire me with a desire and determination to learn.

In learning to read, I owe almost as much to the bitter opposition of my master, as to the kindly aid of my mistress. I acknowledge the benefit of both. . . .

My mistress was, as I have said, a kind and tender-hearted woman; and in the simplicity of her soul she commenced, when I first went to live with her, to treat me as she supposed one human being ought to treat another. . . . Slavery proved as injurious to her as it did to me. . . . Under its influence, the tender heart became stone, and the lamblike disposition gave way to one of tiger-like fierceness.

The first step in her downward course was in her ceasing to instruct me. She now commenced to practice her husband's precepts. She finally became even more violent in her opposition than her husband himself. She was not satisfied with simply doing as well as he had commanded; she seemed anxious to do better. Nothing seemed to make her more angry than to see me with a newspaper. She seemed to think that here lay the danger. I have had her rush at me with a face made all up of fury, and snatch from me a newspaper, in a manner that fully revealed her apprehension. She was an apt woman; and a little experience soon demonstrated, to her satisfaction, that education and slavery were incompatible with each other.

From this time I was most narrowly watched. If I was in a separate room any considerable length of time, I was sure to be suspected of having a book, and was at once called to give an account of myself. All this, however, was too late. The first step had been taken. Mistress, in teaching me the alphabet, had given me the *inch*, and no precaution could prevent me from taking the *ell*.

The plan which I adopted, and the one by which I was most successful, was that of making friends of all the little white boys whom I met in the street. As many of these as I could, I converted into teachers. With their kindly aid, obtained at different times and in different places, I finally succeeded in learning to read. When I was sent on errands, I always took my book with me, and by doing one part of my

errand quickly, I found time to get a lesson before my return. I used also to carry bread with me, enough of which was always in the house, and to which I was always welcome; for I was much better off in this regard than many of the poor white children in our neighborhood. This bread I used to bestow upon the hungry little urchins, who, in return, would give me that more valuable bread of knowledge. I am strongly tempted to give the names of two or three of those little boys, as a testimonial of the gratitude and affection I bear them; but prudence forbids—not that it would injure me, but it might embarrass them; for it is almost an unpardonable offence to teach slaves to read in this Christian country. It is enough to say of the dear little fellows, that they lived on Philpot Street, very near Durgin and Bailey's shipyard. I used to talk this matter of slavery over with them. I would sometimes say to them, I wished I could be free as they would be when they got to be men. "You will be free as soon as you are twenty-one, *but I am a slave for life!* Have not I as good a right to be free as you have?" These words used to trouble them; they would express for me the liveliest sympathy, and console me with the hope that something would occur by which I might be free.

I was now about twelve years old, and the thought of being *a slave for life* began to bear heavily upon my heart. Just about this time, I got hold of a book entitled *The Columbian Orator*. Every opportunity I got, I used to read this book. Among much of other interesting matter, I found in it a dialogue between a master and his slave. The slave was represented as having run away from his master three times. The dialogue represented the conversation which took place between them, when the slave was retaken the third time. In this dialogue, the whole argument in behalf of slavery was brought forward by the master, all of which was disposed of by the slave. The slave was made to say some very smart as well as impressive things in reply to his master—things which had the desired though unexpected effect; for the conversation resulted in the voluntary emancipation of the slave on the part of the master. . . .

The idea as to how I might learn to write was suggested to me by being in Durgin and Bailey's shipyard, and frequently seeing the ship carpenters, after hewing, and getting a piece of timber ready for use, write on the timber the name of that part of the ship for which it was intended. When a piece of timber was intended for the larboard side, it would be marked thus— "L." When a piece was for the starboard side, it would be marked thus—"S." A piece for the larboard side forward would be marked thus—"L. F." When a piece was for starboard side forward, it would be marked thus—"S. F." For larboard aft, it would be marked thus—"L. A." For starboard aft, it would be marked thus—"S. A." I soon learned the names of these letters, and for what they were intended when placed upon a piece of timber in the shipyard. I immediately commenced copying them, and in a short time was able to make the four letters named.

After that, when I met with any boy who I knew could write, I would tell him I could write as well as he. The next word would be, "I don't believe you. Let me see you try it." I would then make the letters which I had been so fortunate as to learn, and ask him to beat that. In this way I got a good many lessons in writing, which it is quite possible I should never have gotten in any other way.

During this time, my copy-book was the board fence, brick wall, and pavement; my pen and ink was a lump of chalk. With these, I learned mainly how to write. I then commenced and continued copying the Italics in *Webster's Spelling Book*, until I could make them all without looking on the book. By this time, my little Master Thomas had gone to school, and learned how to write, and had written over a number of copy-books. These had been brought home, and shown to some of our near neighbors, and then laid aside. My mistress used to go to class meeting at the Wilk Street meetinghouse every Monday afternoon, and leave me to take care of the house. When left thus, I used to spend the time in writing in the spaces left in Master Thomas's copy-book, copying what he had written. I continued to do this until I could write a hand very similar to that of Master Thomas. Thus, after a long, tedious effort for years, I finally succeeded in learning how to write.

THINK IT OVER

1. *What do you think Frederick Douglass meant when he said that learning to read was his "pathway from slavery to freedom"?*

2. *Why did Mrs. Auld stop giving Frederick Douglass lessons?*

3. *How did Frederick Douglass cleverly obtain lessons in reading and writing?*

WRITE

Write a few paragraphs relating your memories of first learning to read or write.

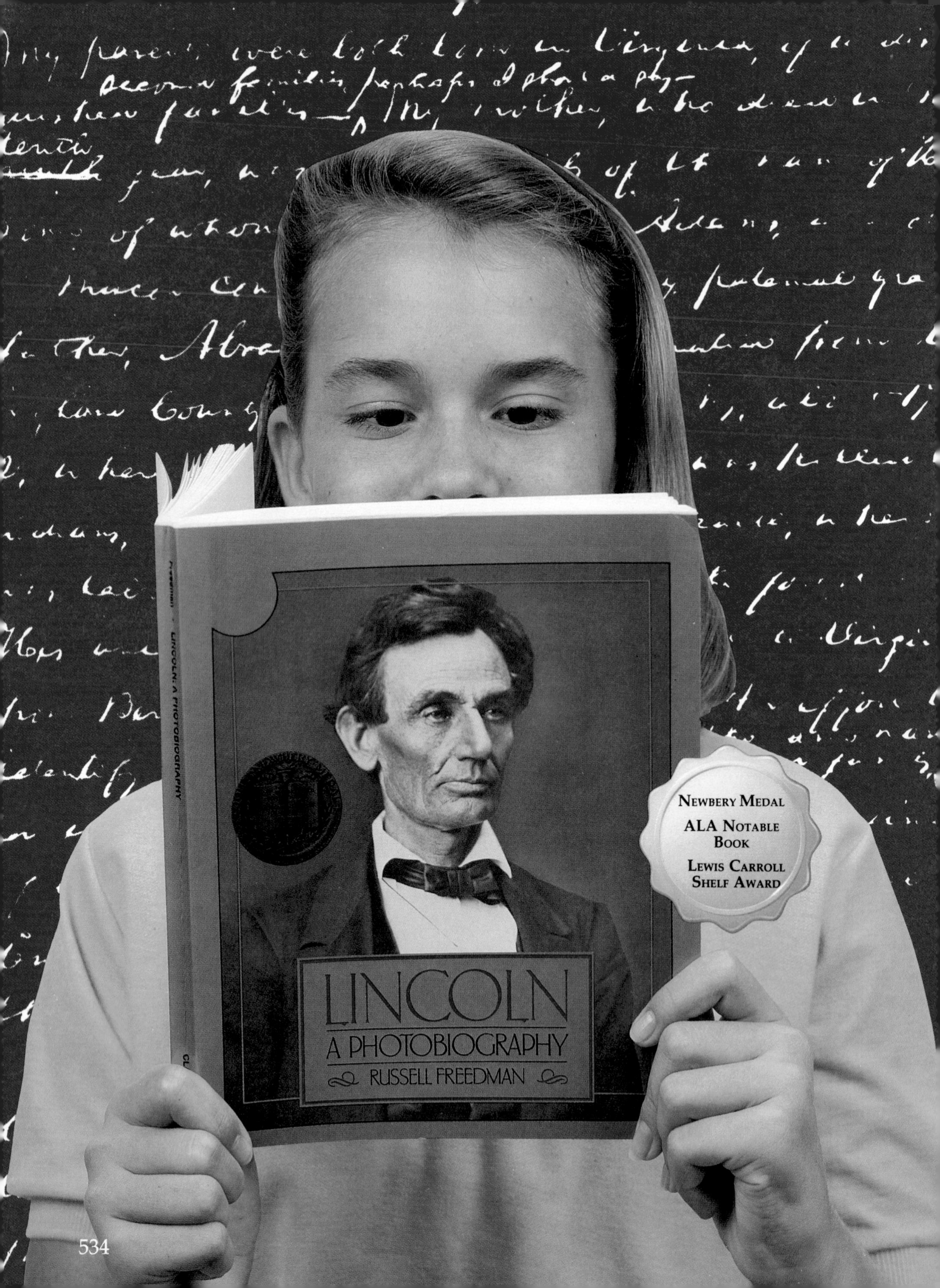
LINCOLN
A PHOTOBIOGRAPHY
RUSSELL FREEDMAN
NEWBERY MEDAL
ALA NOTABLE BOOK
LEWIS CARROLL SHELF AWARD

A Backwoods Boy

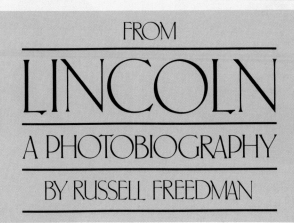

FROM

LINCOLN

A PHOTOBIOGRAPHY

BY RUSSELL FREEDMAN

Abraham Lincoln never liked to talk much about his early life. A poor backwoods farm boy, he grew up swinging an ax on frontier homesteads in Kentucky, Indiana, and Illinois.

He was born near Hodgenville, Kentucky, on February 12, 1809, in a log cabin with one window, one door, a chimney, and a hard-packed dirt floor. His parents named him after his pioneer grandfather. The first Abraham Lincoln had been shot dead by hostile Indians in 1786, while planting a field of corn in the Kentucky wilderness.

Young Abraham was still a toddler when his family packed their belongings and moved to another log-cabin farm a few miles north, on Knob Creek. That was the first home he could remember, the place where he ran and played as a barefoot boy.

He remembered the bright waters of Knob Creek as it tumbled past the Lincoln cabin and disappeared into the Kentucky hills. Once he fell into the rushing creek and almost drowned before he was pulled out by a neighbor boy. Another time he caught a fish and gave it to a passing soldier.

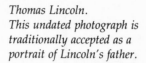

Thomas Lincoln.
*This undated photograph is
traditionally accepted as a
portrait of Lincoln's father.*

*Sarah Bush Lincoln. The
only surviving photograph
of Lincoln's stepmother,
taken about 1865 when she
was seventy-seven.*

Lincoln never forgot the names of his first teachers—Zachariah Riney followed by Caleb Hazel—who ran a windowless log schoolhouse two miles away. It was called a "blab school." Pupils of all ages sat on rough wooden benches and bawled out their lessons aloud. Abraham went there with his sister Sarah, who was two years older, when they could be spared from their chores at home. Holding hands, they would walk through scrub trees and across creek bottoms to the schoolhouse door. They learned their numbers from one to ten, and a smattering of reading, writing, and spelling.

Their parents couldn't read or write at all. Abraham's mother, Nancy, signed her name by making a shakily drawn mark. He would remember her as a thin, sad-eyed woman who labored beside her husband in the fields. She liked to gather the children around her in the evening to recite prayers and Bible stories she had memorized.

His father, Thomas, was a burly, barrel-chested farmer and carpenter who had worked hard at homesteading since marrying Nancy Hanks in 1806. A sociable fellow, his greatest pleasure was to crack jokes and swap stories with his chums. With painful effort, Thomas Lincoln could scrawl his name. Like his wife, he had grown up without education, but that wasn't unusual in those days. He supported his family by living off his own land, and he watched for a chance to better himself.

In 1816, Thomas decided to pull up stakes again and move north to Indiana, which was about to join the Union as the nation's nineteenth state. Abraham was seven. He remembered the one hundred-mile journey as the hardest experience of his life. The family set out on a cold morning in December, loading all their possessions on two horses. They crossed the Ohio River on a makeshift ferry, traveled through towering forests, then hacked a path through tangled underbrush until they reached their new homesite near the backwoods community of Little Pigeon Creek.

Thomas put up a temporary winter shelter—a crude, three-sided lean-to of logs and branches. At the open end, he kept a fire burning to take the edge off the cold and scare off the wild animals. At night, wrapped in bearskins and huddled by the fire, Abraham and Sarah listened to wolves howl and panthers scream.

Abraham passed his eighth birthday in the lean-to. He was big for his age, "a tall spider of a boy," and old enough to handle an ax. He helped his father clear the land. They planted corn and pumpkin seeds between the tree stumps. And they built a new log cabin, the biggest one yet, where Abraham climbed a ladder and slept in a loft beneath the roof.

Soon after the cabin was finished, some of Nancy's kinfolk arrived. Her aunt and uncle with their adopted son Dennis had decided to follow the Lincolns to Indiana. Dennis Hanks became an extra hand for Thomas and a big brother for Abraham, someone to run and wrestle with.

A year later, Nancy's aunt and uncle lay dead, victims of the dreaded "milk sickness" (now known to be caused by a poisonous plant called white snake root). An epidemic of the disease swept through the Indiana woods in the summer of 1818. Nancy had nursed her relatives until the end, and then she too came down with the disease. Abraham watched his mother toss in bed with chills, fever, and pain for seven days before she died at the age of thirty-four. "She knew she was going to die," Dennis Hanks recalled. "She called up the children to her dying side and told them to be good and kind to their father, to one another, and to the world."

Thomas built a coffin from black cherry wood, and nine-year-old Abraham whittled the pegs that held the wooden planks together. They buried Nancy on a windswept hill, next to her aunt and uncle. Sarah, now eleven, took her mother's place, cooking, cleaning, and mending clothes for her father, brother, and cousin Dennis in the forlorn and lonely cabin.

Thomas Lincoln waited for a year. Then he went back to Kentucky to find himself a new wife. He returned in a four-horse wagon with a widow named Sarah Bush Johnston, her three children, and all her household goods. Abraham and his sister were fortunate, for their stepmother was a warm and loving person. She took the motherless children to her heart and raised them as her own. She also spruced up the neglected Lincoln cabin, now shared by eight people who lived, ate, and slept in a single smoky room with a loft.

Abraham was growing fast, shooting up like a sunflower, a spindly youngster with big bony hands, unruly black hair, a dark complexion, and luminous gray eyes. He became an expert with the ax, working alongside his father, who also hired him out to work for others. For twenty-five cents a day, the boy dug wells, built pigpens, split fence rails, felled trees. "My, how he could chop!" exclaimed a friend. "His ax would flash and bite into a sugar tree or a sycamore, and down it would come. If you heard him felling trees in a clearing, you would say there were three men at work, the way the trees fell."

Meanwhile, he went to school "by littles," a few weeks one winter, maybe a month the next. Lincoln said later that all his schooling together "did not amount to one year." Some fragments of his schoolwork still survive, including a verse that he wrote in his homemade arithmetic book: "Abraham Lincoln/his hand and pen/he will be good but/god knows When."

Mostly, he educated himself by borrowing books and newspapers. There are many stories about Lincoln's efforts to find enough books to satisfy him in that backwoods country. Those he liked he read again and again, losing himself in the adventures of *Robinson Crusoe* or the magical tales of *The Arabian Nights*. He was thrilled by a biography of George Washington, with its stirring account of the Revolutionary War. And he came to love the rhyme and rhythm of poetry, reciting passages from Shakespeare or the Scottish poet Robert Burns at the drop of a hat. He would carry a book out to the field with him, so he could read at the end of each plow furrow, while the horse was getting its breath. When noon came, he would sit under a tree and read while he ate. "I never saw Abe after he was twelve that he didn't have a

Lincoln as a flatboatman on the Mississippi River. From an old engraving by H. Brown.

book in his hand or in his pocket," Dennis Hanks remembered. "It didn't seem natural to see a feller read like that."

By the time he was sixteen, Abraham was six feet tall—"the gangliest awkwardest feller . . . he appeared to be all joints," said a neighbor. He may have looked awkward, but hard physical labor had given him a tough, lean body with muscular arms like steel cables. He could grab a woodsman's ax by the handle and hold it straight out at arm's length. And he was one of the best wrestlers and runners around.

He also had a reputation as a comic and storyteller. Like his father, Abraham was fond of talking and listening to talk. About this time he had found a book called *Lessons in Elocution*, which offered advice on public speaking. He practiced before his friends, standing on a tree stump as he entertained them with fiery imitations of the roving preachers and politicians who often visited Little Pigeon Creek.

Folks liked young Lincoln. They regarded him as a good-humored, easy-going boy—a bookworm maybe, but smart and willing to oblige. Yet even then, people noticed that he could be moody and withdrawn. As a friend put it, he was "witty, sad, and reflective by turns."

At the age of seventeen, Abraham left home for a few months to work as a ferryman's helper on the Ohio River. He was eighteen when his sister Sarah died early in 1828, while giving birth to her first child.

That spring, Abraham had a chance to get away from the backwoods and see something of the world. A local merchant named James Gentry hired Lincoln to accompany his son Allen on a twelve hundred-mile flatboat voyage to New Orleans. With their cargo of country produce, the two boys floated down the Ohio River and into the Mississippi, maneuvering with long poles to avoid snags and sandbars, and to navigate in the busy river traffic.

New Orleans was the first real city they had ever seen. Their eyes must have popped as the great harbor came into view, jammed with the masts of sailing ships from distant ports all over the world. The city's cobblestone streets teemed with sailors, traders, and adventurers speaking strange languages. And there were gangs of slaves everywhere. Lincoln would never forget the sight of black men, women, and children being driven along in chains and auctioned off like cattle. In those days, New Orleans had more than two hundred slave dealers.

The boys sold their cargo and their flatboat and returned upriver by steamboat. Abraham earned twenty-four dollars—a good bit of money at the time—for the three-month trip. He handed the money over to his father, according to law and custom.

Thomas Lincoln was thinking about moving on again. Lately he had heard glowing reports about Illinois, where instead of forests there were endless prairies with plenty of rich black soil. Early in 1830, Thomas sold his Indiana farm. The Lincolns piled everything they owned into two ox-drawn wagons and set out over muddy roads, with Abraham, just turned twenty-one, driving one of the wagons himself. They traveled west to their new homesite in central Illinois, not far from Decatur. Once again, Abraham helped his father build a cabin and start a new farm.

He stayed with his family through their first prairie winter, but he was getting restless. He had met an enterprising fellow named Denton Offutt, who wanted him to take another boatload of cargo down the river to New Orleans. Abraham agreed to make the trip with his stepbrother, John Johnston, and a cousin, John Hanks.

When he returned to Illinois three months later, he paid a quick farewell visit to his father and stepmother. Abraham was twenty-two now, of legal age, free to do what he wanted. His parents were settled and could get along without him. Denton Offutt was planning to open a general store in the flourishing village of

New Salem, Illinois, and he had promised Lincoln a steady job.

Lincoln arrived in New Salem in July 1831 wearing a faded cotton shirt and blue jeans too short for his long legs—a "friendless, uneducated, penniless boy," as he later described himself. He tended the counter at Denton Offutt's store and slept in a room at the back.

The village stood in a wooded grove on a bluff above the Sangamon River. Founded just two years earlier, it had about one hundred people living in one- and two-room log houses. Cattle grazed behind split-rail fences, hogs snuffled along dusty lanes, and chickens and geese flapped about underfoot. New Salem was still a small place, but it was growing. The settlers expected it to become a frontier boom town.

With his gifts for swapping stories and making friends, Lincoln fit easily into the life of the village. He showed off his skill with an ax, competed in footraces, and got along with everyone from Mentor Graham, the schoolmaster, to Jack Armstrong, the leader of a rowdy gang called the Clary's Grove boys. Armstrong was the wrestling champion of New Salem. He quickly challenged Lincoln to a match.

On the appointed day, an excited crowd gathered down by the river, placing bets as the wrestlers stripped to the waist for combat. They circled each other, then came to grips, twisting and tugging until they crashed to the ground with Lincoln on top. As he pinned Armstrong's shoulders to the ground, the other Clary's Grove boys dived in to join the scuffle. Lincoln broke away, backed against a cliff, and defiantly offered to take them all on— one at a time. Impressed, Armstrong jumped to his feet and offered Lincoln his hand, declaring the match a draw. After that, they were fast friends.

Lincoln also found a place among the town's intellectuals. He joined the New Salem Debating Society, which met once a week in James Rutledge's tavern. The first time he debated, he seemed nervous. But as he began to speak in his high, reedy voice, he surprised everyone with the force and logic of his argument. "He

Lincoln the Rail Splitter. *Painting by J. L. G. Ferris.*

was already a fine speaker," one debater recalled. "All he lacked was culture."

Lincoln was self-conscious about his meagre education, and ambitious to improve himself. Mentor Graham, the schoolmaster and a fellow debater, took a liking to the young man, lent him books, and offered to coach him in the fine points of English grammar. Lincoln had plenty of time to study. There wasn't much business at Offutt's store, so he could spend long hours reading as he sat behind the counter.

When the store failed in 1832, Offutt moved on to other schemes. Lincoln had to find something else to do. At the age of twenty-three, he decided to run for the Illinois state legislature. Why not? He knew everyone in town, people liked him, and he was rapidly gaining confidence as a public speaker. His friends urged him to run, saying that a bright young man could go far in politics. So Lincoln announced his candidacy and his political platform. He was in favor of local improvements, like better roads and canals. He had made a study of the Sangamon River, and he proposed that it be dredged and cleared so steamboats could call at New Salem—insuring a glorious future for the town.

Before he could start his campaign, an Indian war flared up in northern Illinois. Chief Black Hawk of the Sauk and Fox tribes had crossed the Mississippi, intending, he said, to raise corn on land that had been taken from his people thirty years earlier. The white settlers were alarmed, and the governor called for volunteers to stop the invasion. Lincoln enlisted in a militia company made up of his friends and neighbors. He was surprised and pleased when the men elected him as their captain, with Jack

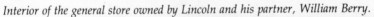

Interior of the general store owned by Lincoln and his partner, William Berry.

Armstrong as first sergeant. His troops drilled and marched, but they never did sight any hostile Indians. Years later, Lincoln would joke about his three-month stint as a military man, telling how he survived "a good many bloody battles with mosquitoes."

By the time he returned to New Salem, election day was just two weeks off. He jumped into the campaign—pitching horse-shoes with voters, speaking at barbecues, chatting with farmers in the fields, joking with customers at country stores. He lost, finishing eighth in a field of thirteen. But in his own precinct, where folks knew him, he received 227 votes out of 300 cast.

Defeated as a politician, he decided to try his luck as a frontier merchant. With a fellow named William Berry as his partner, Lincoln operated a general store that sold everything from axes to beeswax. But the two men showed little aptitude for business, and their store finally "winked out," as Lincoln put it. Then Berry died, leaving Lincoln saddled with a $1,100 debt—a gigantic amount for someone who had never earned more than a few dollars a month. Lincoln called it "the National Debt," but he vowed to repay every cent. He spent the next fifteen years doing so.

To support himself, he worked at all sorts of odd jobs. He split fence rails, hired himself out as a farmhand, helped at the local gristmill. With the help of friends, he was appointed postmaster of New Salem, a part-time job that paid about fifty dollars a year. Then he was offered a chance to become deputy to the local surveyor. He knew nothing about surveying, so he bought a compass, a chain, and a couple of textbooks on the subject. Within six weeks, he had taught himself enough to start work—laying out roads and townsites, and marking off property boundaries.

As he traveled about the county, making surveys and delivering mail to faraway farms, people came to know him as an honest and dependable fellow. Lincoln could be counted on to witness a contract, settle a boundary dispute, or compose a letter for folks who couldn't write much themselves. For the first time, his neighbors began to call him "Abe."

In 1834, Lincoln ran for the state legislature again. This time he placed second in a field of thirteen candidates, and was one of four men elected to the Illinois House of Representatives from Sangamon County. In November, wearing a sixty-dollar tailor-made suit he had bought on credit, the first suit he had ever owned, the twenty-five-year-old legislator climbed into a stagecoach and set out for the state capital in Vandalia.

In those days, Illinois lawmakers were paid three dollars a day to cover their expenses, but only while the legislature was in session. Lincoln still had to earn a living. One of his fellow representatives, a rising young attorney named John Todd Stuart, urged Lincoln to take up the study of law. As Stuart pointed out, it was an ideal profession for anyone with political ambitions.

And in fact, Lincoln had been toying with the idea of becoming a lawyer. For years he had hung around frontier courthouses, watching country lawyers bluster and strut as they cross-examined witnesses and delivered impassioned speeches before juries. He had sat on juries himself, appeared as a witness, drawn up legal documents for his neighbors. He had even argued a few cases before the local justice of the peace.

Yes, the law intrigued him. It would give him a chance to rise in the world, to earn a respected place in the community, to live by his wits instead of by hard physical labor.

Yet Lincoln hesitated, unsure of himself because he had so little formal education. That was no great obstacle, his friend Stuart kept telling him. In the 1830s, few American lawyers had ever seen the inside of a law school. Instead, they "read law" in the office of a practicing attorney until they knew enough to pass their exams.

Lincoln decided to study entirely on his own. He borrowed some law books from Stuart, bought others at an auction, and began to read and memorize legal codes and precedents. Back in New Salem, folks would see him walking down the road, reciting aloud from one of his law books, or lying under a tree as he read, his long legs stretched up the trunk. He studied for nearly three years before passing his exams and being admitted to practice on March 1, 1837.

By then, the state legislature was planning to move from Vandalia to Springfield, which had been named the new capital of Illinois. Lincoln had been elected to a second term in the legislature. And he had accepted a job as junior partner in John Todd Stuart's Springfield law office.

In April, he went back to New Salem for the last time to pack his belongings and say good-bye to his friends. The little village was declining now. Its hopes for growth and prosperity had vanished when the Sangamon River proved too treacherous for steamboat travel. Settlers were moving away, seeking brighter prospects elsewhere.

By 1840, New Salem was a ghost town. It would have been forgotten completely if Abraham Lincoln hadn't gone there to live when he was young, penniless, and ambitious.

THINK IT OVER

1. *Do you think Lincoln's education was a good preparation for a career as a lawyer and public figure? Explain your answer.*

2. *Where and how did Lincoln receive his education?*

3. *What jobs did Lincoln have before becoming a state legislator?*

4. *Was Lincoln successful at everything he undertook? Explain your answer.*

5. *What was Lincoln like as a young man?*

WRITE

As a young boy Lincoln was influenced by reading Robinson Crusoe, The Arabian Nights, *and a biography of George Washington. Write a few paragraphs about a book you particularly enjoyed reading.*

Words from the Author

Russell Freedman

Doing research for a biography is like being a detective. You look for clues, you find clues in other books, you write to sources, such as historical societies. They may not have what you want, but they can send you down the trail somewhere else. And it's like being a detective in the most exciting sense— the best things you find are the things you didn't expect to find, because you didn't know you were looking for them until they turned up.

In doing research for *Lincoln*, for instance, I found the only known photograph taken of a battle in progress. The film was too slow then to take action photographs, so all the pictures you see are of groups or corpses, but not battle shots. In the Library of Congress, I came across this picture taken from the vantage point of a hill. The two opposing armies are in the distance. You are looking down and have the vague impression of soldiers, fighting, dust. It has almost a ghostly quality. I wasn't looking for that photo, because

I didn't know it existed. Another unexpected and lucky find appears in my book *Cowboys of the West*. It's the only known picture of a moving trail drive.

I choose subjects that I am personally interested in learning about for some reason, and I was interested in Lincoln. The Lincoln I grew up with was a cardboard figure, too good to believe. As an adult, I read a couple of books that indicated he was just like everyone else—someone subject to depression, someone who had trouble making up his mind—and that intrigued me. When I had some inkling he was a complicated person in his own right, I decided I wanted to know more about him.

I got to know Lincoln the way I'd try to know anyone in real life. How do you understand people? You observe them, discover their memories, find out their thoughts, their ideas of right and wrong. Once you do that, they become somebody you know. I'd say I know Lincoln better than I know some of my

AWARD-WINNING
AUTHOR

friends because I've studied him more closely.

The most difficult part of writing, whether it's biography or fiction, is deciding what to leave out. You want the reader to bring his own imagination to the piece. In biography you are leaving out most things. Lincoln lived twenty-four hours a day for his whole life. It's the biographer's job to pick out the most significant details, the ones that tell something about the man or woman. There are naturally many, many books written about Lincoln, but that didn't concern me. I thought I could write a biography that would say something special about Lincoln, about the Lincoln I had discovered for myself.

LINCOLN

by Nancy Byrd Turner

There was a boy of other days,
A quiet, awkward, earnest lad,
Who trudged long weary miles to get
A book on which his heart was set—
And then no candle had!

He was too poor to buy a lamp
But very wise in woodmen's ways.
He gathered seasoned bough and stem,
And crisping leaf, and kindled them
Into a ruddy blaze.

Then as he lay full length and read,
The firelight flickered on his face,
And etched his shadow on the gloom,
And made a picture in the room,
In that most humble place.

The hard years came, the hard years went,
But, gentle, brave, and strong of will,
He met them all. And when today
We see his pictured face, we say,
"There's light upon it still."

HUNGRY FOR LEARNING

What message can be found in both "The ABCs" and "A Backwoods Boy"?

. . . .

Frederick Douglass and Abraham Lincoln both faced the challenge of educating themselves. What difficulties did each have to overcome?

. . . .

WRITER'S WORKSHOP You have discovered how Abraham Lincoln and Frederick Douglass managed to educate themselves. Find out about other accomplishments in either Abraham Lincoln's or Frederick Douglass's life. Use what you learn to write a short speech that you will deliver to a group of your classmates.

CIVIL WAR DAYS

If you had lived during the Civil War, you might have faced hardships beyond belief. In the following selections, you will read about a boy who found the courage to meet great responsibilities during the Civil War. You will also read about the man who, as President during the war, bore the responsibilities of the nation.

CONTENTS

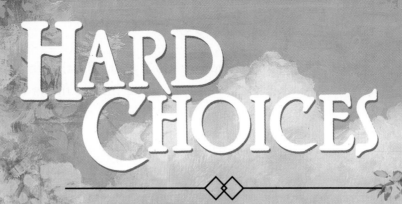

HARD CHOICES

from *Across Five Aprils*

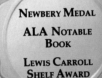

by Irene Hunt

illustrated by Greg Ruhl

Jethro Creighton was too young to enlist in the army when the Civil War began. But Jethro saw his brothers Tom and John, along with his cousin Eb and the local schoolteacher, Shadrach Yale, leave to join the Union army. Tom was killed early in the conflict. Another brother, Bill, left to fight for the Confederacy. Because of his father's illness, Jethro had to work the family's Illinois farm. He and his sister, Jenny, provided not only for their parents, Matt and Ellen, but also for their brother's wife, Nancy, and her two children.

Jethro followed the progress of the war by reading newspapers, when he could get them. What he read depressed him. The Union generals made more mistakes than right moves, and the stories of life on the battlefront were horrible. Starvation and disease drove soldiers to desert in huge numbers. In fact, Jethro's cousin Eb was rumored to be a deserter.

In 1863, two years after the start of the war, Jethro was caught in a battle of his own.

There was an early spring that year. By the first of
March the weather was warm, and the higher fields were
dry enough for plowing. Jethro carried a rifle with him
when he went down to John's place to work; Ellen fretted
a great deal about it, but Matt insisted. Jethro had learned
how to handle a gun properly, and it was always possible
that he might bring down some kind of wild game for the
table, or that he would have need to defend himself
against a desperate man.

The field he plowed that day in early March was bor-
dered on the east by dense woods, and Jethro became
conscious that each time he approached the woods side of
the field, the sharp, harsh call of a wild turkey would
sound out with a strange kind of insistence—almost as if
some stupid bird demanded that he stop and listen. Once
when he halted his team and walked a little distance
toward the woods, the calls came furiously, one after the
other; then when he returned to his team and moved
toward the west, they stopped until he had made the
round of the field.

After several repetitions of this pattern, Jethro teth-
ered his team and, taking up his rifle, walked into the
woods. His heart beat fast as he walked, and his slim
brown hand clutching the rifle was wet with sweat. Ed
Turner was giving him a day's help in the field across the
road, but Jethro chose not to call him although he had a
guilty feeling that he was taking a foolish and dangerous
chance.

He walked slowly and carefully, pausing now and
then to listen. The calls stopped for a while, and he was
half convinced that they had actually come from a wild
bird; he made no move for a few minutes, and they began
again, softer now and more certainly coming from the
throat of a man.

Jethro stood quite still. "Hello," he called finally. "What is it you want of me?"

There was no answer. Then the call came again, softly, insistently, from a clump of trees, one of which was a tremendous old oak—long since hollowed out, first by lightning and then by decay.

Jethro walked closer, his gun raised, and after a minute, the human voice which he had been half expecting to hear called out to him.

"Put yore gun down, Jeth; I ain't aimin' to hurt ye. I didn't dast take the chancet of Ed Turner hearin' me call to ye."

He thought joyfully of Bill at first. He shouldn't have; almost every night he heard his parents talking of Eb and of what uncertainties they would face if he were really a deserter and if he should suddenly appear. But Jethro had forgotten Eb for the moment; the possibility of Bill's return was always a hope far back in his mind.

"Who is it?" he asked again. "Come out and let me see your face."

Then a skeleton came out from among the trees. It was the skeleton of a Union soldier, though the uniform it wore was so ragged and filthy it was difficult to identify. The sunken cheeks were covered with a thin scattering of fuzz; the hair was lank and matted. It fell over the skeleton's forehead and down into its eyes. The boy stared at it without speaking.

"Jeth, you've grown past all believin'. I've bin watchin' you from fur off, and I couldn't git over it—how you've growed."

Then Jethro realized who it was. "Eb," he exclaimed in a voice hardly above a whisper. "It's Eb, ain't it?"

There was utter despair in the soldier's voice.

"Yes," he said, "I reckon it's Eb—what there's left of him."

For a few seconds Jethro forgot the Federal Registrars and the fact that not only the word which preceded Eb, but his method of announcing himself gave credence to the suspicion that he was a deserter. But for those first few seconds Jethro could only remember that this was Eb, a part of the family, the boy who had been close to Tom, the soldier who would have more vivid stories to tell of the war than ever a newspaper would be able to publish. He held out his hand.

"Eb, it's good—it's so good to see you. Pa and Ma will be—" he stopped suddenly. He noticed that Eb ignored his outstretched hand.

"Yore pa and ma will be scairt—that's what you mean, ain't it? Scairt fer themselves and ashamed of me." He paused for a second and then added defiantly, "I deserted, you know; I up and left Ol' Abe's Army of the United States."

Jethro could only stare at his cousin; he could find no words.

"Desertin' ain't a purty word to you, is it? Well, I done it—I don't jest know why. We'd had another skirmish and there was dead boys that we had to bury the next day—and we'd bin licked agin. All at oncet I knowed I couldn't stand it no longer, and I jest up and left. Oncet a man has left, he's done fer. I've bin a long time gittin' home, and now that I'm here, it ain't no comfort."

"Eb, couldn't you just come up to the house and see them for a few hours or so? Couldn't you have a good meal and get cleaned up and tell the folks all you know about Tom?"

"I cain't. I could git 'em into awful trouble. Besides, they would prob'ly jest as soon not set eyes on the likes of me agin."

"But, Eb, if you can't come up to the house, what *did* you come for?"

Eb's face showed quick anger. "I come because I couldn't help myself, that's why. *You* don't know what it's like—you that was allus the baby and the pet of the fam'ly. There be things that air too terr'ble to talk about—and you want to see the fields where you used to be happy, you want to smell the good air of old Illinois so much that you fergit—you go crazy fer an hour or so—and then you don't dare go back."

He shivered and leaned back against a tree trunk as if just talking had taken more strength than he had to spend.

"Have you been down to the Point Prospect camp?" Jethro asked after a while.

"A couple days. It's worse than the war down there with fellers afraid and gittin' meaner as they git more afraid. I didn't come back to be with soldiers anyway. I'm sick of soldiers, livin' and dead; I'm sick of all of 'em." He threw himself down on a thick padding of dead leaves and motioned Jethro to do the same.

"I want ye to tell me about 'em, Jeth—Uncle Matt and Aunt Ellen, Jenny . . ."

"You knew Pa had a heart attack; he's not been himself since. Ma's tolerable, and Jenny's fine. We do the work of the farm together, Jenny and me."

"And John, Shad—where air they? They jined up, didn't they?"

"Yes, John's in Tennessee under a general named Rosecrans. And Shad's in the East with the Army of the Potomac. He was at Antietam Creek and Fredericksburg; you heard of them two battles, didn't you?"

"We hear precious little except what's happenin' in the part of the country we're in. I've heered of Ol' Abe kickin' out that fine McClellan;[1] it's a pity he don't kick out a

---

[1] George McClellan: general in chief of all Union armies from November 1861 to March 1862. Lincoln relieved him of duty because he did not move quickly against the Confederates.

passel of 'em out in the West." Eb seemed absorbed in his angry thoughts for a while; then he looked up at Jethro again.

"And Bill, did ever you hear from him?"

"Not a word," Jethro replied in a voice that was hardly audible.

"I guess you took that hard. You were allus a pet of Bill's."

"All of us took it hard."

"Yore pa wrote Tom and me about it. Tom tried to pertend he didn't keer, but I know he did. He cried oncet—I wouldn't tell that 'cept now it's no matter."

"No," Jethro agreed dully, "now it's no matter."

Eb took a dry twig and broke it up into a dozen pieces, aimlessly.

"How did you git the word about Tom?" he asked finally.

"Dan Lawrence was home on sick leave. His pa brought him over; he told us all about it."

"I was at Pittsburg Landing too, but I didn't know about Tom—not fer two or three days. I wanted to write, but somehow I couldn't do it. Tom and me had bin in swimmin' the day before the Rebs su'prised us; we was both of us in good spirits then, laughin' and carryin' on like we done in the old days back home. Somehow all the spirit in me has bin gone ever since. I could stand things as long as I had Tom along with me."

He ran his hand across his eyes as if to shut out a picture or a memory. "Tell me about little Jenny; is she still in love with Shad Yale?"

"More than ever, I guess. She writes to him a lot; he sets great store by her letters."

"He ought to. A man needs a girl's nice letters when he's sufferin' with the homesick. I wisht I'd had a girl like Jenny to write to me, but there ain't many such as her, I reckon."

Jethro studied Eb's sunken cheeks and dull eyes.

"How do you manage to eat, Eb?"

"I don't do it reg'lar, that's shore. I live off the land—steal a little, shoot me a rabbit or squirrel and cook 'em over a low fire late at night. It ain't good eatin', but nothin's good these days like it used to be."

Jethro's insides twisted in sympathy. "Are you hungry now, Eb?"

"I'm allus hungry. Ye git used to it after a while."

"Nancy fixed me some grub to bring to the field with me; I'll go get it for you."

He ran to the fencerow where he had left two pieces of bread and the cuts from a particularly tender haunch of beef that Nancy had wrapped in a white cloth for him. Ordinarily he would have eaten the snack by midafternoon, but the wild-turkey calls had made him forget it. He returned to Eb minutes later with the food and a jug of water.

They sat together in the shadows, while Eb ate with an appetite that was like a hungry animal's.

"Eb, I've got to tell you," Jethro said quietly after a while. "The soldiers that call themselves the Federal Registrars was at the house lookin' for you last month."

Eb seemed to shrink within himself. He looked at his hands carefully, as if he really cared about inspecting them, and his mouth worked in a strange, convulsive grimace. He wouldn't look at Jethro when he finally spoke.

"I was an awful fool—at least you got a chancet in battle—maybe it's one in a hunderd, but it's a chancet. This way, I got none. There's no place on this earth fer me

to go. Even the camps of deserters don't want fellers as weak and sick as I am; they let me know that quick at Point Prospect. I'll either freeze or starve—or be ketched. I'd give jest about anythin' if I could walk back to my old outfit and pitch into the fightin' again. A soldier don't have to feel ashamed."

Jethro sat for a while trying to think of some way out of the situation; it appeared more hopeless the more he thought. He was frightened—for the despairing man in front of him, for himself, and his family. When he finally spoke, he tried hard to sound reassuring, but the pounding of his heart made his voice shake.

"Well, you stay here till we can think of somethin', Eb. I'm goin' to get you some quilts and things from Nancy's place; I'll bring you what grub I can lay hands on—I can always get eggs and a chicken for you. I think you'd best eat all you can and rest for a spell; we'll think of what's to be done when once you get a little stronger."

Eb looked up then. "You all but fool me into believin' that somethin' *kin* be done, Jeth, but I know better. You ner no one else kin help me now—not even Ol' Abe hisself."

Ol' Abe. Mr. Lincoln. Mr. President.

"I ought to go back to work now, Eb."

"I guess so." Eb looked at him with a suggestion of a smile. "I cain't git used to it—you bein' big enough to handle a team alone. You seem almost a man these days, Jeth; even yore hair ain't quite as yaller and curly as it used to be."

Jethro turned away. "I'll bring you a quilt from Nancy's before I go in for the night," he said shortly.

He walked back to his waiting team; there was still time to plow a dozen furrows before sunset—and to think.

He had faced sorrow when Bill left and fear the night Guy Wortman tried to pull him down from the wagon; he had felt a terrible emptiness the day Shadrach and John went away and deep anger the night he watched the barn burn at the hands of the county ruffians. But in his eleven years he had never been faced with the responsibility of making a fearful decision like the one confronting him.

The authority of the law loomed big in his mind; he remembered, "You and your family will be in serious trouble." Loyalty to his brother Tom and the many thousands who had fought to the last ditch at Pittsburg Landing, at Antietam, Fredericksburg, and all the other places that were adding length to the long list—how could loyalty to these men be true if one were going to harbor and give comfort to a man who simply said, "I quit."

But, on the other hand, how did one feel at night if he awoke and remembered, "I'm the one that sent my cousin to his death." Eb was not a hero, certainly—not now, anyway. People scorned the likes of Eb; sure, so did Jethro, and yet—

"How do I know what *I'd* be like if I were sick and scared and hopeless; how does Ed Turner or Mr. Milton or *any* man know that ain't been there? We got to remember that Eb has been in battles for two years; maybe he's been a hero in them battles, and maybe to go on bein' a hero in a war that has no end in sight is too much to ask. . . . Sure, deep down in me, I want Eb to get out, to leave me free of feelin' that I'm doin' wrong to give him grub, or takin' the risk of keepin' it a secret that he's here. Yes, it would leave me free if he'd just move on—but no, it wouldn't—I ain't goin' to be free when he moves on; I can't set down to a table and forget that someone sick as Eb looks to be is livin' off the land, that he's livin' scared like a wild animal that's bein' hunted.

"But what's it goin' to be like if more and more soldiers quit and go into the woods and leave the fightin' to them that won't quit? What do you say to yourself when you remember that you fed and helped someone like Eb and maybe you get a letter from the East that Shad is killed and you see Jenny grievin', or that John is killed and Nancy and her little boys is left all alone—how do you feel when things like that come up?

"Of course, right now I could say to Pa 'I leave it up to you'—and then what could he do? Why, he'd be caught in the same trap I'm in now; I'd wriggle out of it and leave the decidin' to a sick old man; I'd put him in the spot where any way he decided would be bad—hurtful to a man's conscience. No, there ain't an answer that's any plainer to an old man than it is to me. And what was it that man said the day of the barn-raisin'? 'It's good that you're a boy and don't have to worry yourself about this war.' Why yes, no doubt about it, eleven-year-old boys ain't got a thing to worry about; this year of 1863 is a fine, carefree time for eleven-year-old boys. . . ."

Jenny noticed his preoccupation at supper that night. She waited until the others were out of the kitchen, and she and Jethro were left alone.

"What is it that's on your mind, Jeth?"

"Nothin'. Just tired." He threw himself down in front of the fireplace and closed his eyes. He knew it would be hard to deceive his sister; there was a determination about Jenny.

"You'd better tell me, Jeth. I'll find out, you know."

"You don't give me any worry; there's nothin' to find out."

"Jeth, have you had some news about Shad or John?"

"No, how could I? You know what mail has come."

"You might ha' talked to someone."

"Well, I ain't. Not to anyone that knows a word about Shad or John."

She worked at her dishpan for a while in silence; then she walked over and poked him a little with the toe of her shoe.

"There's somethin', Jeth. Nancy noticed it too. Now I want to know—is it somethin' about Eb? Is he here with the deserters?"

He turned his head away from her; he couldn't remember when he had lied to Jenny, and he wasn't sure that he could do it well.

"Jenny, you vex me when I'm not feelin' so well. Can't I have an upset stummick without you firin' a passel of questions at me?"

She stood looking down at him thoughtfully for a while, and then an idea stemming from experience with older brothers suddenly struck her. She dropped down beside him and whispered her suspicion gleefully in his ear.

"Jeth Creighton, have you been smokin' on the sly? Is *that* what's givin' you an upset stummick?"

He kept his eyes closed and did not answer, knowing his silence would confirm her guess. Jenny was triumphant.

"That's it! I know without your sayin' it," she crowed. "You look white, the way Tom and Eb did once when they tried it."

It was very simple to lie without words; he merely opened his eyes and grinned sheepishly at her.

"I'm su'prised you would be that silly, Jeth. With so much spring work to do, you don't have time to get sick over smokin'." She shook her head. "How do you expect to keep goin' when you didn't more than touch your meal tonight?"

He seized the opportunity to get some food for Eb without detection. "Would you fix me a little bread and meat and slip it up to my room later on, Jenny? I'll likely feel better after a while, and I'm goin' to be hungry when I do."

She sighed, but with a certain satisfaction. There was an adventurous streak in Jenny; she would have liked to try smoking herself if she had dared, and she was a little amused that her sober young brother had been tempted in this direction of most young males.

Jethro lay awake in his room that night and wrestled with his problem. He wondered if, after all, it wouldn't be better to ask his father's advice, but he decided against that almost immediately and as firmly as he had rejected the idea that afternoon. What about Ed Turner, staunch, levelheaded neighbor? No, Ed had two sons in the army; it wouldn't do to lay this responsibility upon Ed's shoulders. He thought of Eb's words, "You ner no one else kin help me now—not even Ol' Abe hisself."

Ol' Abe. Mr. Lincoln. Mr. President. Not even Mr. Lincoln himself!

Jethro turned restlessly in his bed. What if one put it up to Mr. Lincoln? What if one said, "I will abide by the word of him who is highest in this land"? But wasn't that word already known? Wasn't the word from the highest in the land just this: turn in deserters or there will be terrible trouble for you and your family?

But Mr. Lincoln was a man who looked at problems from all sides. Mr. Lincoln was not a faraway man like General McClellan or Senator Sumner or Secretary of State Seward. Mr. Lincoln had plowed fields in Illinois; he had thought of the problems men came up against; he was not ready to say, "Everything on this side of the line is right, and everything on the other side is wrong."

But would one dare? A nobody, a boy on a southern Illinois farm—would he dare? Mr. Lincoln held the highest office in the land; what would he think? Would it vex him that a boy from southern Illinois could be so bold? And anyway, how could one say it? What manner of words could one use so as not to be too forward, too lacking in respect toward the President of the United States?

Jeth realized he was not going to be able to go to sleep. There was a candle in his room; there was some ink and an old pen that Bill had sometimes used. There was also Ross Milton's book—the book on English usage. Jethro got up in the quiet of the night, lighted his candle, opened Ross Milton's book, and began to write on a piece of rough lined paper.

The next morning he hid Jenny's sandwiches inside his coat, and at the barn he picked up a few eggs from the nests up in the loft. He dug an apple out of the straw in the apple-cave; no one would question that—a boy needed something to munch on in midmorning. He would like to have taken some coffee beans—a man lying out in the woods all night needed a hot drink; but that item was one he would not take. Not for Eb, not even for Bill or Shad, would he have taken his mother's coffee. He knew where there were good sassafras roots in the woods; maybe he would burn some brush in the fencerows and heat a little water for sassafras tea. He filched an old kettle and two lumps of sugar, just in case.

Eb was feeling a little better that morning. The quilts Jethro had taken from Nancy's house had made the long night more comfortable; he had washed himself in the creek and looked refreshed.

"You've brung me a feast, Jeth," he said gratefully.

They sat together for a while and talked in low voices.

"I'll be gittin' out in a day or so, Jeth. I cain't hev you takin' all this risk."

"If you could go back to the army, you would, wouldn't you, Eb?"

"You're askin' a man if he had a chancet to live, would he take it. But I've told you, Jeth—a deserter cain't go back. I'll be hunted the rest of my days—but the rest of my days ain't goin' to be too many."

Jethro said nothing, but as he plowed that morning he made up his mind to send the letter. It was a frightening thing to do, but if one did nothing—well, that was frightening too. He knew Eb was not really planning to leave—Eb was a lost and frightened boy, and there was nowhere else to go. For Jethro there was nothing to do but send the letter.

The plowshares needed sharpening, Jethro told his father that noon. Hadn't he better drive over to Hidalgo and get that work done? He'd pick up the mail, too, for themselves and for Ed Turner. Was that all right with his father?

Matt seldom questioned Jethro's decisions. The boy was doing a man's work; he was due the dignity accorded to a man. Matt assented to the trip readily, and Jethro, with the letter in his pocket, drove off down the road, his heart pounding with excitement.

In Hidalgo the old man who took care of the mail glanced sharply at Jethro when he noticed the inscription on the envelope. But he was a silent man with problems of his own; as long as a letter was properly stamped and addressed it was no affair of his. Privately he thought that some people were allowing their young ones to become a little forward, but that was their concern. He threw Jethro's letter in a big bag that would be taken by wagon down to Olney that evening.

The long wait for an answer was interminable. Jethro tossed at night and wondered: had he done an impudent thing, had he laid himself open to trouble, had he been a fool to think that a boy of his age might act without the advice of his elders? Sometimes he got up and walked about his narrow room, but that was bad, for Jenny would hear him. Once she came to his door, and she was crying.

"Jeth—Jeth, what is it? What's botherin' you? Ain't we good friends anymore, ain't you goin' to tell me?"

He had to be curt with her to forestall any more questions. After that she didn't come to his door again, but he knew that if he stirred or moaned under his burden of worry, both Jenny and Nancy would hear him and worry through a sleepless night.

Eb's often reiterated, "I'll be goin' on soon, Jeth; I won't be a burden to you much longer," became like the whippoorwill's cry—always the same and never ending. Jethro closed his ears to it, but the tensions within him mounted, and the necessity of providing for Eb's needs in strictest secrecy became a task that seemed to grow in magnitude as the days went by.

"If I could be sure I'm doin' the right thing," he would say to himself, as he watched the dark earth fall away from his plowshares. "If I could feel really set-up about doin' a fine thing, but I don't know. Maybe I'm doin' somethin' terrible wrong; maybe the next time they come, the Federal Registrars will take me."

The letter came one noon when they were all seated at dinner. As so often happened, it was Ed Turner who brought the mail out from town. Jenny ran to the door, eager for a letter from Shadrach; Nancy's eyes pleaded for word from John.

But Ed held only one large envelope, and that was addressed to Jethro in a small, cramped handwriting done in very black ink. It was postmarked Washington, D.C.

"Looks like purty important mail you're gittin', Jethro," Ed said quietly. His eyes were full of puzzled concern.

Jethro's head swam. This was the showdown; now, all the family, Ed Turner, and soon the neighborhood would know everything. In the few seconds that passed before he opened the envelope, he wished with all his heart that he had not meddled in the affairs of a country at war, that he had let Eb work out his own problems, that he, Jethro, were still a sheltered young boy who did the tasks his father set for him and shunned the idea that he dare think for himself. He looked at the faces around him, and they spun in a strange mist of color—black eyes and blue eyes, gray hair and gold and black, pink cheeks and pale ones and weather-beaten brown ones.

He read the letter through, word for word, and while he read, there wasn't a sound in the cabin beyond the slight rustle of the page in the shaking hand that held it. When he was through, he held the letter out to Jenny, with a long sigh.

"You can read it out loud, Jenny."

Jenny stared at him as if he were a stranger; then she shook her head.

"It's your letter, Jeth; you'd best do the readin'."

He didn't know whether he could or not—there was a great pounding in his ears and his breath was short—but he ran his hand across his eyes and swallowed hard. After the first few words, his voice grew steady, and he read the letter through without faltering.

Master Jethro Creighton
Hidalgo, Illinois

Dear Jethro,

Mr. Hay has called my attention to your letter, knowing as he does the place in my affection for boys of your age and the interest I have in letters coming from my home state of Illinois.

The problem which you describe is one, among so many others, that has troubled both my waking thoughts and those that intrude upon my sleep. The gravity of that problem has become of far-reaching significance and is one in which the authority of military regulations, the decline of moral responsibility, and the question of ordinary human compassion are so involved as to present a situation in which a solution becomes agonizingly difficult.

I had, however, made a decision relative to this problem only a few days before receiving your letter. There will be much criticism of that decision, but you will understand when I say if it be a wrong one, I have then erred on the side of mercy.

The conditions of that decision are as follows: all soldiers improperly absent from their posts, who will report at certain points designated by local recruit offices by April 1, will be restored to their respective regiments without punishment except for forfeiture of pay and allowances for the period of their absence.

This information you may relay to the young man in question, and I pray that the remorse and despair which he has known since the time of his desertion will bring his better self to the cause for which so many of his young compatriots have laid down their lives.

May God bless you for the earnestness with which you have tried to seek out what is right; may He guide both of us in that search during the days ahead of us.

Yours, very sincerely and respectfully,
Abraham Lincoln

THINK IT OVER

1. In your opinion, did Jethro handle the situation with Eb in a mature way? Explain your answer.

2. How did the Civil War change the lives of Jethro and his family?

3. Why didn't Jethro tell anyone about Eb?

WRITE

Do you feel that President Lincoln made the right decision in allowing the deserters to rejoin the army? Write an opinion paragraph explaining your answer.

Lincoln Monument: WASHINGTON

by Langston Hughes

Let's go see Old Abe
Sitting in the marble and the moonlight,
Sitting lonely in the marble and the moonlight,
Quiet for ten thousand centuries, old Abe.
Quiet for a million, million years.

Quiet—

And yet a voice forever
Against the
Timeless walls
Of time—
Old Abe.

AWARD-WINNING
POET

CIVIL WAR DAYS

In what ways are both President Lincoln and Jethro from "Hard Choices" heroes of the Civil War?

. . . .

Compare the letter in the story with the poem "Lincoln Monument: Washington." What does each say about President Lincoln's character?

. . . .

WRITER'S WORKSHOP Think about how Eb will feel when Jethro tells him about President Lincoln's letter. Write a letter from Eb to President Lincoln, expressing Eb's feelings about having deserted as well as his gratitude to President Lincoln for letting him rejoin the Union army.

CONNECTIONS

Nat Love

COWHANDS IN THE AMERICAN WEST

Most people know that cowhands helped open up the American West, but few realize that about a third of all cowhands were Mexicans and African Americans.

The first cowhands were Mexican *vaqueros* (Spanish for "cowhands"). The *vaqueros* introduced the skills of roping and riding as well as much of the gear cowhands use—the large hat, the chaps, the lasso, and the spurs. Many Mexicans took part in the great cattle drives from Texas to Kansas.

African American cowhands also joined the cattle drives, and some later became famous. Nat Love earned the name "Deadwood Dick" by winning roping and shooting contests in Deadwood, South Dakota. Bill Pickett and Jesse Stahl were among the first great rodeo stars. Today, African American cowhands continue to compete in rodeos.

■ *If you were a cowhand, which part of your job would you like the best? Choose a nickname for yourself, as Nat Love did. Then explain to your classmates why you chose your nickname and which part of a cowhand's job you would like the best.*

LIFE IN THE OLD WEST

Choose a feature of western life to research, such as rodeos, cattle drives, ranching, famous cowhands, or women's roles. Organize your information in an outline like the one below. Then give an oral report in a small group, and join in a discussion of your classmates' reports.

(FAMOUS COWHAND)

I. **Youth**
   A.
   B.

II. **Early cowhand days**
   A.
   B.

III. **Champion cowhand**
   A.
   B.

BUFFALO BILL'S WILD WEST
CONGRESS, ROUGH RIDERS OF THE WORLD

MISS ANNIE OAKLEY,
THE PEERLESS LADY WING-SHOT.

LANGUAGE ARTS CONNECTION

LETTERS FROM THE WEST

A few hardy tourists visited the West in the days of the great cattle drives. Imagine that you are one of these tourists. Write a letter to your family back home, telling them about your experiences in the "Wild West."

Cowhands of the
Duke Ranch, Texas, 1930

Modern cowhand
Jesse Jones

Handbook for Readers and Writers

ACTIVE READING STRATEGIES

Chances are that you are familiar with using reading strategies. You probably preview and set your purposes for reading automatically now, and don't even have to think about predicting. Just to refresh your memory, however, look at this chart of some useful reading strategies.

BEFORE READING	DURING READING	AFTER READING
✓ preview	✓ check predictions	✓ evaluate
✓ think about the topic	✓ make new predictions	✓ summarize
✓ predict	✓ visualize	✓ compare
✓ set a purpose	✓ check understanding	
	✓ reread	
	✓ summarize parts	
	✓ take notes	
	✓ compare to what you know	
	✓ ask questions, read for answers	
	✓ adjust reading rate	

Now that you are familiar with these helpful reading strategies, you need to learn how to decide which ones to use when. You can make your reading more difficult for yourself if you struggle to use every strategy with everything you read. Here are some helpful hints.

Before reading

Use all these strategies. They are always helpful. You may not even realize you are thinking about the topic and predicting when you tell yourself that you want to read another mystery story by an author whose books you have read before. However, that is just what you are doing, and it helps.

During reading

Your purpose for reading can help
you decide which strategies to use.

If you are reading for pleasure,
you often don't need
- ✓ to check your
  understanding
- ✓ to stop to reread
- ✓ to take notes
- ✓ to summarize

**If your purpose is to learn from
what you are reading,** you will
probably need
- ✓ to read carefully and
  pay attention to details
- ✓ to visualize, or try to see in your mind how
  something looks
- ✓ to reread, summarize, and take notes
- ✓ to think about what you already know about the subject. This
  is very important when you are reading to learn more. You
  need to change and add to what you know as you read, and
  always think about the connections between the new
  information and your prior knowledge.

After reading

Always take a minute to **evaluate.** Did you like the story? Was
the article useful? If you were reading to learn information,
evaluating will help you to **summarize.** You may automatically
compare by thinking about whether you enjoyed the mystery
story more than one you read earlier.

Finally, remember that you are the one who knows best how to
help yourself read better. Know **how** to use the strategies, and
know **when** to use them.

READING FICTION

When you read fiction, your main purpose is often entertainment. But even when you are reading for pleasure, it is worthwhile to use strategies. Previewing, predicting, visualizing, and drawing conclusions—to name only a few—can help you get more out of your reading.

As Guido reads the first pages of "Milo's Mystery Tour," he puts the strategies he knows to good use. Follow his thoughts in the sidenotes.

From the words Mystery *and* Phantom *in the title, I'd say this is going to be a fantasy, not a realistic story.*

The first sentence shows that Milo has a bad problem. Maybe he is the problem! I know that a fiction story usually is about a problem and its solution. I predict that something will happen to solve Milo's problem.

Milo is really bored. I've felt the way he does, but not all the time about everything.

Milo's Mystery Tour
from
The Phantom Tollbooth
by Norton Juster

There was once a boy named Milo who didn't know what to do with himself—not just sometimes, but always.

When he was in school he longed to be out, and when he was out he longed to be in. On the way he thought about coming home, and coming home he thought about going. Wherever he was he wished he were somewhere else, and when he got there he wondered why he'd bothered. Nothing really interested him—least of all the things that should have.

"It seems to me that almost everything is a waste of time," he remarked one day as he walked dejectedly home from school. "I can't see the point in learning to solve useless problems, or subtracting turnips from turnips, or knowing where Ethiopia is or how to spell February." And, since no one bothered to explain otherwise, he regarded the process of seeking knowledge as the greatest waste of time of all.

As he and his unhappy thoughts hurried along (for while he was never anxious to be where he was going, he liked to get there as quickly as possible) it seemed a great wonder that the world, which was so large, could sometimes feel so small and empty.

"Punctuated"? This is a funny way to use this word, but I can tell what the author means.

This part about the sparrow is sort of funny and exaggerated. I think I'm right about this being a fantasy.

Wow! Is Milo rich! How can he be bored and depressed with all that stuff? Maybe the story will tell me.

OK. Here's something mysterious. Maybe it will help Milo. This is getting good!

I'd better read this paragraph again. I can't see in my mind what the package is like . . . oh, I get it. The description is supposed to be strange. This story is definitely a fantasy.

What is in the package? Let's see . . . a tollbooth and a trip are mentioned in the title. I wonder if there's a connection between the trip, the tollbooth, and this mysterious package. I want to read the rest of the story to find out.

"And worst of all," he continued sadly, "there's nothing for me to do, nowhere I'd care to go, and hardly anything worth seeing." He punctuated this last thought with such a deep sigh that a house sparrow singing nearby stopped and rushed home to be with his family.

Without stopping or looking up, he rushed past the buildings and busy shops that lined the street and in a few minutes reached home—dashed through the lobby—hopped onto the elevator—two, three, four, five, six, seven, eight, and off again—opened the apartment door—rushed into his room—flopped dejectedly into a chair, and grumbled softly, "Another long afternoon."

He looked glumly at all the things he owned. The books that were too much trouble to read, the tools he'd never learned to use, the small electric automobile he hadn't driven in months—or was it years?—and the hundreds of other games and toys, and bats and balls, and bits and pieces scattered around him. And then, to one side of the room, just next to the phonograph, he noticed something he had certainly never seen before.

Who could possibly have left such an enormous package and such a strange one? For, while it was not quite square, it was definitely not round, and for its size it was larger than almost any other big package of smaller dimension that he'd ever seen.

Attached to one side was a bright-blue envelope which said simply: "FOR MILO, WHO HAS PLENTY OF TIME."

(See pages 22–41 for the entire selection "Milo's Mystery Tour.")

READING NONFICTION

How are an article on spiders, a book about the Vietnamese, and an encyclopedia entry for hockey alike? They are all non-fiction and contain facts, or information, about their topics.

The information is often organized under headings. Illustrations and diagrams may be included to make things clear. Whatever the topic or form of a nonfiction selection, special strategies can help you read it more effectively. One of these is known as **K-W-L.** Margarita uses it as she reads "A New Way of Life." Here is how she applies the strategy.

- **K** stands for "What I **K**now." She asks herself what she already knows about the topic. Then she previews the selection.

- **W** means "What I **W**ant to Know." She thinks of questions that she wants to answer as she reads. They are based on what she already knows about the topic and on what she sees in her preview.

- **L** is for "What I **L**earned." After she reads, she summarizes what she has learned. She reviews her questions to see whether she has learned what she hoped to.

Before she reads, Margarita makes a chart with a column for each of the three steps of **K-W-L.** She fills the first two columns with notes as she goes through the **K** and **W** steps before she reads.

K-W-L Strategy

What I **K**now	What I **W**ant to Know	What I **L**earned
The United States fought a war in Vietnam. Vietnam is a country in Southeast Asia. Immigrants from Vietnam live in the United States.	What problems do they face here? What are their families like?	

The sidenotes on the next page show Margarita's thoughts as she starts to read this part of the selection and thinks about her **W** questions. Afterward, she will write her answers and summary in the third column of her chart.

A New Way of Life
from
The Vietnamese in America
by Paul Rutledge

Immigrants have been coming to the United States since early in its history. Among the most recent groups of immigrants are people from Vietnam, a country in Southeast Asia.

Almost every aspect of daily life changes for Vietnamese refugees who settle in the United States. Attitudes toward the family, methods of education, language, even as common a matter as shopping for food—all these can be sources of culture shock for the Vietnamese. Their backgrounds, habits, and ways of everyday life are sometimes the opposite of American customs, and trying to blend the old ways with the new may cause the refugees bewilderment, pain, and conflict.

Here are some problems the Vietnamese face.

Family

The Vietnamese family is under a great deal of pressure in trying to adjust to the American way of life. In the United States, a family usually consists of father, mother, and children. In Vietnam, a family is an extended one that includes the parents and the younger children, grandparents, married children, aunts, uncles, and a variety of other relatives. In some cases, all the members of an extended family live in the same house.

The family is the center of Vietnamese society, and it is the responsibility of every member to help the family survive. But the size of an extended Vietnamese family can make it difficult to find housing in America. Families want to establish themselves as close units but often cannot find adjacent housing large enough to accommodate 20 or 30 relatives.

This section tells about Vietnamese families.

In the Vietnamese culture, the older a person is, the more he or she is respected. Young people are always expected to seek the advice of older persons within the family. Children are taught to listen to and accept the decisions of their elders. In the traditional American family, however, individual members are more independent. In the United States, children are taught and advised by their parents in a less structured way.

When young Vietnamese refugees become friends with young Americans and see the more informal relationships between them and their families, the Vietnamese are likely to want the same kind of independence—something their Vietnamese parents find difficult to accept.

Here is another problem the Vietnamese have in the United States.

Education

The Vietnamese culture places a high value on education. As persons of knowledge, teachers are considered some of the most important members of society.

Before the Europeans entered Vietnam, the Confucian system of education dominated the country. This system was based on memorization.

This part tells about Vietnamese education.

(See pages 208–215 for the entire selection "A New Way of Life.")

VOCABULARY STRATEGIES

Many English words are taken from other languages. Words with Greek and Latin origins became part of the English language centuries ago. Even today, scientists and technicians use Greek and Latin roots to form new words.

Knowing the meanings of Greek and Latin roots can help you figure out some unfamiliar words. When you break down an unfamiliar word into parts that you recognize, you are using a strategy called **structural analysis.** Keep in mind that a word may include a prefix and a suffix added to a Latin or a Greek root. When you know the meanings of just a few of these word parts, you can figure out many words.

Another vocabulary strategy is using **context clues,** or hints from the text surrounding the unknown word.

When all else fails, a **dictionary** or a **glossary** can give you a word's definition.

Sometimes a word's **denotation,** or dictionary definition, doesn't tell exactly what it means in context. This is because a word often has **connotations**—ideas or feelings suggested that go beyond the dictionary definition.
Look at these sentences.

Dolphins are <u>friendly</u> animals with <u>turned-up</u> mouths and <u>bottle-shaped noses</u>.

Dolphins are <u>social</u> animals with <u>crooked</u> mouths and <u>beaklike snouts</u>.

The underlined words in the first sentence have almost identical denotations to the underlined words in the second sentence. The first sentence makes you think well of dolphins. The underlined words have mostly positive connotations. But the second sentence doesn't suggest such good feelings. The words *beaklike snout* even have negative connotations. Wouldn't you rather have a nose than a snout?

The paragraph in the box below contains some underlined words that you may not recognize. The sidenotes show how to use structural analysis and context clues to figure them out. Sometimes you can combine these strategies.

The sentence tells you that <u>depict</u> has something to do with describing dolphins. The same Latin root, *pict*, is in the word *picture*.

<u>Biology</u> is formed from two Greek roots. *Bio* means "life" and *logy* means "study of."

The words *entertained*, *audiences*, and *tales* should tell you what <u>bards</u> are.

<u>Regaled</u> is defined by the **appositive** following it.

Two Latin roots combine in <u>transformed</u>. *Trans* means "over." *Form* is "shape."

The words *instead of* show that <u>deity</u> is an **antonym**, or opposite, of *human*.

Capt, the Latin root for "seize," is the base of <u>captor</u>. The suffix *-or* means "one who."

Myths <u>depict</u> dolphins differently than do the cold descriptions of <u>biology</u>. Ancient Greek <u>bards</u> <u>regaled</u>, or entertained, their audiences with tales of these sea creatures. They said that the god Apollo <u>transformed</u> himself into a dolphin, seized a ship, and steered it to land. He persuaded the passengers to become priests in his temple. The Greeks also believed that pirates once captured the god Dionysus. The pirates thought that he was a human instead of a <u>deity</u>. Dionysus changed his <u>captors</u> into dolphins. The Greeks said the reason dolphins are friendly to humans is that they were once <u>mortals</u> themselves.

This sentence suggests that *humans* is a **synonym** for <u>mortals</u>.

SPEAKING

Speaking effectively is one of the most important skills you'll ever learn. Speaking is our main way of communicating our ideas, opinions, and feelings to other people. The best way to become a confident and effective speaker is to identify your purpose, prepare, and practice.

IDENTIFY PURPOSE: Think about your purpose for speaking. Decide what you want to say and why you think it's important. The four general purposes for speaking are **sharing information, giving directions, entertaining,** and **persuading.**

PREPARE: Prepare your speech well ahead of time by researching your subject and making notes. Study your notes so you are thoroughly familiar with your subject.

PRACTICE: By yourself or with a partner, practice giving your speech. Speak clearly, slowly, and loudly enough to be understood. Refer to your notes when necessary.

Ms. Alvarez has asked her students to give a presentation in front of the class. The students will choose their own topics and identify their purposes. Miko and Juanita are practicing their presentations together.

- Miko plans to talk about the importance of recycling. Her purpose is to **share information** about our environment and **persuade** her classmates to recycle. Juanita suggests that Miko include specific information about how to recycle. Miko decides to **give directions** about how to sort the trash for recycling.

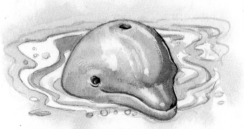

- Juanita has written a story about a dolphin named Gabriella for her class presentation. Her purpose is to **entertain.** Miko suggests ways that Juanita can improve her reading style. Juanita practices slowing down and adding more emotion as she reads.

LISTENING

Listening well doesn't come naturally for many people. Like reading, writing, and speaking, listening is an important skill that takes practice.

IDENTIFY PURPOSE: Just as you set a purpose for reading to help you read better, you should also think about your purpose for listening. Decide what you are listening for. Three general purposes for listening are **listening for information, listening for directions,** and **listening for appreciation.**

THINK ABOUT YOUR BEHAVIOR: Listen to others as you would like them to listen to you. Keep your mind open to other people's feelings and ideas. Show respect by giving your attention to the speaker. Don't interrupt. Respond appropriately. That can mean clapping after a performance in a theater, or asking questions after your classmate gives an oral report.

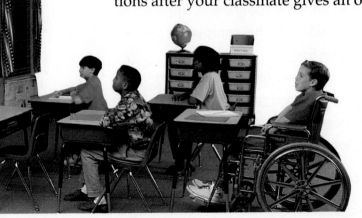

- Miko's classmates are **listening for information** about environmental problems and the importance of recycling. They are also **listening for directions.** They are finding out how to recycle. At the end of Miko's presentation, several students ask questions about recycling.

- Juanita's classmates are **listening for appreciation.** They are enjoying her story about Gabriella, the dolphin. They listen quietly but laugh at the funny things that Gabriella does in the story.

THE WRITING PROCESS

To communicate effectively in writing, you need to start with a plan. The writing process can help. Before you begin, decide the **what, who,** and **why** of your writing.

1. **What** is your **task**? What kind of writing will you be doing?
2. **Who** is your **audience**? Who will read or listen to your work?
3. **Why** are you writing? What is your **purpose**?

Roger answers these questions by deciding to write some comparison-and-contrast paragraphs for the purpose of informing his classmates about something that interests him. Now he is ready to start the process.

PREWRITING

Roger's first step is to choose a subject. He considers Asia and Africa, but they are too big and varied for an effective comparison and contrast. He has read a lot about Egypt, but what can he compare it to? He decides to compare ancient and modern Egypt.

Once he has his topic, Roger lists subtopics to compare and contrast. Three that interest him are farming, houses, and games.

After reading and taking notes, Roger draws a Venn diagram for each subtopic. His diagram for farming looks like this. Similarities are shown where the two circles overlap.

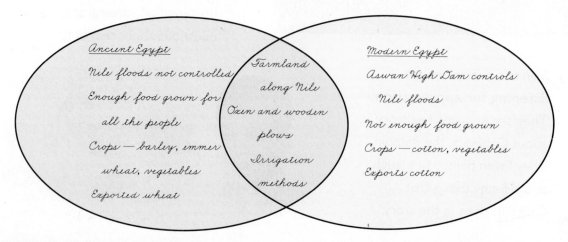

Ancient Egypt
Nile floods not controlled
Enough food grown for
all the people
Crops — barley, emmer
wheat, vegetables
Exported wheat

Farmland along Nile
Oxen and wooden plows
Irrigation methods

Modern Egypt
Aswan High Dam controls
Nile floods
Not enough food grown
Crops — cotton, vegetables
Exports cotton

DRAFTING

When Roger is satisfied with his planning, he begins writing by drafting a paragraph about similarities in ancient and modern farming. Then he drafts a paragraph about the differences. He writes freely, without worrying about errors. He knows he can correct any errors later. He also knows he can go back to the prewriting stage if it's necessary to collect more information.

RESPONDING AND REVISING

Now Roger is ready to ask his writing group to respond to his draft. Here are some questions they ask themselves as they read:

- Does the beginning catch the reader's interest?
- Is there anything the reader doesn't understand?
- Are the main points and details presented in order?
- Are there any details that could be left out?

Roger thinks about the suggestions of his writing group and uses editor's marks to make some revisions.

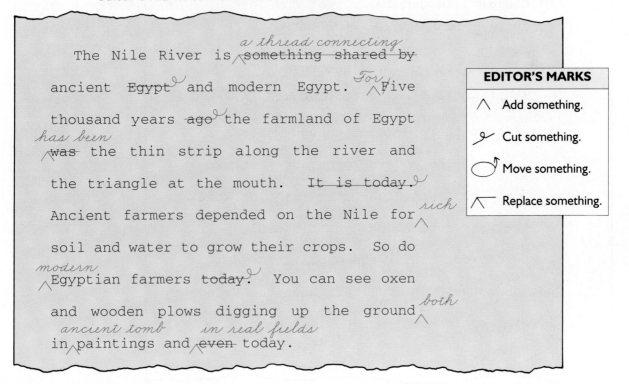

The Nile River is ^*a thread connecting* something shared by ancient Egypt~~ and modern Egypt. ^*For* ~~Five~~ thousand years ~~ago~~ the farmland of Egypt ^*has been* ~~was~~ the thin strip along the river and the triangle at the mouth. ~~It is today.~~ Ancient farmers depended on the Nile for ^*rich* soil and water to grow their crops. So do ^*modern* Egyptian farmers ~~today~~. You can see oxen and wooden plows digging up the ground ^*both* in ^*ancient tomb* paintings and ~~even~~ ^*in real fields* today.

EDITOR'S MARKS

∧	Add something.
✄	Cut something.
⟳	Move something.
∧̷	Replace something.

PROOFREADING

When Roger has made his revisions, he is ready to check his writing for errors. He corrects them with more editor's marks.

EDITOR'S MARKS	
☰ Capitalize.	↻ Transpose.
⊙ Add a period.	◯ Spell correctly.
⋀ Add a comma.	⊬ Indent paragraph.
ＶＶ Add quotation marks.	/ Make a lowercase letter.

Roger made corrections in the part of his contrast paragraph shown below. Compare these corrections with the checklist that he used. You will find it at the top of the next page.

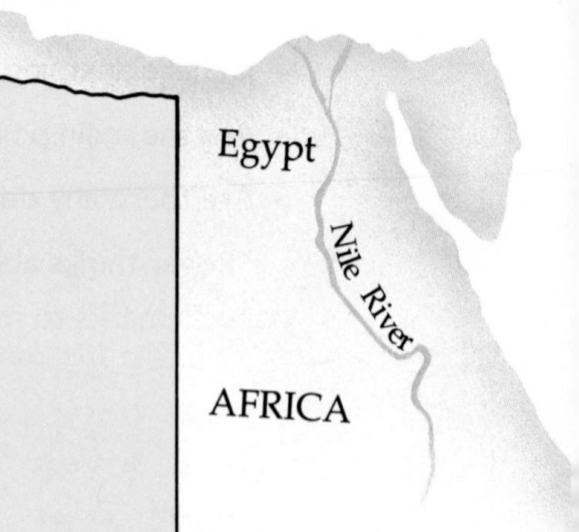

⊬ Some things are different for ~~M~~odern

Egyptian farmers⊙ In ancient times, the

Nile ~~r~~iver flooded every year and left

behind ⟨furtile⟩ *fertile* soil. ~~s~~ome years it

overflowed too much and destroyed

everything. Sometimes it flooded too

little, so there ~~weren't~~ *wasn't* enough water for

the crops. The ~~M~~odern Egyptians⋀however⋀

~~builded~~ *built* the Aswan High Dam. It holds some

of the waters back so that it doesn't

cause ⟨damige⟩ *damage*. This water ⟨in a lake⟩ is
                                              ↻

saved and used in dry years when the Nile

River doesn't have enough water to grow

the crops.

Egypt

Nile River

AFRICA

PROOFREADING CHECKLIST

- Use this symbol to show where to indent paragraphs: ⁋ .
- Use this mark to capitalize a letter: ≡ . Make a letter lowercase with this: ╱ .
- Use this symbol to replace a word: ∧‾ .
- Add a period with this mark: ⊙ . Add a comma with this: ⋀ .
- Circle misspelled words. Write the correct spelling above. Write the words in your spelling notebook.
- Use these symbols to change the order of things: ∽ and ↶ .

PUBLISHING

Roger neatly copies his paragraphs, making all the corrections. He can publish his work by letting his classmates read his clean copy, or he can come up with some other ideas.

- Roger could make a book about ancient and modern Egypt. He could illustrate the similarities and differences with drawings.
- With his writing group, he might turn his paragraphs into a dramatization about some ancient Egyptians "time traveling" to modern Egypt.
- He could present his paragraphs as a speech to his class and use a chart like the one below to point out similarities and differences in the two Egypts.

Egypt		
	Ancient	**Modern**
Similarities		
Differences		

RESEARCHING INFORMATION

Research is not just something you need to do for school. Think of researching as a helpful learning tool that you can use for many different purposes. For example, suppose that your favorite basketball player is Michael Jordan and you want to find out what he was like when he was younger. You can go to a library and use your research skills to find magazine and newspaper articles as well as books about Michael Jordan's life. What if your uncle gives you a puppy? You can do research to learn how to take care of it. **Skimming, scanning,** and **taking notes** are useful skills that will help you do research more effectively.

SKIMMING means looking over a book or reference source quickly to identify its subject and find out how it is organized. Pay attention to divisions and headings. The purpose of skimming is to help you locate sections that you want to go back to and read carefully. Skimming saves time because it shows you which sections do not relate to your topic.

SCANNING means looking quickly through a passage to find key words or phrases. Scanning is a fast way to locate specific information.

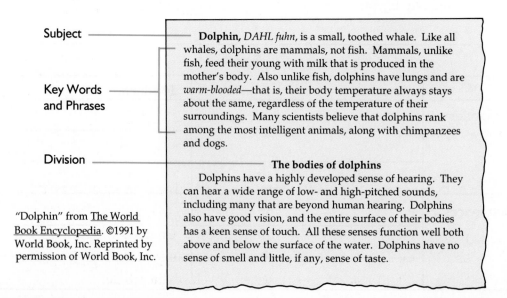

Subject

Key Words and Phrases

Division

"Dolphin" from The World Book Encyclopedia. ©1991 by World Book, Inc. Reprinted by permission of World Book, Inc.

Dolphin, *DAHL fuhn,* is a small, toothed whale. Like all whales, dolphins are mammals, not fish. Mammals, unlike fish, feed their young with milk that is produced in the mother's body. Also unlike fish, dolphins have lungs and are *warm-blooded*—that is, their body temperature always stays about the same, regardless of the temperature of their surroundings. Many scientists believe that dolphins rank among the most intelligent animals, along with chimpanzees and dogs.

The bodies of dolphins
Dolphins have a highly developed sense of hearing. They can hear a wide range of low- and high-pitched sounds, including many that are beyond human hearing. Dolphins also have good vision, and the entire surface of their bodies has a keen sense of touch. All these senses function well both above and below the surface of the water. Dolphins have no sense of smell and little, if any, sense of taste.

TAKING NOTES is a good way to summarize your research. You can take notes in a notebook or on index cards, depending on what method you find easier. Here is an example of notes taken from the encyclopedia article on the previous page.

■ Write the topic at the top. ·········

■ Write only what you need to remember.

■ Use your own words. ·······

■ Use short phrases instead of sentences.

■ Write the name of the source. ·······

Dolphins

small, toothed whales

mammals (not fish):

  lungs, warm-blooded,

  constant body temp

intelligent

highly developed hearing,

  vision, touch

no sense of smell

little or no sense of taste

World Book Encyclopedia, 1991

Notes are for you to use when you give a speech or write a report, so it is important for you to use your own words and include only what you think you want or need. Usually you should look in several different sources as you do research on a topic. Don't limit yourself to one encyclopedia article!

THE LIBRARY

A library is a great resource for anyone who is interested in learning. Whatever you want to find out, the library has information about it or can direct you somewhere that does.

Libraries contain books; periodicals such as magazines and newspapers; reference materials such as atlases, encyclopedias, and almanacs; government documents; and audiovisual materials. Libraries are organized to make it easy to find the materials you need. For example, most libraries have separate rooms or sections for **fiction, nonfiction, juvenile books,** and **reference sources.** When you visit a library for the first time, take a few minutes to find where each kind of material is located.

NONFICTION: You can locate **nonfiction** books by using the **card catalog.** Each book is listed on three different cards by **title, author,** and **subject.** Cards are filed in alphabetical order in drawers.

The subject card lists the subject of the book first.

599.5   DOLPHINS

The author card lists the author's last name first.

599.5   Patent, Dorothy Hinshaw
         Dolphins and Porpoises / Dorothy

The title card lists the title of the book first.

         Dolphins and Porpoises
599.5   Patent, Dorothy Hinshaw
         Dolphins and Porpoises / Dorothy
            Hinshaw Patent
         New York: Holiday House, ©1987.

Many libraries now use **computerized catalogs** instead of drawers of cards because computers are faster and easier to use. Like card catalogs, computerized catalogs are organized by title, author, and subject. Although computerized systems vary from library to library, they all have instructions printed on the keyboard and screen to help you. If you want to find books on dolphins, you might begin by typing your system's subject command and the word *dolphins* on the keyboard. When you have followed the steps shown on the screen, the computer will give you a list of the titles and **call numbers** of books on dolphins.

Each nonfiction book has a call number that is listed on its three cards or on the computer screen and on the book itself. The library shelves are labeled with the call numbers of the books they contain. As you can see, *Dolphins and Porpoises* has a call number of 599.5. Based on the **Dewey Decimal System**, call numbers are used to arrange nonfiction books by subject area. The chart shows the Dewey Decimal System call numbers, with the subject areas and topics found within each.

000—099	General works (encyclopedias, atlases, newspapers)
100—199	Philosophy (ideas about the meaning of life)
200—299	Religion (world religions, myths)
300—399	Social Science (government, law, business, education)
400—499	Language (dictionaries, grammar books)
500—599	Pure Science (mathematics, chemistry, plants, animals)
600—699	Applied Science (how–to books, engineering, radio)
700—799	Arts and Recreation (music, art, sports, hobbies)
800—899	Literature (poems, plays, essays)
900—999	History (travel, geography, biography)

(Note: Many libraries separate biographies from the 900s and organize them in alphabetical order by the subject's last name.)

FICTION: Books of fiction do not have call numbers. They are organized in alphabetical order by the author's last name. They are listed in the card catalog just as nonfiction books are.

PERIODICALS: You can locate information in a magazine or newspaper by using the *Readers' Guide to Periodical Literature.* This reference source lists articles by subject and by author. Many libraries also store information about periodicals in computers.

REFERENCE SOURCES: Libraries have many references, including specialized dictionaries, atlases, indexes, and maps.

GLOSSARY

The **pronunciation** of each word in this glossary is shown by a phonetic respelling in brackets; for example, [dis′ri·gärd′]. An accent mark (′) follows the syllable with the most stress: [in·koun′tər]. A secondary, or lighter, accent mark (′) follows a syllable with less stress: [kar′ə·sel′]. The key to other pronunciation symbols is below. You will find a shortened version of this key on alternate pages of the glossary.

Pronunciation Key*

a	add, map	m	move, seem	u	up, done
ā	ace, rate	n	nice, tin	û(r)	burn, term
â(r)	care, air	ng	ring, song	yōō	fuse, few
ä	palm, father	o	odd, hot	v	vain, eve
b	bat, rub	ō	open, so	w	win, away
ch	check, catch	ô	order, jaw	y	yet, yearn
d	dog, rod	oi	oil, boy	z	zest, muse
e	end, pet	ou	pout, now	zh	vision, pleasure
ē	equal, tree	ŏŏ	took, full	ə	the schwa,
f	fit, half	ōō	pool, food		an unstressed
g	go, log	p	pit, stop		vowel representing
h	hope, hate	r	run, poor		the sound spelled
i	it, give	s	see, pass		a in *above*
ī	ice, write	sh	sure, rush		e in *sicken*
j	joy, ledge	t	talk, sit		i in *possible*
k	cool, take	th	thin, both		o in *melon*
l	look, rule	th	this, bathe		u in *circus*

*Adapted entries, the Pronunciation Key, and the Short Key that appear on the following pages are reprinted from *HBJ School Dictionary*. Copyright © 1990 by Harcourt Brace Jovanovich, Inc. Reprinted by permission of Harcourt Brace Jovanovich, Inc.

A

affectionately

archaeologist

artisan

ac·co·lade [ak′ə·lād′] *n.* A great honor; praise: **The honor students were given** *accolades* **for their achievements.** *syn.* recognition

ac·com·mo·date [ə·kom′ə·dāt′] *v.* To hold or house comfortably: **We rented a larger apartment to** *accommodate* **our growing family.** *syn.* fit

ac·knowl·edge [ak·nol′ij] *v.* **ac·knowl·edged, ac·knowl·edg·ing** To indicate that one has received something.

ad·e·quate [ad′ə·kwit] *adj.* Enough for what is needed: **We did not take an** *adequate* **amount of food on our camping trip, so we were hungry the last day.** *syn.* sufficient

ad·ja·cent [ə·jā′sənt] *adj.* Close by; next to: **Miguel and Gus lived in** *adjacent* **homes, and one was always running next door to see the other.** *syn.* nearby

ad·o·les·cent [ad′ə·les′ənt] *n.* A person or an animal who is no longer a child but is not yet an adult: **The students in high school are** *adolescents.*

aer·o·nau·ti·cal [âr′ə·nô′ti·kəl] *adj.* Of or related to flying an aircraft: **Commercial pilots receive** *aeronautical* **training.**

af·fec·tion·ate·ly [ə·fek′shən·it·lē] *adv.* In a way that shows love or kindness. *syn.* lovingly

af·firm·a·tive [ə·fûr′mə·tiv] *adj.* Showing agreement or answering yes.

al·lot·ment [ə·lot′mənt] *n.* A specific share or amount. *syn.* portion

am·u·let [am′yə·lit] *n.* A charm worn to keep away evil or bad luck: **People in ancient Egypt believed that wearing** *amulets* **would keep them safe.**

an·i·mos·i·ty [an′ə·mos′ə·tē] *n.* Hatred: **Because he had been bitten once, Oscar felt nothing but** *animosity* **toward dogs.**

an·tic·i·pate [an·tis′ə·pāt′] *v.* **an·tic·i·pat·ed, an·tic·i·pat·ing** To look forward to something. *syn.* expect

anx·ious [angk′shəs] *adj.* Nervous or worried: **The shy girl felt** *anxious* **about going to a new school.** *syn.* uneasy

ap·prais·al [ə·prā′z(ə)l] *n.* The act of evaluating someone or something. *syn.* judgment

apt [apt] *adj.* Quick to learn. *syns.* bright, smart

ap·ti·tude [ap′tə·t(y)ōod′] *n.* Natural or special ability: **She easily passed the exam because she had an** *aptitude* **for math.** *syn.* talent

ar·chae·ol·o·gist [är′kē·ol′ə·jist] *n.* A person who studies past cultures, usually by examining ancient artifacts.

a·ris·to·crat [ə·ris′tə·krat′] *n.* A person of inherited high rank; an upper-class person: **In that nation, an aristocrat had more wealth and power than someone of the middle class.** *syn.* patrician

ar·ti·san [är′tə·zən] *n.* A highly trained worker, such as a carpenter: **The king hired the country's most skilled** *artisans* **to build his special furniture.** *syn.* craftsperson

a·skew [ə·skyōō′] *adj.* Sideways or out of line. *syn.* awry

as·pect [as′pekt] *n.* A part, an angle, or an appearance of something.

as·sess [ə·ses′] *v.* **as·sessed, as·sess·ing** To look at and figure out. *syn.* evaluate

as·sur·ance [ə·shŏŏr′əns] *n.* Something a person says to keep someone else from worrying.

ba·leen [bə·lēn'] *n.* Whalebone, which is a flexible material hanging from the upper jaw of some types of whales: **A whale's *baleen* separates sea water from the tiny plants and animals the whale eats.**

bar [bär] *v.* **barred, bar·ring** To prevent someone from doing something: **Students are *barred* from entering the teachers' lounge.** *syn.* exclude

bar·na·cle [bär'nə·kəl] *n.* A shellfish that attaches itself to objects or other animals: **When the sailor turned the boat over to clean it, he noticed that its bottom was covered with *barnacles*.**

be·grudge [bi·gruj'] *v.* To envy someone because of something he or she has: **Don't *begrudge* him his success—he worked hard for it.**

bel·lig·er·ent·ly [bə·lij'ər·ənt·lē] *adv.* In an argumentative or challenging manner.

be·stow [bi·stō'] *v.* To give as a gift, usually in a formal way: **When I move into my new apartment, my mother plans to *bestow* her antique oak desk upon me.** *syn.* confer

bi·zarre [bi·zär'] *adj.* Odd or unusual: **We were puzzled by the stranger's *bizarre* behavior.** *syns.* strange, weird

bray [brā] *n.* A loud, harsh sound made by a donkey: **Each morning on the farm we awoke to the *brays* of the hungry donkeys.**

bus·tle [bus'(ə)l] *v.* **bus·tled, bus·tling** To move around with excitement: **The students *bustled* around the stage, getting ready for the next act of the play.**

cal·cu·late [kal'kyə·lāt'] *v.* **cal·cu·lat·ed, cal·cu·lat·ing** To think out or plan. *syns.* figure, estimate

cap·stan [kap'stən] *n.* A large spool on a ship's deck that cables or ropes are wound around: **Teams of sailors worked together to turn the *capstans* and wind the heavy cables around them.**

car·ou·sel [kar'ə·sel'] *n.* A merry-go-round: **The wooden horses moved up and down as the *carousel* turned.**

cas·u·al·ly [kazh'oo·əl·ē] *adv.* Done off-handedly or without thinking. *syn.* informally

ca·tas·tro·phe [kə·tas'trə·fē] *n.* A sudden great disaster: **The famous Chicago Fire was an enormous *catastrophe* because it cost so many lives and destroyed so much property.** *syns.* calamity, misfortune, cataclysm

cat·e·chism [kat'ə·kiz'əm] *adj.* Relating to religious education: **Some students attend *catechism* classes at church one afternoon a week.**

chant [chant] *n.* A simple, rhythmic melody sung or shouted: **The monks joined together to sing *chants* after their evening meal.** *syn.* song

cir·cum·stance [sûr'kəm·stans'] *n.* Surrounding condition or situation: **The *circumstances* at his mother's house made it impossible for us to talk there in private.** *syn.* context

claus·tro·pho·bi·a [klôs'trə·fō'bē·ə] *n.* Fear of being in a small or enclosed place: **Her *claustrophobia* kept her from using the small walk-in closet in her bedroom.**

belligerently Today we use *belligerently* to describe any hostile or threatening way of acting. The Latin ancestor of this word—*bellum gerere*—was military. It meant "to wage war." If individuals or nations behave *belligerently*, watch out! They may be angry enough to go to war.

capstan

carousel

a	add	oͦo	took
ā	ace	ōͦo	pool
â	care	u	up
ä	palm	û	burn
e	end	yōͦo	fuse
ē	equal	oi	oil
i	it	ou	pout
ī	ice	ng	ring
o	odd	th	thin
ō	open	th	this
ô	order	zh	vision

ə = { a in *above*   e in *sicken*
      i in *possible*
      o in *melon*   u in *circus* }

conspirator *Conspirators,* those who plot together in secret, agree completely with one another. They may be so close that they almost breathe together. In fact, *conspirator* comes from the Latin prefix *con-,* "together" and *spirare,* meaning "to breathe."

cordially

cordially When you welcome a friend *cordially,* you are doing so in a warm and sincere way. You are acting from your heart. In fact, *cordially* goes back to the Latin word *cor,* meaning "heart." If you are in *accord* with someone, you agree with him or her. Your hearts are together. When there is *discord* between you, your hearts are far apart. *Ac-* has the sense of "to" or "toward," and *dis-* means "away."

clout [klout] *v.* In baseball, to hit the ball a great distance: **Gilberto hit a home run yesterday, and he hopes he can** *clout* **another one today.**

co·in·ci·dence [kō·in′sə·dəns] *n.* An unlikely event; the appearance of two things at the same place or time.

com·mence [kə·mens′] *v.* **com·menced, com·menc·ing** To start or begin. *syn.* initiate

com·pa·ra·ble [kom′pər·ə·bəl] *adj.* Similar enough to be compared.

com·pen·sate [kom′pən·sāt′] *v.* **com·pen·sat·ed, com·pen·sat·ing** To make up for or balance out.

com·pli·ment [kom′plə·mənt] *n.* Speech or action that shows praise for someone.

com·pro·mise [kom′prə·mīz′] *v.* **com·pro·mised, com·pro·mis·ing** To adjust to something less than expected or desired. *syn.* settle

con·cil·i·a·to·ry [kən·sil′ē·ə·tôr′ē] *adj.* In a soothing or peacemaking manner: **The salesclerk spoke to the angry customer in a** *conciliatory* **tone and soon calmed him down.**

con·de·scend·ing·ly [kon′di·sen′ding·lē] *adv.* In a way that looks down on something or someone. *syns.* arrogantly, patronizingly

con·serve [kən·sûrv′] *v.* To save: **Hiroshi sat quietly by the track because he wanted to** *conserve* **his energy for the relay race.** *syns.* preserve, protect

con·sole [kən·sōl′] *v.* To comfort someone in sadness: **The mother tried to** *console* **her son when his dog was sick by telling him that it would recover.** *syns.* reassure, cheer

con·spir·a·tor [kən·spir′ə·tər] *n.* A person involved in an illegal plot. *syn.* plotter

con·ster·na·tion [kon′stər·nā′shən] *n.* A feeling of fear, confusion, and helplessness. *syn.* dismay

con·sti·tute [kon′stə·t(y)o͞ot′] *v.* **con·sti·tut·ed, con·sti·tut·ing** To make up or form. *syn.* compose

con·su·late [kon′sə·lit] *n.* A country's office in a foreign country, designed to help and protect its citizens living or traveling there: **When our friend lost his passport in France, we went to the American** *consulate* **in Paris to get help.**

con·sul·ta·tion [kon′səl·tā′shən] *n.* A meeting to discuss ideas or get advice: **Maria held a** *consultation* **with her lawyer to discuss her rights in the dispute.** *syn.* conference

con·verge [kən·vûrj′] *v.* **con·verged, con·verg·ing** To come together or meet at the same point.

con·verse [kən·vûrs′] *v.* To have a conversation with someone. *syns.* speak, talk

con·vic·tion [kən·vik′shən] *n.* Strong belief in something.

cor·dial·ly [kôr′jəl·ē] *adv.* With friendliness and sincerity: **Smiling with delight, Mr. Cortez greeted his guests** *cordially.* *syns.* warmly, heartily

cre·dence [krēd′(ə)ns] *n.* Belief; acceptance: **Knowing her truthfulness, we had to give** *credence* **to her report.**

cre·scen·do [krə·shen′dō] *n.* A gradual increase in loudness: **The thundering sound at the height of the symphony's final** *crescendo* **woke George up.**

cru·cial [kro͞o′shəl] *adj.* Extremely important. *syns.* key, significant

D

dav·it [dav′it] *n.* One of two cranes on the side of a ship, used for lowering and raising smaller boats: **One** *davit* **did not let out the cable, so we could not lower the lifeboat into the water.**

de·bris [də·brē′ *or* dā·brē′] *n.* Broken pieces left over: **After the store burned down, there was nothing left except charred wood and other** *debris. syns.* fragments, remains

de·cree [di·krē′] *v.* **de·creed, de·cree·ing** To decide or cause to happen: **The heavy storm** *decreed* **that we stay inside all day.** *syn.* proclaim

de·fi·ant·ly [di·fī′ənt·lē] *adv.* In a fiercely resistant manner: **The child stamped her feet and** *defiantly* **refused to go to bed.**

de·jec·ted·ly [di·jek′tid·lē] *adv.* In a downcast or depressed manner. *syn.* unhappily

de·lib·er·ate·ly [di·lib′ər·it·lē] *adv.* With care and intention: **Santiago** *deliberately* **arranged the pictures to hide the holes in the wall.** *syns.* consciously, methodically

de·scent [di·sent′] *n.* The act of going or coming down to a lower point.

des·o·late [des′ə·lit] *adj.* Lonely; without any people. *syns.* deserted, remote

des·per·a·tion [des′pə·rā′shən] *n.* A state of great need or helplessness leading to reckless behavior: **The child was overcome by a sense of** *desperation* **when he couldn't find his mother.** *syns.* terror, hopelessness

de·spon·dent·ly [di·spon′dənt·lē] *adv.* In a discouraged way. *syn.* despairingly

des·ti·ny [des′tə·nē] *n.* An unavoidable outcome. *syn.* fate

di·ag·nos·tic [dī′əg·nos′tik] *adj.* Having to do with analyzing or evaluating a condition or situation: **The** *diagnostic* **exam helped the school determine which grade the new student belonged in.**

dil·i·gent·ly [dil′ə·jənt·lē] *adv.* With persistence and care. *syns.* conscientiously, assiduously

dis·dain·ful·ly [dis·dān′fəl·ē] *adv.* In a scornful or disgusted manner. *syn.* contemptuously

di·shev·eled [di·shev′əld] *adj.* Rumpled and untidy.

dis·re·gard [dis′ri·gärd′] *n.* Lack of concern: **Miguel did not vote in the election because he had a** *disregard* **for politics.**

dis·taste [dis·tāst′] *n.* Dislike. *syns.* disgust, revulsion

dis·tinct [dis·tingkt′] *adj.* Clear and definite.

di·vert [di·vûrt′] *v.* **di·vert·ed, di·vert·ing** To throw someone off his or her planned course. *syn.* distract

doc·ile·ly [dos′(ə)l·ē] *adv.* Obediently; without struggle or difficulty: **The violent criminal changed and behaved** *docilely* **for the rest of his time in prison.** *syn.* tamely

dol·drums [dōl′drəmz *or* dol′drəmz] *n.* A bored or inactive state of mind. *syns.* dullness, listlessness

dom·i·nate [dom′ə·nāt′] *v.* **dom·i·nat·ed, dom·i·nat·ing** To control or have power over.

dou·blet [dub′lit] *n.* A tight-fitting jacket with or without sleeves: **A** *doublet* **was worn as commonly by a man in the fifteenth century as a suit jacket is worn today.**

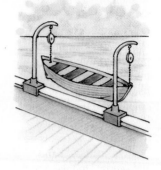

davit

diagnostic This word and its relatives *diagnose, diagnosis,* and *diagnostician* go back to the ancient Greek *dia,* "between" and *gignoskein,* "to know." A doctor who knows the differences between diseases is a *diagnostician.* Incidentally, the English word *know* and the Greek *gignoskein* both come from the same ancient word *gno,* "to know."

a	add	o͞o	took
ā	ace	o͞o	pool
â	care	u	up
ä	palm	û	burn
e	end	yo͞o	fuse
ē	equal	oi	oil
i	it	ou	pout
ī	ice	ng	ring
o	odd	th	thin
ō	open	th	this
ô	order	zh	vision

ə = { a in *above*   e in *sicken*
i in *possible*
o in *melon*   u in *circus* }

609

emancipation When a Roman master bought slaves, he took or touched them with his hand. This symbolized that he possessed them. To free his slaves, he "took his hand away" or *emancipated* them. *Emancipation* is formed from three Latin roots—*e*, "away," *manus*, "hand," and *capere*, "to take."

embed

ethnic

exaggerate In Latin *agger* means "heap" or "pile." A person who *exaggerates* something really "piles it on" by making it seem more than it is. Sometimes people who exaggerate their troubles are said to "make mountains out of molehills."

du·bi·ous·ly [d(y)o͞o′bē·əs·lē] *adv.* With doubt or suspicion: **Brett looked at Meg *dubiously* when she claimed she spoke seven languages.** *syns.* doubtfully, questioningly

E

ed·i·ble [ed′ə·bəl] *adj.* Fit to be eaten. *syns.* eatable, palatable, appetizing

ef·fi·gy [ef′ə·jē] *n.* A crude model of a disliked person, held up for display and ridicule: **The *effigies* hanging in the streets of the troubled city looked amazingly like the tyrant.**

ef·fu·sive [i·fyo͞o′siv] *adj.* Gushing with emotion or enthusiasm.

e·lec·tive [i·lek′tiv] *n.* A course that a student may or may not choose to take.

e·lu·sive [i·lo͞o′siv] *adj.* Difficult to find or hold on to: **The *elusive* bird kept flying away when we came near it.** *syn.* evasive

e·man·ci·pa·tion [i·man′sə·pā′shən] *n.* The act of freeing from slavery. *syn.* liberation

em·bed [im·bed′] *v.* **em·bed·ded, em·bed·ding** To put an object deeply into something: **The tiles were so deeply *embedded* in the concrete of the patio that we could not free them.** *syn.* implant

e·mit [i·mit′] *v.* **e·mit·ted, e·mit·ting** To give or send out, usually light or sound.

em·pha·size [em′fə·sīz′] *v.* **em·pha·sized, em·pha·siz·ing** To point out or call attention to: **We *emphasized* our team spirit by wearing the school colors.** *syns.* accentuate, stress

en·coun·ter [in·koun′tər] *n.* An unexpected meeting.

en·light·en [in·līt′(ə)n] *v.* To inform or explain.

err [ûr *or* er] *v.* **erred, err·ing** To make an error; to be wrong: **Because he hated stinginess, he often *erred* by giving too much away.**

etch [ech] *v.* **etched, etch·ing** To engrave a pattern or image: **The artist *etched* the image of her mother's face into the stone.**

eth·nic [eth′nik] *adj.* Belonging to a specific group of people who share the same language and culture. *syn.* cultural

e·val·u·ate [i·val′yo͞o·āt′] *v.* **e·val·u·at·ed, e·val·u·at·ing** To measure or judge the worth of something: **The teacher *evaluated* his students' spelling abilities by giving weekly tests.** *syn.* measure

e·ven·tu·al·ly [i·ven′cho͞o·əl·ē] *adv.* At some point in the future. *syn.* ultimately

ex·ag·ger·at·ed [ig·zaj′ə·rāt′əd] *adj.* Larger than life or reality; much more than is real or possible.

ex·as·per·at·ed [ig·zas′pə·rāt′əd] *adj.* Very irritated or annoyed. *syn.* frustrated

ex·cur·sion [ik·skûr′zhən] *n.* A short trip or journey, usually for pleasure: **Harry and his cousin often went on *excursions* to the park for picnics.** *syn.* outing

F

fal·ter [fôl′tər] *v.* **fal·tered, fal·ter·ing** To hesitate or seem uncertain: **When he gave his speech without *faltering* once, he was glad he had practiced.**

fea·si·ble [fē′zə·bəl] *adj.* Able to be done. *syns.* likely, possible

fe·roc·i·ty [fə·ros′ə·tē] *n.* Fierceness. *syn.* savagery

flaw [flô] *n.* A crack or defect. *syns.* imperfection, blemish

flot·sam [flot′səm] *n.* Pieces of a wrecked ship or its contents, floating on water: **After the ship sank, the ocean was littered with broken suitcases, pieces of oars, and other *flotsam*.**

flus·ter [flus′tər] *v.* To confuse or make upset.

foil [foil] *v.* To outwit or prevent. *syn.* thwart

for·bid·ding [fər·bid′ing] *adj.* Unfriendly and frightening. *syns.* repellent, intimidating

for·fei·ture [fôr′fi·chər] *n.* The act of being forced to give up something as punishment.

fraud [frôd] *n.* A dishonest trick or act of deception.

frig·id [frij′id] *adj.* Extremely cold.

frus·tra·tion [frus·trā′shən] *n.* Anger or impatience at wasted effort or ineffectiveness. *syn.* exasperation

her·o·ine [her′ō·in] *n.* A girl or woman who is known for acts of courage and intelligence: **Everyone called her a *heroine* after she rescued the drowning child.**

hi·er·o·glyph·ics [hī′ər·ə·glif′iks *or* hī′rə·glif′iks] *n.* A written language of pictures and symbols, such as that used by the ancient Egyptians: **The explorer was able to read the *hieroglyphics* carved into the walls of the Egyptian tomb.**

hoax [hōks] *n.* A trick or practical joke: **Their story about seeing the UFO was a *hoax* that tricked many people.** *syn.* deception

hos·til·i·ties [hos·til′ə·tēz] *n.* Warfare or unfriendly feelings or acts: ***Hostilities* between the two nations resulted in many deaths.** *syns.* opposition, fighting

hum·drum [hum′drum′] *adj.* Dull and boring: **Kim could not sit through the entire *humdrum* television show.**

hys·te·ri·a [his·tir′ē·ə *or* his·ter′ē·ə] *n.* A state of uncontrolled excitement or emotion: **She was overcome by *hysteria* when she learned that her daughter had been in an accident.** *syn.* frenzy

flotsam

hieroglyphics

G

gra·cious [grā′shəs] *adj.* Kind and polite. *syn.* courteous

H

hearth·fire [härth′fīr′] *n.* A fire in a fireplace or hearth: **We stood near the burning logs and warmed ourselves by the *hearthfire*.**

I

il·lu·mi·na·tion [i·lōō′mə·nā′shən] *n.* Lighting; an amount of light.

im·mo·bi·lized [i·mō′bə·līzd] *adj.* Not able to move: **The rabbit froze in its tracks, *immobilized* by fear.**

im·pas·sioned [im·pash′ənd] *adj.* Filled with strong emotion. *syns.* passionate, ardent, fervent

a	add	o͞o	took
ā	ace	o͞o	pool
â	care	u	up
ä	palm	û	burn
e	end	yo͞o	fuse
ē	equal	oi	oil
i	it	ou	pout
ī	ice	ng	ring
o	odd	th	thin
ō	open	t͟h	this
ô	order	zh	vision

ə = { a in *above* e in *sicken*
i in *possible*
o in *melon* u in *circus* }

im·pe·ri·ous [im·pir′ē·əs] *adj.*
Proud and haughty: **The cat gave
us an** *imperious* **look as it sat like
a queen on the chair.** *syns.* arro-
gant, domineering

im·pli·ca·tion [im′plə·kā′shən] *n.*
Something that is hinted at but
not directly said: **The** *implication*
**was that she did not want to go
to the party, though she clearly
did not want to say so.**

im·pres·sion [im·presh′ən] *n.* A
feeling or idea: **Even though
George was polite to the guests,
I had the** *impression* **that he
would rather be alone.** *syn.*
perception

im·pu·dent [im′pyə·dənt] *adj.*
Rude and uncooperative. *syns.* in-
solent, belligerent

in·com·pat·i·ble
[in′kəm·pat′ə·bəl] *adj.* Not able
to be combined or exist together.

incompatible

in·di·cate [in′də·kāt′] *v.* To show:
Anna's high test scores *indicate*
that she is an excellent student.
syns. attest, testify

in·dig·nant·ly [in·dig′nənt·lē] *adv.*
With anger at something unjust or
untrue: **The audience shouted** *indignantly* **at the speaker's lies.**

in·di·vid·u·al·ize
[in′də·vij′o͞o·ə·līz] *v.* To treat
separately and independently: **He
tries to** *individualize* **his teaching
by giving students assignments
suited to their own interests.** *syn.*
particularize

in·for·mal [in·fôr′məl] *adj.* On a
relaxed or friendly basis: **I often
have** *informal* **talks in the hallway with my English teacher.**
syn. casual

ingratitude

in·grat·i·tude [in·grat′ə·t(y)o͞od′]
n. A lack of appreciation: **After
all the help we gave her, we were
angered by her** *ingratitude* **when
she didn't even thank us.** *syn.*
ungratefulness

in·her·i·tance [in·her′ə·təns] *n.*
Something passed on through
family or received from a parent
or an ancestor: **This house was
left to us as part of our** *inheritance* **when our father died.**

in·ju·ri·ous [in·jo͞or′ē·əs] *adj.*
Harmful or damaging: **Long per-
iods of typing can be so** *injurious*
**to the hands that they require a
doctor's care.**

in·quis·i·tive [in·kwiz′ə·tiv] *adj.*
Eager to know something or to
ask a question. *syn.* curious

in·tact [in·takt′] *adj.* Whole or without any damage.

in·tel·lec·tu·al [in′tə·lek′cho͞o·əl]
n. A well-educated person: **Eva
was one of a group of** *intellectuals* **at the university who loved
art and literature.** *syn.* scholar

in·ter·me·di·ate [in′tər·mē′dē·it]
adj. Occurring between two
things: **After the class in beginning French, the students took
an** *intermediate* **class before they
entered the advanced level.** *syn.*
middle

in·ter·mi·na·ble
[in·tûr′mə·nə·bəl] *adj.* Seemingly
endless and tiresome.

in·trigue [in·trēg′] *v.* **in·trigued,
in·tri·guing** To produce great interest or curiosity: **We were** *intrigued* **by her travels in Africa
and were eager to hear more
about them.** *syn.* fascinate

in·val·u·a·ble [in·val′y(o͞o·)ə·bəl]
adj. Valuable beyond any price.
syn. priceless

J

jest [jest] *n.* An act or comment intended to provoke laughter. *syn.*
joke

L

leg·en·dar·y [lej′ən·der′ē] *adj.* Famous: The *legendary* pyramids attract visitors from all over the world.

le·vi·a·than [lə·vī′ə·thən] *n.* A huge animal or thing: The great white shark is a *leviathan* that frightens many deep-sea divers.

lin·ger [ling′gər] *v.* **lin·gered, lin·ger·ing** To stay or hang around: The smell of her perfume *lingered* in the room for days. *syn.* loiter

lore [lôr] *n.* Knowledge or stories about a subject: Sitting around the campfire, the children heard the *lore* of ancient tribes.

lu·gu·bri·ous [loo·goo′brē·əs] *adj.* Full of sadness: The lost, hungry dog let out a *lugubrious* howl. *syn.* mournful

lu·mi·nous [loo′·mə·nəs] *adj.* Glowing; brightly lit. *syn.* aglow

M

mag·ni·tude [mag′nə·t(y)ood′] *n.* Great importance.

ma·raud·er [mə·rôd′ər] *n.* Someone who roams around and steals things. *syns.* robber, thief

mas·sive [mas′iv] *adj.* Extremely large and heavy. *syns.* bulky, huge

mea·gre or **mea·ger** [mē′gər] *adj.* Inadequate or inferior. *syn.* paltry

meas·ly [mēz′lē] *adj.* Not having much worth: When Cathy looked in the cookie jar, all she found were a few *measly* crumbs. *syn.* meager

me·di·o·cre [mē′dē·ō′kər] *adj.* Of average quality. *syns.* ordinary, so-so

med·i·tate [med′ə·tāt′] *v.* To think deeply and quietly: She sat down to *meditate* about how to thank her aunt for the special gift. *syn.* contemplate

mirth [mûrth] *n.* Laughter; feeling of silliness or happiness: The children at the birthday party were filled with *mirth*. *syns.* gaiety, joy

mo·men·tum [mō·men′təm] *n.* The force of a moving body. *syn.* force

mo·not·o·nous [mə·not′ə·nəs] *adj.* Unchanging or boringly repetitive. *syn.* tedious

mus·ter [mus′tər] *v.* **mus·tered, mus·ter·ing** To gather together: Sergio was so exhausted that he had trouble *mustering* the energy to lift the heavy box. *syn.* collect

myr·i·ad [mir′ē·əd] *n.* A huge number: *Myriads* of flowers filled the garden with color.

N

nau·ti·cal [nô′ti·kəl] *adj.* Having to do with the sea: The *nautical* mile, which is longer than the usual mile, is used to measure the length of a ship's journey.

no·bil·i·ty [nō·bil′ə·tē] *n.* People of noble birth with inherited titles or rank; those possessing fine qualities: Although she was not born into the *nobility*, her intelligence and generosity made her noble. *syn.* aristocracy

nom·i·nate [nom′ə·nāt′] *v.* **nom·i·nat·ed, nom·i·nat·ing** To select someone for a position, sometimes as a candidate for elected office: Diego's classmates *nominated* him to represent them in the spelling contest. *syns.* appoint, elect

mirth

monotonous A voice that doesn't change in tone is a monotone. *Monos* is the Greek word for "single." Listening to someone who speaks in a monotone is difficult. In fact, it is downright boring! So *monotonous* has come to refer to anything that bores us because it is always the same.

myriad

a	add	oo	took
ā	ace	oo	pool
â	care	u	up
ä	palm	û	burn
e	end	yoo	fuse
ē	equal	oi	oil
i	it	ou	pout
ī	ice	ng	ring
o	odd	th	thin
ō	open	th	this
ô	order	zh	vision

ə = { a in *above*   e in *sicken*
       i in *possible*
       o in *melon*   u in *circus* }

non·de·script [non′də·skript′] *adj.* Not special or distinctive: **Her shoes were so *nondescript* that I don't remember anything about them.** *syns.* common, ordinary

paleontologist

ob·li·ga·tion [ob′lə·gā′shən] *n.* A commitment or duty: **She felt an *obligation* to go to the party because she had told her friend that she would go.**

ob·scure·ly [əb·skyŏŏr′lē] *adv.* Unclearly or faintly: **The moon glimmered *obscurely* behind the clouds.** *syn.* vaguely

ob·struc·tion [əb·struk′shən] *n.* Something that gets in the way: **Harry could not walk straight across the yard because piles of dirt and rocks were *obstructions* in his path.** *syn.* obstacle

ob·vi·ous [ob′vē·əs] *adj.* Clear or easy to see or understand: **It was *obvious* that the student hadn't read the assignment after the teacher asked him a few questions.** *syns.* evident, visible

oc·cu·pa·tion [ok′yə·pā′shən] *n.* Forced military take-over and possession.

oc·cur·rence [ə·kûr′əns] *n.* Something that happens: **Tornadoes are a common *occurrence* in this area during spring.** *syns.* event, incident

om·i·nous·ly [om′ə·nəs·lē] *adv.* In a way that points to something bad or frightening: **The clouds gathered *ominously* before the storm.** *syn.* threateningly

or·tho·pe·dist [ôr′thə·pē′dist] *n.* A doctor who specializes in treating bones and joints: **The *orthopedist* put a cast on my broken leg.**

pa·le·on·tol·o·gist [pā′lē·on·tol′ə·jist] *n.* A person who studies ancient forms of life, usually by looking at fossils: **The *paleontologist* carefully examined the fossil skull of a small dinosaur.**

pa·py·rus [pə·pī′rəs] *n.* A kind of paper used by the ancient Egyptians, Greeks, and Romans, made from the papyrus plant: **The ancient manuscript was written on *papyrus*.**

pa·tent·ly [pāt′(ə)nt·lē] *adv.* Clearly or obviously: **Benita was *patently* lying, and everyone in the room knew it.**

pa·tri·cian [pə·trish′ən] *n.* An upper-class or noble person: **In ancient Rome, a *patrician* often lived in luxury, served by members of the lower classes.** *syn.* aristocrat

pe·des·tri·an [pə·des′trē·ən] *n.* A person walking or traveling on foot: **The young bicyclist almost ran into two *pedestrians* who were walking slowly along the path through the park.**

per·plex·ing [pər·pleks′ing] *adj.* Confusing or puzzling: **It was a *perplexing* question that none of us knew how to answer.** *syns.* bewildering, complicated

per·spec·tive [pər·spek′tiv] *n.* A way of seeing the relative importance of things: **Studying world history has given me a new *perspective* on the events of today.** *syn.* outlook

phos·phor·es·cence [fos′fə·res′əns] *n.* The condition of giving off light but not noticeable heat: **The *phosphorescence* of lightning bugs is a fascinating aspect of the natural world.**

piv·ot [piv′ət] *v.* **piv·ot·ed,
piv·ot·ing** To turn in place, as on
a center pin, shaft, or hinge: **The
soccer player** *pivoted* **on one foot
and kicked the ball the other direction into the goal.**

plank·ton [plangk′tən] *n.* Tiny animals and plants that float in
water but cannot swim: **Many
fish and other sea animals eat**
plankton **as the major part of
their diet.**

port [pôrt] *n.* A place where ships
arrive and depart: **Frank always
enjoyed going to the** *port* **to
watch the ships coming in.** *syn.*
harbor

prac·ti·cal [prak′ti·kəl] *adj.* Having
to do with actual use or practice
rather than theories or ideas: **She
learned theories in class, but
gained** *practical* **experience on
the job.**

prat·tle [prat′(ə)l] *n.* Talk that is not
important: **Part of the school
council president's speech was
about serious issues, but another
part was just silly** *prattle* **about
table tennis and video games.**
syn. foolishness

pre·cau·tion·ar·y
[pri·kô′shən·ər′ē] *adj.* Serving to
prevent or avoid harm: **Fastening
your seat belt is a good** *precautionary* **measure.** *syn.*
preventative

pre·cede [pri·sēd′] *v.* **pre·ced·ed,
pre·ced·ing** To come or occur
before: **World War I** *preceded*
**World War II by about twenty
years.**

prec·e·dent [pres′ə·dənt] *n.* A decision or ruling used as a guide for
a similar situation that occurs
later: **The judge strongly believed that if he ruled the defen-
dant innocent in this case, it
would set a** *precedent* **for all future cases like this.**

pre·cept [prē′sept′] *n.* A rule of
conduct or action: **Being polite
and courteous are strict** *precepts*
in Ms. Pardo's class.

pre·cious [presh′əs] *adj.* Highly val-
ued: **The pirates discovered gold
coins and** *precious* **jewels in the
treasure chest.**

pre·cise [pri·sīs′] *adj.* Carefully
planned or exact. *syn.* accurate

pre·ci·sion [pri·sizh′ən] *n.* Accu-
racy: **Being a good surgeon re-
quires great care and** *precision.*
syn. exactness

pre·dic·a·ment [pri·dik′ə·mənt] *n.*
A dangerous or difficult situation.

pre·oc·cu·pa·tion
[prē·ok′yə·pā′shən] *n.* A fully
absorbed state of mind. *syn.*
obsession

prim·i·tive [prim′ə·tiv] *adj.* Old-
fashioned or not advanced. *syns.*
archaic, crude

pro·cras·ti·nate [prō·kras′tə·nāt′]
v. **pro·cras·ti·nat·ed,
pro·cras·ti·nat·ing** To avoid or
put off until later.

pros·pec·tor [pros′pek′tər] *n.*
Someone who explores an area,
usually looking for gold or other
mineral deposits: **The** *prospectors*
**searched the area, hoping to find
oil.**

pros·per·i·ty [pros·per′ə·tē] *n.*
Wealth and success.

pru·dent·ly [prōō′dənt·lē] *adv.* In a
responsible or carefully considered manner. *syn.* wisely

prospector

procrastinate Do you
ever *procrastinate*, or put
off until the future
something that you
should do right now?
Everybody does, and so
did the ancient Romans.
They had a word for it—
procrastinare. It was
formed from *pro,*
"forward" and *cras,*
"tomorrow."

Q

quin·tes·sen·tial [kwin′tə·sen′shəl]
adj. Possessing the purest or most
essential part or quality of something: **Fans of jazz think that it is
the** *quintessential* **form of music.**

a	add	o͞o	took
ā	ace	o͞o	pool
â	care	u	up
ä	palm	û	burn
e	end	yo͞o	fuse
ē	equal	oi	oil
i	it	ou	pout
ī	ice	ng	ring
o	odd	th	thin
ō	open	th	this
ô	order	zh	vision

ə = { a in *above* e in *sicken*
      i in *possible*
      o in *melon* u in *circus* }

R

receptionist

rendezvous This word for a planned meeting or joining of forces comes from a command in French. *Rendez vous* means "present yourself." Don't be late for a rendezvous!

respective

ra·tion [rash′ən *or* rā′shən] *v.* **ra·tioned, ra·tion·ing** To limit the amount of something scarce.

ra·tion·al [rash′ən·əl] *adj.* Sensible or reasonable.

re·as·sure [rē′ə·shŏŏr′] *v.* To free from doubt or fear: **Mrs. Allen tried to *reassure* the frightened boy by telling him that nothing would harm him.** *syns.* console, encourage

re·cep·tion·ist [ri·sep′shə·nist] *n.* A person employed in an office to answer the telephone and greet people.

re·flec·tive [ri·flek′tiv] *adj.* Quiet and thoughtful. *syns.* contemplative, introverted

reg·is·ter [rej′is·tər] *v.* **reg·is·tered, reg·is·ter·ing** To enter the mind or awareness of someone: **The importance of his remark had not *registered* in her mind before he left.**

re·it·er·ate [rē·it′ə·rāt′] *v.* **re·it·er·at·ed, re·it·er·at·ing** To do or say again. *syn.* repeat

re·lent [ri·lent′] *v.* To become less severe and more gentle and cooperative. *syn.* slacken

rel·ic [rel′ik] *n.* Something remaining from a past culture or time period. *syn.* artifact

re·lieve [ri·lēv′] *v.* To reduce or lessen: **Esteban took some medicine to *relieve* his stomachache.** *syn.* alleviate

re·mark·a·ble [ri·mär′kə·bəl] *adj.* Worthy of notice: **The pilot was known all over the country for her *remarkable* airplane stunts.** *syn.* extraordinary

re·morse [ri·môrs′] *n.* Deep regret. *syn.* self-reproach

ren·dez·vous [rän′dā·vōō′] *n.* A planned meeting.

rep·u·ta·tion [rep′yə·tā′shən] *n.* An image or set of qualities that represents how someone is viewed by others: **Her jokes gave her a *reputation* for being one of the funniest people in our junior high school.**

re·sis·tance [ri·zis′təns] *n.* A group of people fighting to oppose a military invasion.

re·spec·tive [ri·spek′tiv] *adj.* Specific and separate: **Each day we separate to attend our *respective* classes, and then we meet again in the afternoon.**

re·trieve [ri·trēv′] *v.* **re·trieved, re·triev·ing** To get something back. *syns.* recover, regain

re·vert [ri·vûrt′] *v.* **re·vert·ed, re·vert·ing** To go back to a previous condition or attitude.

right·eous [rī′chəs] *adj.* Being exactly right according to rules or principles: **The coach knew the rules so well that he felt *righteous* in arguing with the umpire about the play.**

rig·or [rig′ər] *n.* A harsh or difficult condition: **The sailors were exhausted from the *rigors* of sailing on rough seas.** *syn.* severity

S

sar·cas·ti·cal·ly [sär·kas′tik·lē] *adv.* In a way that makes fun of someone; with mocking insincerity. *syns.* jokingly, tauntingly

self-con·scious [self′kon′shəs] *adj.* Feeling embarrassed because people are watching.

sen·ti·ments [sen′tə·mənts] *n.* Feelings or attitudes. *syns.* emotions, opinions

shun [shun] *v.* **shunned, shun·ning** To avoid or stay away from.

sig·nif·i·cant [sig·nif′ə·kənt] *adj.* Important or noteworthy: **I have noticed a *significant* difference in my health since I started exercising.**

skir·mish [skûr′mish] *n.* A small battle or fight between troops: **There was a *skirmish* between small groups of soldiers the day before war was officially declared.**

so·cia·ble [sō′shə·bəl] *adj.* Friendly and agreeable. *syn.* social

sol·emn·ly [sol′əm·lē] *adv.* With great seriousness and formality. *syn.* gravely

spire [spīr] *n.* A long pointed top of a church or tower: **A small cross was at the top of the church's tall *spire*.** *syn.* steeple

spon·ta·ne·ous [spon·tā′nē·əs] *adj.* Done on impulse without planning. *syns.* impulsive, unplanned

star·board [stär′bərd] *n.* The right, in nautical language; the right-hand side of a ship when one is on board facing the front: **The captain shouted the command to turn the ship to the right—"Hard a-*starboard*!"**

staunch [stônch *or* stänch] *adj.* Dependable and strong: **She was a *staunch* friend, and I turned to her for help and advice many times over the years.** *syns.* steadfast, faithful, loyal

stern [stûrn] *n.* The rear part of a ship: **The fishing nets hanging from the *stern* spread out behind us as we moved along.**

stew·ard [st(y)ōō′ərd] *n.* Someone who manages someone else's finances, property, or other personal affairs.

strat·o·sphere [strat′ə·sfir′] *n.* A layer of the atmosphere starting about seven miles above the earth's surface: **The plane flew up into the cloudless *stratosphere*.**

sub·merge [səb·mûrj′] *v.* **sub·merged, sub·merg·ing** To go under water: **Chiang *submerged* herself in the cool water of the lake.**

sub·side [səb·sīd′] *v.* **sub·sid·ed, sub·sid·ing** To become less violent or intense: **After my anger had *subsided*, I was able to apologize.** *syns.* lessen, calm

sup·press [sə·pres′] *v.* To hold back; to keep from getting out or becoming known. *syn.* control

sus·pense [sə·spens′] *n.* A state or condition of uncertainty and intense curiosity: **The storyteller held us in *suspense* by not revealing the secret until the very end.**

spire

T

tact·ful·ly [takt′fəl·ē] *adv.* In a manner that does not offend or hurt others: **She declined his invitation to dinner so *tactfully* that his feelings were not hurt.** *syns.* skillfully, gracefully

tan·ta·lize [tan′tə·līz′] *v.* To tease someone by offering something and then not letting that person have it: **Tim could *tantalize* the dog by holding out a cookie and then pulling it back.** *syn.* torment

te·di·ous [tē′dē·əs] *adj.* Tiresome and boring: **She felt irritable after a long day of *tedious*, unexciting work.** *syn.* monotonous

tem·per·a·men·tal [tem′prə·men′təl] *adj.* Easily excited or upset: **Because they are afraid and nervous, caged animals are often *temperamental* and not to be trusted.** *syns.* sensitive, edgy

tantalize The ancient Greeks tell the story of Tantalus, an evil man who was punished by the gods after he died. In the land of the dead he was condemned to stand forever in a pool of cool water beneath branches laden with delicious fruits. Whenever he bent down to drink, the water receded. Whenever he reached up for fruit, it withdrew from his hand. He was never allowed the slightest taste of either. Think about Tantalus whenever you want something you can't quite reach.

a	add	o͞o	took
ā	ace	o͞o	pool
â	care	u	up
ä	palm	û	burn
e	end	yo͞o	fuse
ē	equal	oi	oil
i	it	ou	pout
ī	ice	ng	ring
o	odd	th	thin
ō	open	th	this
ô	order	zh	vision

ə = { a in *above*   e in *sicken*
     i in *possible*
     o in *melon*   u in *circus* }

ten·den·cy [ten'dən·sē] *n.* A leaning toward something. *syn.* habit

ten·ta·tive·ly [ten'tə·tiv·lē] *adv.* Cautiously or with hesitation: **Aiko walked *tentatively* along the wall of the dark room, feeling for the light switch.** *syn.* reluctantly

tes·ti·mo·ni·al [tes'tə·mō'nē·əl] *n.* An expression of praise or thanks: **She wrote a poem about me as a *testimonial* to our friendship.** *syn.* tribute

tex·ture [teks'chər] *n.* The feel of something's surface: **The *texture* of the cloth was rough and prickly.**

to·nal [tō'nəl] *adj.* Of or having to do with tones, pitches, or certain sounds: **In *tonal* languages the same word can have different meanings depending on the pitch at which it is spoken.**

trait [trāt] *n.* A special quality or feature: **The dog's most pleasing *traits* are its intelligence and loyalty.** *syns.* aspect, characteristic

tra·jec·to·ry [trə·jek'tər·ē] *n.* The curved path followed by an object thrown or launched upward as it rises and then falls back down: **Lin misjudged the *trajectory* of the baseball as it flew into the outfield, so he didn't catch it.**

treach·er·ous [trech'ər·əs] *adj.* Unsafe or hazardous: **We had been warned about *treacherous* quicksand on the path.** *syn.* dangerous

tread [tred] *v.* To step on: **The worker put a barrier around the sidewalk so that no one would *tread* on the wet cement.** *syn.* trample

trib·ute [trib'yo͞ot] *n.* An action that shows admiration or respect for someone: **The city paid a *tribute* to the astronaut by holding a parade in her honor.**

trajectory

unscrupulous To the ancient Romans a *scrupulus* was a small sharp stone. It also meant "uneasiness" or "doubt" about matters of right and wrong. Just as a sharp stone in your shoe may prick your foot, so your doubts about something may prick your conscience. Those who have *scruples* are sensitive to right and wrong. *Unscrupulous* people don't feel the prickings of doubt and will do almost anything they please.

tur·ban [tûr'bən] *n.* A headdress made of a long cloth twisted around the head or around a cap: **It is common for a man in the Middle East to wear a *turban*.**

tur·bu·lent [tûr'byə·lənt] *adj.* Disturbed or moving around a great deal: **As the storm clouds darkened, the sea became *turbulent* and rocked the ship.** *syn.* tumultuous

tu·te·lage [t(y)o͞o'tə·lij] *n.* Instruction and care: **Sandra's assistant learned a great deal under her *tutelage*.** *syn.* guardianship

U

un·daunt·ed [un·dôn'tid] *adj.* Not discouraged or afraid in the face of danger or misfortune: **The mountain climbers were *undaunted* by the cold weather and climbed to the summit anyway.** *syn.* undefeated

un·or·tho·dox [un·ôr'thə·doks'] *adj.* Out of the ordinary: **In many families, it is *unorthodox* to have Thanksgiving dinner without turkey.** *syns.* unconventional, unapproved

un·scru·pu·lous [un·skro͞o'pyə·ləs] *adj.* Having no principles or conscience: **The *unscrupulous* young man lied to his friends and stole their money.** *syns.* dishonest, immoral

un·wav·er·ing [un·wā'və·ring] *adj.* Not faltering or failing: **No matter what trouble the boy got into, his mother's love was *unwavering*.** *syns.* steady, constant

ut·ter [ut'ər] *adj.* Complete: **The politician felt *utter* joy when she won the election.** *syn.* total

vague·ly [vāg′lē] *adv.* Indefinitely or imprecisely: **The boy was only** *vaguely* **aware of the time and didn't realize just how late he was.**

ven·dor [ven′dər] *n.* A person who sells something, often outdoors: **Children from the neighborhood came running when they heard the ice-cream** *vendor* **ring his bell.** *syns.* salesperson, merchant

waif [wāf] *n.* A homeless or helpless child: **The shelter provided food and safety for the** *waif* **who had no parents.** *syns.* orphan, runaway

wea·ry [wir′ē] *v.* **wea·ried, wea·ry·ing** To make tired, discontented, or bored: **I fell asleep because his endless talking** *wearied* **me.**

yoke [yōk] *n.* A wooden bar used to harness two animals together at the head: **The old** *yoke* **split apart as the oxen were plowing, and the farmer had no way to harness them together again.**

vendor

yoke

a	add	o͞o	took
ā	ace	o͞o	pool
â	care	u	up
ä	palm	û	burn
e	end	yo͞o	fuse
ē	equal	oi	oil
i	it	ou	pout
ī	ice	ng	ring
o	odd	th	thin
ō	open	th	this
ô	order	zh	vision

ə = { a in *above*   e in *sicken*
       i in *possible*
       o in *melon*   u in *circus* }

INDEX OF
TITLES AND AUTHORS

Page numbers in light type refer to biographical information.

Acknowledgments continued

illustration by John Suh from *Shadow Shark* by Colin Thiele. Illustration © 1988 by John Suh. "Silent Bianca" from *The Girl Who Cried Flowers* by Jane Yolen. Text copyright © 1974 by Jane Yolen.

Esther R. Heuman: "The Horse That Played the Outfield" by William Heuman from *Pedro's Tall Tales*.

Holiday House: Cover illustration by Leslie Morrill from *Dog Poems* by Myra Cohn Livingston. Illustration copyright © 1990 by Leslie Morrill.

Houghton Mifflin Company: Cover illustration by Liv Osterberg from *Two Short and One Long* by Nina Ring Aamundsen. Illustration copyright © 1990 by Liv Osterberg. From pp. 18-49 in *Number the Stars* (Retitled: "A Test of Courage") by Lois Lowry, cover photograph of Anne Johnson by Lois Lowry. Text and cover photograph copyright © 1989 by Lois Lowry. From pp. 40-47 in *The One Hundredth Thing About Caroline* (Retitled: "Caroline's Hero") by Lois Lowry, cover illustration by Diane de Groat. Text copyright © 1983 by Lois Lowry; cover illustration copyright © 1983 by Diane de Groat. Cover illustration from *Pyramid* by David Macaulay. Copyright © 1975 by David Macaulay. From pp. 73-78 in *Hunter's Stew and Hangtown Fry: What Pioneer America Ate and Why* by Lila Perl. Text copyright © 1977 by Lila Perl. Cover illustration by Ted Lewin from *Island of the Blue Dolphins* by Scott O'Dell. Illustration copyright © 1990 by Ted Lewin. Cover illustration from *Apple Is My Sign* by Mary Riskind. Copyright © 1981 by Mary L. Riskind. Cover illustration from *The Pueblo* by Charlotte and David Yue. Copyright © 1986 by Charlotte Yue and David Yue.

Alfred A. Knopf, Inc: "Lincoln Monument: Washington" from *The Dream Keeper and Other Poems* by Langston Hughes. Text copyright 1932 by Alfred A. Knopf, Inc., renewed 1960 by Langston Hughes.

Lerner Publications, 241 First Avenue North, Minneapolis, MN 55401: From pp. 42-51 in *The Vietnamese in America* (Retitled: "A New Way of Life") by Paul Rutledge. Text © 1973 by Lerner Publications.

Little, Brown and Company: "Books Fall Open" from *One at a Time* by David McCord. Text copyright © 1965, 1966 by David McCord. Cover illustration by Pamela and Walter Carroll from *Life in a Tidal Pool* by Alvin and Virginia Silverstein. Illustration copyright © 1990 by Pamela and Walter Carroll.

Lothrop, Lee & Shepard Books, a division of William Morrow & Company, Inc.: "Basketball Players" from *The Break Dance Kids: Poems of Sport, Motion, and Locomotion* by Lillian Morrison. Text copyright © 1985 by Lillian Morrison.

Macmillan Publishing Company: Cover illustration by Symeon Shimin from *Zeely* by Virginia Hamilton. Illustration copyright © 1967 by Macmillan Publishing Company.

Alan Mazzetti: Cover illustration by Alan Mazzetti from *Taking Sides* by Gary Soto.

Margaret K. McElderry Books, an imprint of Macmillan Publishing Company: Cover illustration by Kinuko Craft from *A Jar of Dreams* by Yoshiko Uchida. Copyright © 1981 by Yoshiko Uchida.

Mendola Ltd.: Cover illustration by Carol Newsom from *Bingo Brown and the Language of Love* by Betsy Byars.

Scott Meredith Literary Agency, Inc., 845 Third Avenue, New York, NY 10022 and Arthur C. Clarke: From pp. 20-35 in *Dolphin Island* (Retitled: "Rescue at Sea") by Arthur C. Clarke. Text copyright © 1963 by Arthur C. Clarke.

Scott Meredith Literary Agency, Inc., 845 Third Avenue, New York, NY 10022 and Ralph Williams: From *Emergency Landing* by Ralph Williams. Text copyright 1940 by Street and Smith Publications, Inc.

Modern Curriculum Press, Inc.: From *Across Five Aprils* by Irene Hunt. Text copyright © 1964 by Irene Hunt.

William Morrow & Company, Inc.: From *Hello, My Name Is Scrambled Eggs* (Retitled: "Tom Win, American") by Jamie Gilson, cover illustration by James Warhola. Text copyright © 1985 by Jamie Gilson; cover illustration copyright © 1986 by James Warhola.

National Council of Teachers of English: "Foreign Student" by Barbara B. Robinson from *English Journal*, May 1976. Text copyright 1976 by the National Council of Teachers of English.

Plays, Inc.: From *Listen to The Hodja* in *Plays from Folktales of Africa and Asia* by Barbara Winther. Text copyright © 1976 by Barbara Winther.

Puffin Books, a division of Penguin Books USA Inc.: Cover illustration by Lino Saffioti from *The Summer of the Swans* by Betsy Byars. Illustration copyright © 1991 by Lino Saffioti.

G. P. Putnam's Sons: From pp. 7-38 in *UFOs, ETs & Visitors from Space* (Retitled: "The UFO Question") by Melvin Berger. Text copyright © 1988 by Melvin Berger.

Raintree Publishers, Inc., a division of Steck-Vaughn Company: Illustrations by Ken Bachaus from *Casey at the Bat* by Ernest Lawrence Thayer. Illustrations copyright © 1985 by Raintree Publishers, Inc.

Random House, Inc.: From pp. 9-31 in *The Phantom Tollbooth* (Retitled: "Milo's Mystery Tour") by Norton Juster, illustrated by Jules Feiffer. Text copyright © 1961 by Norton Juster; text copyright renewed 1989 by Norton Juster. Illustrations copyright © 1961 by Jules Feiffer; illustrations copyright renewed 1989 by Jules Feiffer.

Scholastic, Inc.: From *Exploring the Titanic* by Robert D. Ballard. Text copyright © 1988 by Ballard & Family. A Scholastic/Madison Press Book. From *Amazing But True Sports Stories* (Retitled: "Sports Legends and Laughers") by Phyllis and Zander Hollander. Text copyright © 1986 by Associated Features Inc.

Charles Scribner's Sons, an imprint of Macmillan Publishing Company: Cover illustration by Ronald Himler from *A Gathering of Days* by Joan W. Blos. Copyright © 1979 by Joan W. Blos. Cover illustration by Ernest H. Shepard from *The Wind in the Willows* by Kenneth Grahame. Illustration copyright © 1960 by Ernest H. Shepard.

Sniffen Court Books: From pp. 18-23 in *Behind the Sealed Door: The Discovery of the Tomb and Treasures of Tutankhamun* (Retitled: "Treasures of the Valley") by Irene and Laurence Swinburne. Text copyright © 1977 by Sniffen Court Books.

Michael Steirnagle: Cover illustration by Michael Steirnagle from *How Smart Are Animals?* by Dorothy Hinshaw Patent. Illustration © by Michael Steirnagle.

Marjorie Filley Stover: From pp. 129-141 in *Trail Boss in Pigtails* (Retitled: "Red River Crossing") by Marjorie Filley Stover. Text copyright © 1972 by Marjorie Filley Stover. Published by Atheneum Publishers.

Viking Penguin, a division of Penguin Books USA, Inc.: Cover illustration by Melodye Rosales from *My Sister, My Science Report* by Margaret Bechard. Illustration copyright © 1990 by Melodye Rosales. From *Bingo Brown and the Language of Love* (Retitled: "The Photo Session") by Betsy Byars. Text copyright © 1989 by Betsy Byars. Cover illustration by Carol Newsom from *Bingo Brown, Gypsy Lover* by Betsy Byars. Illustration copyright © 1990 by Carol Newsom. From pp. 64-72 in *Mojo and the Russians* (Retitled: "Kwami Green, Teacher Supreme") by Walter Dean Myers. Text copyright © 1977 by Walter Dean Myers.

Handwriting models in this program have been used with permission of the publisher, Zaner-Bloser, Inc., Columbus, OH.

Every effort has been made to locate the copyright holders for the selections in this work. The publisher would be pleased to receive information that would allow the correction of any omissions in future printings.

Photograph Credits

Key: (t) top, (c) center, (b) bottom, (l) left, (r) right, (bg) background.

UNIT 1:
20, HBJ/Britt Runion; 22, HBJ; 44, HBJ/Maria Paraskevas; 46, HBJ; 73, AP/Wide World Photos; 75, NASA; 78, NASA; 80(l), NASA; 80(r), NASA; 94(t), Andrew Rakoczy/Bruce Coleman, Inc.; 94(b), Robert Frerck/Odyssey Productions; 95, Larry S. Gordon/The Image Bank.

UNIT 2:
97(t), HBJ/Debi Harbin; 97(c), HBJ/Britt Runion; 100-101, HBJ/ Harbin; 118-128, All photos Courtesy Ron Jones; 130-131, H Runion; 132, HBJ; 140(l), Bob Burch/Bruce Coleman, Inc. Courtesy Houghton Mifflin Co.; 142-143(bg), Bob Coleman, Inc.; 144, HBJ/Chris Lowery; 189, Courtes Griffin/A Better Chance, Inc.; 190, "Washington' Officers" by Alonzo Chappel, #X.39: Chicago

194(l), Culver Pictures; 194–195(b), Bruce Davidson/Magnum Photos; 195(tl), AP/Wide World Photos; 195(tr), AP/Wide World Photos.

UNIT 3:
197(t), HBJ/Britt Runion; 200, HBJ/Britt Runion; 202(t), Steve Elmore/The Stock Market; 202(b), Alan Schein/The Stock Market; 202(l), Berenholtz/The Stock Market; 202(l)(inset), Blaine Harrington/The Stock Market; 202(r), Berenholtz/The Stock Market; 203(t), Courtesy Julia Alvarez; 203(t)(inset), HBJ/Beverly Brosius; 203(b), P. Robert Garvey/The Stock Market; 203(b)(inset), Peter Beck/The Stock Market; 204(l), Wes Thompson Photography/The Stock Market; 204(r), Courtesy Julia Alvarez; 204–205(b)(inset), Ronnie Kaufman/The Stock Market; 205(tl)(inset), Lynn Johnson/Black Star; 205(tr), Richard Steedman/The Stock Market; 205(cl), Tom Bean/The Stock Market; 205(br)(inset), Luis Villota/The Stock Market; 206(tl), Sara Eichner, Courtesy Algonquin Books; 206(tr)(inset), HBJ/Julie Fletcher; 206(b), Tom Bean/The Stock Market; 207(t), Naoki Okamoto/The Stock Market; 207(bl)(inset), Harvey Lloyd/The Stock Market; 207(bc), Courtesy Julia Alvarez; 207(br)(inset), Stephanie Pfriender/The Stock Market; 208, Geoffrey Clifford/Woodfin Camp & Associates; 209, Allen Russell/Black Star; 210(t), Keza/Gamma-Liaison; 210(b), Larry Barns/Black Star; 211, Chris Harris/Gamma-Liaison; 212, David A. Harvey/Woodfin Camp & Associates; 213, David A. Harvey/Woodfin Camp & Associates; 214, Bill Nation/Sygma Photos; 242, The Granger Collection; 243(l), Scala/Art Resource, NY; 243(r), Superstock; 244(t), Cairo Museum, Egypt/Superstock; 244(l), Art Resource, NY; 244(r), Borromeo/Art Resource, NY; 245(tr), Scala/Art Resource; 245(lc), North Wind Picture Archives; 245(b), Scala/Art Resource; 246(t), Robert Frerck/Odyssey Productions; 246(r), Scala/Art Resource, NY; 247(t), Scala/Art Resource, NY; 247(b), John Ross/Photo Researchers; 248, Giraudon/Art Resource, NY; 249, Bridgeman/Superstock; 250–251, HBJ; 271, Photo Bob Newey/Courtesy Bantam Doubleday; 296, Lionel Isy-Schwart/The Image Bank; 297(bl), Hoa-Qui/Viesti Associates; 297(br), David Austen/T.S.W.; 297(t), Robert Frerck/Odyssey Productions.

UNIT 4:
299(c), HBJ/Debi Harbin; 332–333, HBJ/Debi Harbin; 334, HBJ; 358(bg), HBJ/Britt Runion; 358, Courtesy Betsy Byars; 368–369, HBJ/Debi Harbin; 389 Courtesy, New Orleans Saints; 391, HBJ; 396(l), UPI/Bettmann Newsphotos; 396(r), Culver Pictures; 397(t), UPI Bettmann Newsphotos; 397(c), Cherokee Nation; 397(b), Cherokee Nation.

UNIT 5:
399(c), HBJ/Debi Harbin; 404, Jim Holland/Black Star; 407, Francisco Erize/Bruce Coleman, Inc.; 410–411, Mark Sexton; 412–413(bg), HBJ/Britt Runion; 412(inset), HBJ/Ken Rogers, Black Star; 414–415, Original art by Ken Marschall; 416–417, R.J. Bowen/Woods Hole Oceanographic Institution; 418–419, Original art by Ken Marschall; 422–423, Ira Wyman/Sygma Photos; 424, Original art by Ken Marschall; 426–427, Original art by Ken Marschall; 429, Sygma Photos; 430–431, Original art by Ken Marschall; 432, Woods Hole Oceanographic Institution/Sygma Photos; 434–435, HBJ/Debi Harbin; 436(t), DiMaggio-Kalish/Peter Arnold, Inc.; 436(c), HBJ; 436(b), Eric Martin/Marine Mammal Images; 437, Silvan Wick/Marine Mammal Images; 438, Eric Martin/Marine Mammal Images; 439, Silvan Wick/Marine Mammal Images; 457, Dana Fineman/Sygma Photos; 458, NASA; 460, HBJ/Debi Harbin; 472–473, Courtesy Jean Craighead George; 474(t), Erwin & Peggy Bauer/Bruce Coleman, Inc.; 474(c), Grapes-Michaud/Photo Researchers; 474(b), /Rodney Jones; 475(t), Jeff Foott/Bruce Coleman, Inc.; 475(c), Parker/Tom Stack & Associates; 475(b), Erwin & Peggy ce Coleman, Inc.; 477, HBJ.

Lou Collection; 494–495(b), The Granger Collection; Libra Riger, Contact/Woodfin Camp & Associates; Britt Rossi/The Image Bank; 497(t), Louis M. union; 500, HBJ/Britt Runion; 500 (bg), stock; 524–525, HBJ/Britt Runion; 526, Granger Collection; 524–525, HBJ; Collection; 531, Library of Con-

gress; 534, HBJ; 534, (book cover),Chicago Historical Society, Photo by Hesler, 1860; 534 (bg), Library of Congress; 536(l), Illinois State Historical Library; 536(r), Library of Congress; 539, Library of Congress; 543, Library of Congress; 544, Illinois State Historical Library; 548(bg), Library of Congress; 549, Courtesy Clarion Books; 550, Library of Congress; 580, Art Stein/Folio; 580(bg), Comstock; 582–583(b), Dennis O'Connor II/Paul Bardagjy Photography; 582(l), The Bettmann Archive; 583(t), The Granger Collection; 583(b), Louise S. O'Connor/Paul Bardagjy Photography; 587, HBJ/Maria Paraskevas; 594-595, HBJ/Les Stone; 610, Joe Viesti/Viesti Associates; 613, Jay King/PP/FA; 617, David Carol/The Image Bank; 619, Gail Denham/PP/FA.

Illustration Credits

Key: (t) top, (c) center, (b) bottom, (l) left, (r) right.

Table of Contents Art
Abby Carter, 6 (bl), 9 (tr), 11 (br),12 (c), 13 (c); Regan Dunnick, 5 (br), 6–7 (c), 12 (bl), 15 (br); Cameron Eagle, 5 (tr), 7 (br) 8–9 (c), 14 (bl); Jennifer Hewitson, 4 (tl), 7 (tr), 9 (br), 10–11 (c), 14 (tl); Tracy Sabin, 4–5 (c), 8 (tl), 11 (tr), 13 (tr); Rhonda Voo, 6 (tl), 8 (bl), 10 (bl), 14–15 (c).

Unit Opening Patterns
Tracy Sabin.

Bookshelf Art
Cindy Clark; 198–199, 400–401; Tuko Fujisaki, 18–19; Kenton Nelson, 300–301; Amanda Schaffer, 498–499; James Staunton, 98–99.

Theme Opening Art
Gerald Bustamante, 44–45; Ray-Mel Cornelius, 20–21; Normand Cousineau, 240–241; David Davis, 66–67; Mark Frueh, 402–403; Marty Gunsaullus, 170–171; Benton Mahan, 100–101, 302–303; Ed Martinez, 552–553; Louis Police, 500–501; Walter Stuart, 433, 459; Jean and Mou-sien Tseng, 460–461; Randy Verougstraete, 368–369; Terry Widener, 274–275.

Theme Closing Art
Seymnour Chwast, 43; Regan Dunnick, 93, 523; Cameron Eagle, 395; Mark Freuh, 493; Peter Horjus, 367; Dave Jonason, 65, 295; Paul Meisel, 169; Walter Stuart, 239; Lynn Tanaka, 129; Mary Thelan, 273; Gregg Valley, 193, 581; Randy Verougstraete, 331; Edward Martinez, 551.

Connections Art
HBJ

Selections Art
Gil Ashby, 58–64; Ken Bachaus, 390–394; Debra Becker (Computer Illustration), 271, 272, 457, 458; Catherine Farley (Charts), 407, 421; Jules Feiffer, 22–41; Edward Feldman (Background, Computer Illustration), 334–357; Laura Fernandez, 288–294; Michael Garland, 102–115; Hector Garrido, 360–366; Kevin Ghiglione, 42, 216, 217, 317; Keith Gold, 68–83, (Borders) 208–215; Jody Hugo, 276–287; Oleana Kassian, 304–316; Murray Kimber, 440–456; Deborah Nourse Lattimore, 250–270; Bernadette Lau, 218–238, 318, 319; Jay Leach, 384–389; Mike Lester, 370–383; Charles Lilly, 320–330; Ken Marschall, 414–432; Wayne McLoughlin, 476–492; Susan Melrath, 334–357; Wendell Minor, 508–521; Julian Mulock, 462–471; Rita Neuhaus (Calligraphy), 578–579; Buster O'Connor (Map), 248, (Backgrounds) 304–316, 508–521; Clarence Porter, 116, 117, 118–128; Rodica Prato, 46–56; Charles Pyle, 132–139; Paul Rivoche, 88–92; Greg Ruhl, 554–579; Terry Schoffner, 502–507; Margot Tomes, 172–187; Bill Watterson, 84, 85; David Wilgus, 144–168; J. E. Buttersworth, 410, 411; Robert Lindneux, 522.